"I TOLD YOU YESTERDAY THAT WHEN I SAW SOMETHING I WANTED,

I WENT AFTER IT. NOW I'LL ALSO ADD THAT I KEEP IT."

She made a sound of protest. "You make it all sound so . . . possessive."

"Oh, no, I didn't mean it that way. But I do love you."

"Sh-h, not now, Jake." She put a finger across his lips. "We'll have almost a month together. Let's not spoil it by getting too serious in the beginning. Let's wait and see how it goes."

She thought again of telling him about her father, the reason for this journey, and the strange, threatening notes. Yet it was far too early to confide so much to him. Even if he was a cop, he was still a stranger . . . a man who had ignited her passions and now invited her trust. But she couldn't afford to love, couldn't afford to trust. Not until the mystery of her father was solved. No matter where the path would lead. . . .

MIDNIGHT LAVENDER

MIDNIGHT LAVENDER

Patricia
and
Clayton Matthews

BANTAM BOOKS
TORONTO • NEW YORK • LONDON • SYDNEY • AUCKLAND

*For a world-class bookworm
and dear friend, Bobbie Lefkowitz,
who is always there with a
kind and supportive word.*

MIDNIGHT LAVENDER

A Bantam Book / June 1985

ISBN 0-553-24979-7

Published simultaneously in the United States and Canada

PRINTED IN THE UNITED STATES OF AMERICA

H   0 9 8 7 6 5 4 3 2 1

MIDNIGHT LAVENDER

NORDIC STAR

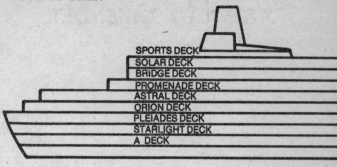

SPORTS DECK
SOLAR DECK
BRIDGE DECK
PROMENADE DECK
ASTRAL DECK
ORION DECK
PLEIADES DECK
STARLIGHT DECK
A DECK

SPORTS DECK: Ping Pong; Shuffleboard; etc.

SOLAR DECK: Penthouse Suites; Nova Lounge, Solar Bar; Pool; Casino.

BRIDGE DECK: Officer's Cabins; Pool; Casino.

PROMENADE DECK: Suites; A & B Class Staterooms; Gemini Bar; Pisces Lounge; Milky Way Club; Card Room; Library, Open Promenade.

ASTRAL DECK: Dining Room; Astral Lounge, Lunar Lounge; Swimming Pool; Changing Rooms.

ORION DECK:	Reception Area; Shops; Staterooms, Beauty Parlour; Barber Shop.
PLEIADES DECK:	Less expensive staterooms (most of the performers are quartered here).
STARLIGHT DECK:	Theatre; Gym and Sauna; Hospital, Indoor Swimming Pool.
A DECK:	Engine Room, Hold, etc.

One

Standing in front of her apartment door, Cassandra Kanaris juggled the awkward dress box as she dug into her purse for her keys. Why was it that whatever you needed was invariably at the bottom of your purse?

Muttering a mild expletive, she finally found the keys and unlocked the door.

Still muttering to herself, she headed for the bedroom, where she dropped the dress box onto the bed. Her arm was numb and she felt vaguely out of sorts. It had been one of those days. First, her garbage disposal had backed up, and when she called the building super, he had told her that he couldn't possibly get to it until tomorrow. Then she had blown a tire on the way to the shopping mall, the spare had mysteriously disappeared, and the gas station attendant had taken forever to repair the flat.

It obviously wasn't her day, someone else's perhaps, but not hers. It was enough to make her wish that she was still on the cruise ship. There, at least, all mundane details were taken care of for her. All she had to do was her job. Usually, shopping cheered her, but after the flat, even that hadn't helped. Besides, she wasn't at all certain that she was happy with her purchase.

With a put-upon sigh, she tossed her purse down beside the dress box and began to undress. A glance at the bedside clock told her that it was already five o'clock; Ron Wilson was supposed to pick her up at six. Just barely time enough to shower and change. She almost wished that she hadn't

1

agreed to go out with him tonight. In her present mood, she would much rather have remained home and watched television. After being at sea for two months, watching television, and being alone, were luxuries, and she wasn't sure that she was all that crazy about Ron, anyway. He was handsome, yes, and could be charming company, but she suspected he was rather shallow, and he had a reputation for being a ladies' man.

Deciding on a bath rather than a shower, Cassandra turned on the water, threw in a handful of perfumed bath salts, and then returned to the bedroom to lay out her clothes for the evening.

Catching a glimpse of her pouting face and naked body in the mirror, she suddenly realized just how ridiculous she was being. "You're really in a lousy mood, kiddo," she said aloud, and started to laugh at her own scowling reflection.

Reminding herself that bad moods could be generated by negative thoughts, she laughed again, and then opened the dresser drawer in search of a scarf with which to tie up her hair while bathing. She really *was* being silly. She had been looking forward to this time at home. Life on board ship was elegant, comfortable, and exciting, but it was also insular, confining, and hectic for the staff and crew. The credo of the Nordic cruise line was: "The passenger always comes first," and unfortunately some passengers were quite demanding.

Cassandra had been looking forward to shopping, seeing her old friends, and last but not least, being by herself for a while. Aboard ship, the only time she was not with other people was when she was asleep, and even then she often had a cabin mate. The rest of the time, from early morning until late at night, she was working, and working as an assistant cruise director, meant being with people constantly.

That was why she now regretted making the date with Ron, who was assistant purser on the *Nordic Rover*. She had anticipated going out with old friends, but after being away from Los Angeles for months, she always found that it wasn't easy to fit into their lives again, particularly when she was only home for a few days at a time. They seemed almost strangers to her.

Well, she *had* made the date, and she might as well make the best of it and try to enjoy herself. She would relax in her bath, think good thoughts, put on a happy face, and maybe, just maybe, the evening would turn out better than the rest of her day.

Turning again to the bed, she reached for the dress box, trying to decide whether or not she would wear the new outfit tonight.

As she moved the box her eye was caught by a flash of lavender—her favorite color. Picking up the box, she uncovered a large, square lavender envelope. Where on earth could it have come from? Perhaps it had been placed beneath the ribbons on the box by someone in the dress shop as some kind of an advertisement.

She picked up the envelope, which had no address on it, and opened it. Inside was a single fold of thick, lavender paper. She unfolded it, and quickly scanned the written message inside. The message was written with purple ink: "Cassandra, your father is alive and living on an island in the Mediterranean. We thought you should finally know the truth."

It was signed: "A friend."

Cassandra felt the prickle of hair rising along her spine and neck as she read the message again. What did it mean? Was this some kind of a sick joke?

The note said, "A friend," but she seldom discussed her family with friends, and when she did, she talked mainly of her mother, who had died the year before, the tragic victim of a hit-and-run accident. The only thing Cassandra ever told anyone about her father was that he was dead. How could any of her friends know anything about him, when she knew so little herself?

The sudden sound of dripping water aroused Cassandra, and she dropped the note onto the bed and hastened into the bathroom to find the tub overflowing. Quickly, she turned off the water and pulled the plug, trying to keep her mind fastened on the simple task, trying to distance herself from the message.

Snatching a towel from the rack, she used it to mop up the water on the floor, and when this was done, she finally felt calm enough to return to the bedroom.

She picked up the note and read it again, handling it gingerly. She had hoped that somehow the words would have changed, but they were the same—inexplicable and frightening. What could it mean? Could it *possibly* be true? Could her father be alive?

Cassandra had never known her father, and the only things she knew *of* him were what her mother had told her, stories that had become mythlike through constant repetition. When she was very young, Cassandra had listened avidly to the stories about her father and of how he and her mother had met, but as she had grown older, she could not help but question some of the glowing accounts. In fact, she had sometimes wondered if her father and mother had really been married at all. Penelope, her mother, had been a charming woman, a warm and loving mother; yet she had been given to soaring flights of fancy and had not been above adorning the truth to make it fit her vision of reality. Was it possible that she had conceived the story of Cassandra's father's death to disguise the fact that he had abandoned her?

According to Penelope, she had met her husband-to-be on the island of Rhodes. His name had been Jason Kanaris, and, according to Penelope, he had been a beautiful man— "So beautiful, Cassandra, that you wouldn't believe it unless you saw him in person. He looked just the way I had always imagined a Greek god would look, tall, beautifully made, with broad shoulders and a slim waist. His hair was thick, dark, and curly, and his eyes were green, but they burned with a deep light. I was simply swept off my feet. I couldn't resist him. I left the cruise ship at Rhodes so that I could stay with him. We were married two weeks later."

It was a romantic tale, but one that, according to Penelope at any rate, ended tragically. After one brief month of idyllic marriage, Jason was drowned while swimming in the bay at Lindos, leaving Penelope pregnant with his child and in a state of confused shock. His body was never found, and strangely enough, her mother had only one faded photograph of him.

Penelope had always claimed that such was her despair that she could never remember just how she made her way back to the United States and to her own mother, who was alive at the time. She said that it was as if a "dark curtain" had descended mercifully over the long months that passed before Cassandra was born. Luckily, money was not a problem, for Penelope's father had left her a substantial trust, and her mother had money of her own.

It was only with Cassandra's birth, that Penelope had come back to the world of the living, and all of the love that she had felt for Jason she then lavished on the child, making Cassandra her whole life and reason for being.

This part of the story, at least, Cassandra knew was true. Her mother had been very devoted, and very caring, but luckily not in an unhealthy, obsessive way. They had been very close.

Penelope had seemed to have no interest in men, in a romantic sense, and indeed, Cassandra knew, had turned down a number of proposals of marriage; for she had been a beautiful woman, and men had been much attracted to her.

Cassandra, who in her early years sorely missed having a father, had finally asked her mother why she did not marry again, and Penelope had replied, "I could never find another man like your father, Cassandra. In my mind he is still my husband. He is the only man I could ever love."

It had sounded very romantic, but as Cassandra grew older and became interested in boys herself, she often wondered at her mother's enduring devotion.

There were also the unanswered questions, the queries that her mother evaded, or flatly refused to answer.

Why, after Jason's death, didn't Penelope try to contact his family?

Well, Penelope didn't know much about his family. After all, she and Jason had only been married a month. They really hadn't had time to learn everything about each other.

But didn't she know *anything* about his family?

Very little. Penelope was sure that they were Greek, but she didn't know where they lived.

What had Jason done? What was his work, his profession?

Jason didn't seem to have a job, although he did seem to have money; Penelope thought that his family was wealthy.

What had Jason been doing on Rhodes then?

Penelope wasn't certain. A vacation perhaps. He was there, he had told her, to view the ruins of the Acropolis at Lindos.

It was all very vague, and it drove Cassandra up the wall. She longed to know more about her handsome father so that she could feel close to his memory, but her mother's descriptions and stories made him seem more like some character out of a fairy tale—the handsome prince with no past and no future, existing only in the story.

And now this!

Feeling a chill of uneasiness along her spine, Cassandra went to her dresser, opened the top drawer, and took out a small, leather box.

She opened the box and took out a snapshot, the only physical evidence of her father's existence, taken, her mother had told her, on the day before his death.

Holding the picture up to the light, Cassandra studied it intently, as she had so many times before, looking for some kind of an answer in the image that stared back at her.

The picture had been taken at Lindos. It showed a slender, broad-shouldered young man in old-fashioned swim trunks. He looked directly into the camera, unsmiling. Even in the small snapshot it was obvious that he was intense and very handsome.

Penelope had often told Cassandra that she was "the perfect image" of her father, and now Cassandra raised her gaze from the photo to her own image in the mirror. She was, she supposed, just about the age he had been when the picture was taken, and she had to admit the resemblance—the same, wide-cheekboned, narrow-chinned face; the same dark, curly hair. Her short haircut intensified the resemblance. Even the body structure was much the same—broad shoulders, narrow hips, long legs; an athletic build, she supposed. Her face was somewhat softer, of course, more feminine, but they were obviously cast from the same mold.

The photo was too small, too faded, to show the color of his eyes, but according to her mother, his eyes had been the same unusual hazel-green of Cassandra's . . .

The musical chime of the telephone intruded on Cassandra's dark thoughts, and as she picked up the receiver she noticed that it was already five-thirty.

"Hello," she said tentatively; her voice, she realized, was a trifle shaky.

"Cass, is that you? Have you got a cold or something? I can hardly hear you."

It was Ron, and she went weak with relief. What, or who, had she been expecting?

She cleared her throat. "No, Ron, no cold. You caught me taking a bath."

He laughed. "Sorry about that. Although I do wish there

was a view-screen on the phone. I just called to make sure that you remembered our date."

"No, I haven't forgotten. That's why I was taking a bath. But I would appreciate it if you could make it a half hour later. I was late getting back from shopping."

"Sure, no problem," he said breezily. "Suppose I pick you up at six-thirty or so. Okay?"

"Okay. I'll be ready."

Slowly, Cassandra put down the phone, finding herself suddenly reluctant to break off human contact. Even a voice on the phone was better than being left alone with her frightened thoughts.

She stared down at the note clutched in her hand. What was she going to do about it? What was she *supposed* to do about it? What had the writer of the note expected her to do? And, how had it gotten into her apartment in the first place? Obviously someone had brought it here and placed it on her bed. But how had they gotten in? A cheering thought came to her. Maybe it had been Mr. Brugg, the building super. Maybe he had found time after all to come up and check her disposal and had brought the envelope in. Since it bore no stamps, address, or name, it must have been hand-delivered; and it would be natural enough for someone to give the note to the building superintendent, rather than putting it in her mailbox. But if it had been Brugg, why had he left the envelope on her bed? Why not in the living room, on the coffee table?

Quickly, she dialed the number of Brugg's apartment. The telephone was answered by Brugg's ill-tempered wife, and Cassandra fidgeted in impatience as she waited for Brugg to come on the line.

Finally: "Yeah? This is Brugg."

Cassandra prayed that her guess was right. "Mr. Brugg, this is Cassandra Kanaris, in three-thirteen. Did you find time after all to look at my disposal?"

A deep sigh answered her. "I told you this morning that I

wouldn't have time to look at it until tomorrow. I been all afternoon trying to fix an electrical short in Mrs. Johnson's apartment."

"Then you haven't been in my apartment at all today?"

"Look, I just told you. What's the matter, you deaf or something?" he said in an aggrieved voice.

"No, of course not. But there was a letter in my apartment. I thought you, or maybe Mrs. Brugg, had brought it up."

"Nope, not me. Not my old lady, either. She's been out all day, gabbing with her mother. Most likely somebody went up and slipped it under your door."

She saw no point in telling him that the envelope was on her bed, not slipped under the door. "Yes, that must be it. Sorry to have bothered you, Mr. Brugg."

Cassandra slowly replaced the receiver. There was no longer any doubt: someone *had* entered her apartment, gone into her bedroom, and left the note on the bed.

She felt violated. The apartment had been locked. If someone had gotten in, they could do it again at any time. Even changing the locks probably wouldn't prevent it. How could she *ever* feel safe here again?

But more important, at least more immediate, was the note. Was it some kind of a joke, or was it true? And what could she do about it?

The man on the telephone hung up and turned to the others, a smile of satisfaction on his lips. "Well, the note was delivered today. She has read it by now."

Their leader said, "All is well then, Hermes?"

"Yes, Hera, all should be well."

One of the three other women said worriedly, "But how can we be sure that she will follow up on the message?"

"I think it is inevitable, Aphrodite," the man called Hermes said confidently. "After all, we know that the girl has always wondered about her father. Penelope never told her a great deal, and much of what she *did* tell Cassandra was not the truth."

A third woman said, "I agree. I think it is logical that she will follow it up. She desperately wants to know about her father, anyone would. To suddenly learn that her father is alive, she will be afire with curiosity."

"Just because you are known for your wisdom, Athena," Aphrodite said with a touch of scorn, "does not mean that you are always right. I still maintain that there must be a better way."

The woman called Athena retorted angrily, "You have been against us from the start. I should think that the goddess of love would be delighted to see a father and daughter brought together."

"I am delighted, if it works. But you know there is more to it than that. And I fear for the girl's safety. You well know that the others will try everything they can to stop her. They may even resort to violence."

"Aphrodite is right, you know," said the one who called herself Demeter. "Zeus and Ares are determined to prevent the meeting. Both are evil men and will stop at nothing to get their way."

"Stop squabbling, the lot of you!" Hera said harshly. She looked at the second man in the room. "You, Poseidon, have said nothing. What do you think?"

Poseidon shrugged. "We have agreed, more or less, to set things in motion. Even if some of us are doubtful, the plans are going ahead. I agree with Aphrodite and Demeter, the others will stop at nothing. The only thing we can do is try and thwart them, protect the girl as much as is in our power."

Hera nodded thoughtfully. "Yes, that we must do at all costs. If Cassandra is harmed in any way, we will have been the cause of it. Are we all agreed on that?"

The six sat in silence for a moment, thinking. Then, one by one, they nodded agreement with their leader.

"Good!" she said. She turned to the Messenger. "Hermes, tell your man to watch Cassandra closely, and inform us at once when it is learned how the girl plans to journey to the islands."

Two

The main trouble with Ron Wilson, Cassandra concluded, was his ego: he obviously considered himself irresistible to women. He *was* handsome, there was no denying that, yet she didn't always consider that an asset in a man, especially when the man knew just how good-looking he was. That was one thing that had always troubled her a little about her mother's description of Jason Kanaris. "So beautiful, Cassandra, that you wouldn't believe it . . ."

She forcibly directed her thoughts away from that subject and realized that Ron had been speaking. She leaned across the table. "I'm sorry, Ron, what were you saying?"

"I said, that orchid becomes you," he said, gesturing to the orchid pinned to her dress. It had been delivered minutes after her frustrating conversation with Bruggs. "I know lavender is your favorite color."

She glanced down at it. It *was* close to lavender in color, which had already raised disturbing questions in her mind. Ron knew her favorite color—God only knew how he'd learned—and she was quite sure that he was one of the few who did. But she couldn't see Ron as the writer of the note. What would be his motive?

If she kept thinking about that damned note, her whole evening was going to be spoiled.

Ron said, "What are you frowning about, Cass?"

She glanced up with a start. "Was I frowning? Nothing, really. Oh . . . I *was* wondering how you knew my favorite color."

"I'm a very observant fellow," he said playfully. "Actually, it wasn't all that difficult. Being a mystery buff, you should know that. I've noticed that you always have a touch of lavender about you, even if it's only a ribbon or piece of jewelry. In fact"—he grinned—"the last time I saw you sunning yourself, you had a lavender-colored bikini, what there was of it."

She felt herself blushing, remembering just how skimpy that bikini was. But then, almost all of the female employees of the *Nordic Rover* wore skimpy costumes when sunbathing, in spite of the fact that the employee deck area was in full view of the passengers from the Promenade deck. Most of the employees, she had always suspected, exposed as much of themselves as possible for that very reason.

"You're blushing!" Ron said, reaching across the table to take her hand. "That's what I like about you, Cass. You're so fresh, so innocent. Most women have lost all ability to blush nowadays. In fact, I can't recall when I last saw it happen."

"Did you ever think that the reason for that might be the company you keep?" she said dryly, and extricated her hand from his grip.

"Touché," he said, assuming a rueful expression, which was, she suspected, supposed to disarm her.

She made no response but concentrated on cutting her steak.

After a few minutes Ron said, "Speaking of mysteries,

have you heard about the special *Nordic Star* cruise leaving Fort Lauderdale on the tenth?"

"No, I haven't." She looked at him with interest. "What connection does that have with mysteries?"

"You know that, with cruise business down somewhat this year, many cruises are being built around themes. Well, this particular cruise is billed as a 'Mystery Cruise.' From what I've been told, it will feature a number of well-known mystery writers, some big names in the field, along with as many mystery fans as will book. The writers will give lectures, there will be mystery games and puzzles, and there will even be a New York City homicide cop along, as well as a reformed criminal who now writes mysteries for a living. Some entrepreneur from New York dreamed it all up, I hear. She conducted a tour to London last year, a Sherlock Holmes tour, covering all the places mentioned in the Holmes books. It sounds like something that would be right up your alley, Cass."

Cassandra felt a tiny prick of excitement. "What's the itinerary?"

"Across the Atlantic, with the usual ports of call along the way, around the Mediterranean and the Aegean Sea, hitting several of the Greek Isles. But the Mystery Cruise itself ends in Genoa."

"A four-week cruise then?"

Ron nodded. "Yes."

Cassandra said slowly, "I wonder if there's any chance I could get transferred to that cruise? There's so little time. The tenth, you said?"

"But why on earth would you want to do that?" Ron said in dismay. "Aren't you working the Orient trip?"

"I'm supposed to, yes, but maybe I could change over."

"But I was looking forward to the Orient cruise with you, Cass. Two months together would be great."

"I'm sure you'll manage to survive," she said dryly.

She was a touch surprised at the excitement the prospect

of the Mediterranean cruise engendered in her. Apparently, subconsciously, she had been thinking of investigating the truth of the note. She could always take an extended leave of absence and fly to the Greek Islands, but that would be terribly expensive, especially since the note had not named a specific island. Strangely enough, although she had worked for the Nordic Line for four years, Cassandra had never worked a Mediterranean cruise. She could have put in for one, yet she had avoided it for some reason. Why, she wondered now? Was it because her father had presumably died there?

Ron's words brought her attention back.

"There's something I've been debating about whether or not to tell you. It's more or less a rumor, but maybe I should pass it along before you do anything rash. Bob Haskins told me that he's thinking of retiring. He's been a cruise ship director for fifteen years, and he's tired of it. I asked him who's in line to replace him and you know what he told me?"

"I don't suppose I'm all that interested. I'd hate to see Bob leave, he's a fine cruise director, but beyond that I can't see that it matters much."

Ron shook his head. "No, no. You don't understand. Bob said that *you* were under consideration."

"*Me?*" She stared at him in disbelief. "You have to be putting me on, Ron."

"No, I swear. That's what he told me."

"I can't see it. To begin with, I'm a woman and I'm only twenty-six, without that much experience."

"But the thing is, Cass, it could happen. But if you ask to be switched to another ship, it might prevent you from ever getting the job."

"I simply can't believe they're considering me. I'm not sure I'd want it, anyway. It's hard enough being an assistant cruise director. Bob works around the clock."

"Don't you have any ambition?"

"Ambition, yes, but I'm not sure it lies with cruise ships. There's no real future in it. It's great for a few years, but I don't think I'd want to make it my life's work."

"It's the greatest job there is," he said enthusiastically.

It was her turn to grin at him. "For you, Ron, yes. All those available females."

"Aw-w, you've been listening to nasty gossip." He wagged a finger at her.

"I can see for myself. I don't have to be a detective to know what *you* like about working cruise ships."

Before Ron could respond the waitress came to inquire if they wanted dessert. Both declined. As they waited for the check, Ron said, "I heard about a new disco not far from here. How does that strike you?"

Cassandra shook her head. "I think not, Ron. Not tonight. It's been a long day, what with this and that. If you don't mind too much, I'd much rather go straight home."

He tried to hide his disappointment with a shrug. "If that's the way you want it."

She reached across to touch his hand lightly. "Some other night perhaps."

They were silent during the cab ride to Cassandra's apartment building. She was busy planning tomorrow. She had about made up her mind; she was going to try and arrange a transfer to the *Nordic Star* and the Mediterranean cruise. The search for her father would probably be futile. She hadn't any idea even where to start looking for him, yet she felt strongly compelled to make the effort.

If only her mother were alive! If she were, Cassandra could force the issue and get more information. One thing was reasonably clear—either her mother had lied about her father's tragic death, or she had been misled, for some reason.

Cassandra came out of her reverie as the cab drew up before her building, and Ron got out his wallet to pay the driver.

"No, Ron. Keep the cab." She placed a hand on his arm. "It's early to bed for me tonight."

He turned a face of dismay to her. "But Cass, aren't you going to even ask me in for a nightcap? I thought . . ."

"I know what you thought, Ron. I really don't have anything to drink in my apartment; I haven't had time to shop for anything yet."

"A cup of coffee would do fine," he said insinuatingly.

"Ron . . ." She sighed. "You are very hard to discourage." She faced him squarely. "Are you the kind of a man who thinks he can take a woman to bed for the price of dinner?"

He stiffened. "That's a hell of a thing to say!"

"Ron, you nagged and nagged about taking me out tonight. I finally gave in to save the wear and tear. But I am *not* going to bed with you, now or any other time. So go chase a more willing female."

He recoiled as though he'd been slapped. "You're a cold bitch, Cass, that's your trouble," he muttered.

She smiled tightly. "You're really conforming to the macho image, aren't you? If a woman won't go to bed with you, she's frigid." She pushed down the door handle. "Good night, Ron. Thanks for the dinner."

Just before she slammed the door in his face, he flared, "I hope you *do* switch cruises. I'd hate to have you along for two whole months."

Cassandra, smiling to herself, went into her building. She supposed she was acting rather a bitch, but even if she had felt inclined to go to bed with Ron, she wasn't in the mood tonight. The note had left her uptight, and despite all her efforts to the contrary, she had thought of little else all evening.

The minute the head office of Nordic Lines opened in San Francisco, she made the telephone call, finally getting through to the personnel supervisor in charge of cruise assignments.

Her reception was chilly. The supervisor, Anne Roberts, said, "You know what you're asking, Kanaris? You were made aware of the proper procedure when you were employed. To get a change of cruise assignment, you must make an application well in advance."

"Yes, I know that, Ms. Roberts, but I only learned about this particular cruise last night. It's rather important to me."

"A matter of life and death, I suppose?" the other woman said sarcastically.

"No, of course not, but important nonetheless. At least to me." Cassandra knew that if she told the supervisor she wanted to switch cruises to search for a perhaps nonexistent father and on the strength of an anonymous note, she would be laughed at. Instead she improvised, "I'm a mystery fan, and I would very much like to meet all those famous mystery writers."

"*That's* vitally important to you?" Anne Roberts said in disbelief. "For that reason you expect me to disrupt our personnel assignments, and with only ten days notice? Not good enough, Kanaris, and you know it!"

"There's something else. There's a man on the *Nordic Rover* who has been trying to get me into bed with him, and two months on the same ship with him would give me the shudders."

"A crew member? Who is it?"

"I can't tell you that, Ms. Roberts."

The woman laughed. "My dear Kanaris, you were clearly informed that one talent required of a woman employed to work our ships is the ability to fend off advances, from crew members as well as passengers. If you can't handle yourself in that kind of a situation, perhaps you're in the wrong line of work."

The woman's supercilious tone was beginning to annoy Cassandra, and she was strongly tempted to tell her to stuff the job, but she was in no financial condition to take that drastic a step. She did not have enough money to quit her job and finance an air flight to the Greek Islands on what might well be a futile mission.

"I understand, Ms. Roberts," she finally said with a sigh. "I knew it was short notice, but I thought it worth a try."

"Perhaps you might be able to work the cruise, Kanaris, if they have it next year," the supervisor said in a warmer voice. "I'm sorry that I couldn't comply with your request. If it will console you any, I can confide in you that I've had nothing but good reports on your work. Hang in there, Kanaris."

Cassandra hung up slowly. All of a sudden she felt a sense of relief. She had made every effort, and the decision had been taken out of her hands. There didn't seem to be any way she could go, not at the present. Maybe the whole thing was a hoax, anyway. She had lived all these years with the thought that her father was dead; she could continue to survive.

She knew, of course, that it would be different now. In her mind there would always be the nagging thought that he *might* be alive, somewhere.

Two days later she came home from an afternoon movie and heard her telephone ringing as she put the key in the lock. Quickly, she opened the door, rushed to the phone, and snatched up the receiver.

"Hello," she said breathlessly.

"Kanaris, did you go over my head?"

"Ms. Roberts?" Cassandra said, startled. "You mean about changing cruises? No, I did not, I swear to you."

"You wouldn't lie to me?" Anne Roberts's icy voice thawed a trifle.

"I swear. I wouldn't know who to go to about it, except you. I haven't even mentioned it to anyone, except . . ." She hesitated.

"Except?"

"Just another crew member. Certainly no one with any kind of clout."

She heard a faint sigh on the other end of the line. "Well, someone found out, and someone with clout acted. I just received a memo signed by the president of the company, no less, transferring you to the *Nordic Star*, their assistant cruise director will take over your Orient cruise. So someone up there must like you. Good-bye, Kanaris, and good luck with all your mystery writers."

Cassandra hung up thoughtfully, her mind filled with questions. She was glad to get the transfer, of course, but who could be responsible? And why, why should anyone intervene in her behalf? But even more important, how could anyone except the supervisor have known that she wanted the transfer? Even Ron didn't know that she had actually requested a transfer.

The man who called himself Zeus said, "It has been arranged then? The girl is going on the cruise ship?"

The man called Pluto said, "Yes, Zeus. Apparently Hera arranged it."

"Damn and blast that woman! She's the one who started this by having that note planted. Ares, what do you think?"

Ares smiled coldly. "Where would be the game, if Hera hadn't alerted the girl?"

"If that girl gets to him, we will lose the game," Zeus snapped. "We can't have that happen."

"Then we'll have to see that it doesn't happen," Ares said with his cold smile.

"Artemis?" Zeus looked at one of the two women in the room.

"I think it would be rather fun," she said with a charming smile. "Where's the game without the hunt?"

"Don't take your persona too literally," Zeus said harshly.

"I have no wish to lose. We stand to lose too much, if the girl gets to him."

Ares said, "We can always kill him first. I advised that course of action at the start."

Zeus was shaking his head. "No, that's too drastic. That is only a last resort."

"Let's kill the girl then."

"You're so bloodthirsty, dear Ares," Artemis said playfully. "The hunt is always more fun than the kill."

The fourth man in the room spoke for the first time. "The first thing to do is send one, or more, of us along on the cruise, to keep a close watch on her."

Zeus sighed. "I've already thought of that, Hephaestus. It's a foregone conclusion that we must do that. We have no alternative. But Hera will also send one or two of the others along, you can be sure of that."

Demeter, the other woman, said, "That will only make it more fun all around."

"The next question is," Zeus said, "which of us shall go?"

"I'll volunteer," Artemis said eagerly. "It will be easier for a woman to gain Cassandra's confidence."

Zeus nodded. "You're right. Who else? You, Ares?"

Artemis said quickly, "Not him. He's too fond of violence."

"My dear Artemis, violence may become necessary, regrettable as that may be. Ares?" Zeus said.

"I shall be delighted to accompany our dear Artemis." Ares bowed mockingly, his eyes the essence of evil.

Three

After meeting the cruise director for the *Nordic Star*, Cassandra knew that it was going to be a difficult trip.

Leland Dawes was arrogant, vain, and obviously jealous of his authority. He also seemed to have a strong prejudice against female cruise directors. Now in his late forties, he had once worked in the Nevada casinos, where he had become fairly well known as a singer. However, with time, his star had faded, and his anger at that fact continued to color his personality.

The *Star* had just completed a two-week Caribbean cruise, and it was during the three-day layover in Fort Lauderdale that Cassandra met Dawes in his office aboard ship.

Entering the rather overdecorated office, Cassandra saw a tallish man with a shock of dark hair, theatrically streaked with gray, piercing green eyes, a prominent nose, and a ruddy complexion. His rather obvious good looks were marred by a petulant expression, and he glared at her with frank displeasure.

Cassandra, with a feeling of foreboding, said, "Mr. Dawes?"

He bared his teeth in a grimace that might have been intended as a smile, teeth so white and even that they had to be capped, and said unpleasantly. "You must be Cassandra Kanaris, Paul's replacement?"

"Yes, I am," she said with more composure than she felt.

"Well, you might as well sit," he said ungraciously, motioning to a chair opposite the desk behind which he sat.

Cassandra took the seat and drew a deep breath. It was clear that she had a problem to deal with, if she was going to get on this man's good side—assuming he *had* a good side.

He stared at her intently, and said sourly, "Did you ask to be transferred to the *Star*? Paul said he certainly didn't request a transfer, and he wasn't too happy about it. I'll be honest with you, Miss Kanaris, I'm not, either. I had just got Paul trained to my satisfaction, and now I'll have to start all over again, with you."

Cassandra felt a pulse of anger, but she kept her voice calm. Dawes was clearly a prima donna; and unless she wanted to spend a miserable cruise she knew she had to placate him, despite the fact that it went against the grain. "I've had four years of experience," she said, making her voice neutral. "Two years as a hostess, and two as an assistant cruise director. It's all there, in my file."

She indicated the manila folder open on his desk before him.

"Papers!" he said with heavy scorn, slapping the folder closed. "Papers tell very little about a person's ability. The whole world is being inundated by papers and more papers. And you didn't answer my question. Did you request a transfer to the *Star*?"

The man was insufferable! Cassandra said steadily, "Yes, Mr. Dawes, I did."

He squinted suspiciously. "But why? Why this particular cruise?"

She gave him the same answer she had given the personnel supervisor, and Dawes shook his head in disbelief. "You put everybody to all this trouble just because you wanted to meet some mystery writers? I don't believe this!"

Cassandra, struggling to hold back what she really wanted to say to this man, shrugged. "But Mr. Dawes, many times a transfer is requested simply because someone wants to visit a particular place. That's the reason many of us work cruise ships in the first place, isn't it? A change of scenery, a change of faces, a search for new adventures?" She tried her sweetest smile, yet his expression didn't soften. "I'm sorry if I've inconvenienced you in any way, but since the transfer *has* been made, and since we will be working together, I hope that you will give me a chance to show you that I do know my job. I am quite good at it, Mr. Dawes."

His glance slid away, and he assumed an expression of patient suffering. "At least you're right on that score. What's done is done." He paused briefly. "All right. There's obviously nothing to be done about the switch at this late date, but I want one thing clearly understood. You are not to expect any special favors from me because you are a woman."

His gaze made contact with hers aggressively, and Cassandra had to suppress her surprise. What on earth was he talking about? She couldn't resist asking, "Haven't you ever worked with a woman assistant cruise director before?"

He appeared to find some implied rebuke in her question for his color heightened. "Happily, no. Although women have their place on cruise ships as performers, hostesses, and, occasionally, guest lecturers, I have never thought that the job of cruise director was suitable for a woman."

Cassandra, fascinated and really curious, had to ask, "Why?"

His expression told her that she had been foolish to ask the question. "Because it is a difficult and demanding job, which requires a strong will and an even stronger personality, not to mention physical stamina. You say you've been working as an assistant cruise director for two years, you should know what I mean."

Cassandra smiled sweetly. "Oh, I do, Mr. Dawes. And I

agree with you as far as the requirements go, but what makes you think that women don't possess the qualities you named?"

Dawes pushed her folder roughly to one side, and Cassandra suspected that he would like to do the same with her. "Observation," he said curtly, "and experience."

Cassandra, realizing that she had succeeded in making him even angrier, tried again to placate him. "Well, I do hope that I will be able to change your opinion, Mr. Dawes. I certainly intend to work very hard at doing so."

"We'll see," he said noncommittally. "We'll see."

After the audience with Dawes, Cassandra was introduced to the other members of the director's staff: the hostess, Betsy Clark, a pert woman of about Cassandra's own age; and Ben Lomax, a very young, brash, energetic man of about twenty, who suffered from a bad case of overenthusiasm.

Cassandra liked Betsy immediately; she sensed that Betsy might be an ally against Dawes; and she was amused at Lomax, who already had picked up many of the salesman-actor techniques, the overfirm handshake, the overforceful direct eye contact, and the plastic smile. He'd be attractive, Cassandra thought with an inward smile, if he'd only relax and be himself. Dawes's influence, probably.

After the meeting with Leland Dawes and the staff, Cassandra was shown to her cabin by Betsy Clark.

Most of the performers and staff had to share cabins, but the cruise director and assistant cruise director were assigned private cabins, a privilege that Cassandra much appreciated. During her two years as a hostess, she had discovered that no matter how much you liked the person you were rooming with, they invariably had habits that differed from your own; and since private time, for the staff, was at a premium, she had been very relieved when she had been promoted to assistant cruise director and allowed to room alone.

"I know he's difficult, but he's really good at his job," Betsy said as they were walking to Cassandra's cabin.

It took Cassandra a moment before she realized that Betsy was talking about Leland Dawes.

"When he's dealing with the passengers, he's a different man, all charm and personality."

Cassandra sighed. "Well, I just hope that he'll give me a chance to show him what I can do." She grinned suddenly. "You see, I'm good at my job, too."

"It'll work out," Betsy said confidently. "Once we're at sea, he'll be too busy, and he'll need you too much to give you too bad a time." They stopped before a door on the Pleiades deck. "Well, here you are, Cassandra. Home!"

She opened the door, and let Cassandra precede her into the cabin. Cassandra dropped her purse onto the table and looked around. "Just the same as my cabin on the *Nordic Rover*. I feel like I'm home again."

Betsy smiled. "I'd give my eyeteeth to have a cabin all to myself. My roommate last trip was a real party girl, up to all hours, and sloppy in the bargain."

"I know just what you mean," Cassandra said. "I had the same problem when I was a hostess."

Betsy handed her a manila folder. "Here is the list of performers who will be working this trip. Leland asked me to give it to you. We'll have to start rehearsals tomorrow."

Cassandra accepted the list and scanned it quickly. There was an orchestra; a jazz trio; a musical director; a quartet of singers, two male and two female; a puppeteer; a magician; a dance team; a male lounge pianist/singer; a female singer; six young women billed as The Lido Dancers; and a country/western trio.

She recognized the names of the orchestra and quartet members. They were Polish musicians with whom she had worked before. The only other name she recognized was that of Gene Thorne, the music director.

"You'll like the music director," Betsy commented, as Cassandra finished reading the list. "I've worked with him before, and he's the best. He really knows how to put on a good show."

Cassandra looked up with a smile. "You must have been reading my mind. I've worked with Gene several times myself. He is great. He'll make things easier all around. Now, have you got any hot gossip that I should know? Since I'm new to the *Star,* I can use all the briefing I can get."

Betsy grinned and plopped down onto the couch. "If you don't mind, I'm going to sit. I've been on my feet all day."

Cassandra took the other end of the couch, and reached for a juicy-looking pear from the basket of fruit on the table.

"Well," Betsy began, "we've got a pretty good crew. The captain is named Helsing. He's good, and a really pleasant man." She giggled. "And one of the doctors is straight out of *The Love Boat.* He's young, he's handsome, and a real ladies' man. You'll have to watch out for him. In fact, we'll *all* have to watch out for him.

"Another one to watch out for is the chief purser. He's another fast operator. He's got a wife in Norway and a steady girlfriend on the ship, but that doesn't stop him from making moves on any of the other female staff members he can talk into his bed, as well as some of the younger female passengers."

Cassandra smiled, remembering Ron Wilson. "I've encountered that kind before. Do we have a full ship?"

Betsy nodded. "At first I thought we might not. You know that they remodeled the *Star* a few months ago, adding all those penthouse suites on the Astral deck. They're beautiful, but awfully expensive, much more than the regular suites, and you know what *they* go for."

Cassandra nodded. "I've heard. Conspicuous consumption."

"Well, up until a week ago, only two of the six penthouse suites had been booked, but just a few days ago, the other four were all booked on the same day, by the same travel agency. It was downright weird. At any rate, we now have a full ship."

Betsy stretched and stood up. "Well, I'd better get back to my own cabin and see if my roommate has arrived yet. This time it's Leslie Lane, the singer. I have a feeling that it's going to be just like last time. Singers are definitely night people." She turned toward the door. "It was nice meeting you, Cassandra, and I can tell you right now that I have a feeling that it's going to be great working with you on this cruise."

Cassandra also got to her feet and walked with the other woman to the door. "I feel the same. I hope we'll be friends."

"We already are," Betsy said warmly, as she went out.

Cassandra again picked up the manila folder containing the list. Well, here they were, the people with whom she would be working closely for the next four weeks. As she always did at the beginning of any cruise, she scanned the list of performers, and wondered what they, and the passengers, were going to be like.

Sailing day was beautiful, warm and clear, with a nice breeze that helped to counteract the Florida humidity.

Cassandra, in a pleated white skirt and blue blazer, bearing the logo of the Nordic Line, stood at the head of the gangplank with Leland Dawes, Betsy Clark, and Ben Lomax, greeting and posing for pictures with the passengers, as they boarded.

Since this was going to be a fairly lengthy cruise, most of the passengers were middle-aged or older, with only a scattering of young couples. Cassandra had learned early on that younger couples generally could not afford the time or the money for long cruises; the average age of the passengers on a cruise like this one was sixty-five years old.

Upon studying the passenger list, she had also learned that this time there were only going to be two children on board, which pleased her. She liked children well enough and certainly intended to have some of her own some day, but children could be a hassle on board ship, and it was always a relief when there wasn't too many of them.

As Cassandra continued to greet the passengers and pose for pictures with them, her cheeks grew stiff from the constant smiling. Over five hundred passengers. A smile and a word of greeting for each one. Of course, that was somewhat of an exaggeration, since she often escaped with a single smile for couples, or groups. Still, the smile, she thought dolefully at one point, felt permanently fixed in place.

During a brief lull, she whispered to Betsy, "I haven't seen any of the mystery writers yet."

"Your mystery writers and their fans will be coming along in a group. They're at a champagne bon voyage party organized by the woman who dreamed up the Mystery Cruise idea."

The conversation was interrupted as another group of passengers came across the gangplank. One was an elderly woman—tall, regal, beautifully dressed, with snow-white hair exquisitely coiffed. Her narrow face was still relatively wrinkle free, and her brown eyes sharp and piercing. Cassandra estimated her to be in her seventies, and she suspected an expensive face-lift or two along the way.

The woman stopped before her, and Cassandra said, "Welcome aboard the *Nordic Star*. I'm Cassandra Kanaris, your assistant cruise director."

"I am Lisa van Horne," the woman said in a low, melodious voice. Her sharp eyes were examining Cassandra closely, seemingly taking in every feature and storing them in her memory, until Cassandra became uncomfortable under her gaze.

As the ship's photographer approached with his camera poised, Lisa van Horne held up one well-manicured hand and said imperiously, "No pictures, young man. When one reaches my age, no picture, no matter how well done, can possibly be flattering."

Cassandra had to laugh. "As you wish, Miss van Horne." She waved the photographer away. "Would you like someone to show you to your cabin? You're in one of the penthouse suites, I believe."

"Heavens, no, child, I'm perfectly capable of finding it on my own. It's my first trip on the *Star*. I want to explore her. What a lovely scarf." She reached out to touch the lavender-colored scarf around Cassandra's neck. "Your favorite color, isn't it?"

Cassandra looked at her in surprise. "Yes, but how did you know that?"

"An old lady's intuition, my dear."

She smiled brilliantly, and lovely as she was now, Cassandra knew that Lisa van Horne must have been an unusually beautiful woman in her prime, a real heartbreaker.

As the woman moved on, Betsy sighed. "Well, this looks like the last batch. And I think this is your mystery group."

With a nod of her head she indicated a group of about thirty people coming on board. They were all bright-eyed and laughing; evidently the champagne party had been a great success.

Betsy's surmise was correct. Most of the group wore name tags with their names and the legend: "I Love a Mystery!" Several of them wore tags that also said, "Speaker."

Cassandra, as a mystery fan, recognized most of the names. One author was famous for espionage novels; another for a series about a tough adventurer. A husband-

and-wife team who wrote comic mysteries. One woman known for her romantic suspense novels. One name, however, Cassandra wasn't familiar with; it belonged to a slender man, with a touch of cynicism about his dark brown eyes and full-lipped mouth. He was blond, deeply tanned, and looked about thirty. The name on his tag was Jake Randle. As she stood next to him she found herself very conscious of him.

After the flash of the photographer's camera, she turned to Jake Randle. "Hello, I'm Cassandra Kanaris, the assistant cruise director. And you're Mr. Randle. Welcome aboard. Are you a mystery writer?"

"I can't write worth a damn, Cassandra, except for crime reports, and I've been told they're almost unreadable." His grin was lopsided, and incongruously, a dimple came and went in his right cheek as he grinned. "Not all of the speakers are mystery writers, you know. One of us is a former con artist, and one of us is a private detective."

"And which one are you?"

His brown eyes warmed toward her. "Can't you guess?"

She tapped the corner of her mouth with her finger. "Let's see . . . If you were the former con man, I'd say you would have to be much older. Therefore, you must be the private detective."

"Very good, Cassandra." He applauded softly. "You hit it right on the button."

She smiled. "Well, I am a mystery fan! So you'll be lecturing to the mystery fans on what it's like to be a private eye, I suppose?"

He nodded. "Yes, I'm supposed to give a couple of talks about my experiences, both as a private cop and a regular cop."

"You were once a policeman?"

"I was. I was with the New York Police Department for seven years, until I . . . uh, retired three years ago, and became a private cop in Miami. That's where I met Alex

Dudley, who writes all those books about Fargo, the detective, adventurer, deep-sea diver, God only knows what else. Alex has been picking my brains ever since."

Cassandra longed to ask him why he had left the police force, but she knew that would be a mistake. She said merely, "Well, welcome aboard the *Star*, Mr. Randle. As a mystery fan, I'm looking forward to this voyage very much."

"So am I, Cassandra, especially now that I've met you."

He gave her his crooked smile and Cassandra felt her color rise. Then he was gone, as those behind him pressed forward.

As he went in search of his cabin Jake's thoughts lingered on the woman he'd just met. He was strongly drawn to her. This would be his first cruise. He'd heard that men and women left their inhibitions behind when they boarded a cruise ship and that sexual connections were easy to make. He wondered now if that held true for the ship's personnel. Alex had told him that this was a gross exaggeration, and Alex was a seasoned voyager. But then Alex, for all the adventures, sexual or otherwise, that he wrote for his popular character, Fargo, was a pragmatic man and a highly moral individual, happily married for twenty years to the same woman, and a lot might well go on that he never saw.

Jake was a neat man, almost obsessively neat, not only about his person and attire, but also about his private and professional life. He had been a good cop, bringing to the job a bright, inquisitive mind. Loose ends always bothered him, and that trait had made him a good homicide officer. A fellow officer, irked by his worrying over a fact that didn't quite fit, had once told him, "You'll drive me into a rubber room, Jake. You remind me of a man who, if he found a loose thread on his suit, would pull and tug at it until the whole suit was unraveled. You keep doing that on this job, buddy, and someday you're going to wind up naked to the world."

And that, in effect, was what had finally happened. Jake had been assigned to a murder case. A prominent politician had been found beaten to death in a seedy hotel off Times Square. On the face of it the death seemed the result of a random mugging. Probably one of the hotel thieves who preyed on hotels in the area had broken into the room and found its occupant in bed. If that was the case, the odds against the killer ever being found were prohibitive.

But Jake wasn't satisfied with that explanation. The one fact that bugged him, the loose thread, was the victim's presence in the hotel in the first place. He certainly could have afforded a better hotel. Usually, in such cases, the man would have rented a room as a place to take a hooker; in this case that did not seem to apply, for a woman could not have given the victim such a brutal beating.

Jake kept plugging away. Slowly, the truth began to emerge. The victim, although married, had been gay and had obviously booked the room for an assignation with another man. The man had beaten the politician to death, then robbed him. Jake began hauling in male hookers and grilling them mercilessly. By this time the preliminary report had worked its way up to somebody high in the city administration, and the word came down to lay off. The reason was obvious: if Jake found the killer, the whole unsavory story would come out in court and be splattered all over the front pages.

But Jake ignored the warning and doggedly continued with his investigation. The next thing he knew he was removed from the homicide squad and assigned to traffic patrol. He promptly resigned.

He also lost his wife in the process. He had been married to Beverly for three years. Unlike many policemen's wives, she loved police work. She loved the thought of being married to a man with a dangerous job; she basked in what she considered the glamour of his profession. Although Jake had often tried to explain to her that it was not that dangerous and was far from glamourous, Beverly refused to believe him, and when he resigned, she simply packed up and moved out. Fortunately, they had postponed children.

Jake was left cynical and disillusioned, both with police work and with women. But since he had joined the force at twenty-two, he knew no other profession, and he was good at it, damned good. So, although policemen generally regarded private detectives with scorn, Jake decided to become one.

He didn't get his license in New York but instead moved to Florida and opened his practice in Miami, working mostly along Florida's Gold Coast. He did very well from the very beginning, steering away from divorce work as much as possible, specializing in industrial jobs and hunting down runaway wives, husbands, and children. After four years he had a thriving agency with a staff of four.

The only thing he missed was the excitement of a murder investigation. When he had first become friends with Alex Dudley, he had hooted in derision when Alex had questioned him about his various cases for information to use in his novels.

"Alex, you writers romanticize private eyes. The life is not all that exciting, believe me. For instance, we seldom get involved in murder investigations."

"But you *have* been involved in several murder cases, Jake. I know that."

Jake nodded. "That's true, three altogether, but all three times I was working on what I consider the wrong side of the fence."

"How so? Murder is murder, Jake."

"As you know, I was working for a law firm, Fenner & Blake. They're a famous defense team, demanding and getting outrageous fees. As a result, all of their clients are wealthy. All three times my job was to find evidence that their clients did *not* commit the crime with which they were charged."

Alex's round face lit up with a sly smile. "People are entitled to a defense, the rich as well as the poor. Isn't that a tenet of our legal system?"

"Of course it is, Alex. But the more money you have, the better defense you'll get. That's an *unwritten* tenet of our court system, if you will."

Alex frowned slightly. "Are you saying they were all three guilty?"

"One was, definitely. And one was clearly innocent. The third I'm not sure about to this day."

"As I recall, all three were found not guilty."

Jake nodded. "And that's what bugs me, you see. The one I did discover to be guilty went free because of me, in a sense. Naturally, Bert Fenner didn't use the evidence I uncovered of his client's guilt."

"Knowing you as I do, I'm surprised you didn't turn what you'd discovered over to the prosecution."

Jake smiled grimly. "I thought about it, believe me. But then I remembered what had happened to me in New York, and I backed away. It's bothered the hell out of me ever since."

It was Alex Dudley who had mentioned the Mystery Cruise to Jake and suggested proposing him as a speaker to talk of his experiences both as a city cop and a private detective. The police officer who had originally been scheduled for the cruise had found it necessary to back out at the last minute. All of Jake's expenses would be paid.

Jake accepted at once. He did not tell Alex that Fenner & Blake had just offered him a new murder case. Jake had not given them a firm answer as yet, and the cruise would give him an excuse to turn it down. He had not taken a vacation since opening his agency, which was now functioning smoothly and could operate without him for a month. Jake had decided to stay on the *Star* after the Mystery Cruise ended and continue on to the Greek Isles. He would have to pay for the extra two weeks out of his own pocket, but he could afford it; he had been making good money and there had been little to spend it on.

Now that he was finally on board the ship, Jake was doubly glad that he had come along. He was looking forward to a good time.

By five o'clock the last passenger had boarded, and those of the staff who had been required to greet the oncoming passengers were free. Cassandra still had a great deal to do and was so busy that she scarcely heard the warning over the loudspeakers: "All visitors are now asked to go ashore. We shall be sailing in thirty minutes."

But when she heard the ship's whistle a half hour later, Cassandra put aside her paperwork and went up on deck. No matter how many times she went through it, sailing time was always thrilling for Cassandra.

As the passengers stood at the railing, throwing bright streamers toward the people seeing them off from the dock, and the ship's orchestra played on the Promenade deck, the ship moved slowly, majestically, up the channel and toward the open sea. The sun was sinking like a fireball in the west, and the sky was a deep blue, with a few white, fluffy clouds drifting across the sky.

The passengers stood three deep along the rail, laughing and waving. Cassandra finally found a place at the aft railing. Leland Dawes commented over the bridge microphone on the sights they passed. Within a very short time they were beyond the breakwater, and the deck began to move under her feet. Cassandra stood away from the rail, feet set wide apart, getting her sea legs back.

She sniffed the salt tang of the freshening breeze. The deck started to empty as the passengers began to leave, going in search of their cabins, or to one of the many bars. Many would be unpacking; others, those who had imbibed too freely, would catch a short nap before dinner; and still others would continue to celebrate.

Cassandra smiled to herself. Although the sea was relatively calm today, she knew that many, especially the first-time passengers, would be seasick and skip dinner. There was nothing more terrible than a bout of seasickness. Victims felt quite willing to die, if it would only relieve their bone-deep misery. Thank goodness, she had always been a good sailor.

Well, she'd better stop loitering and get back to work, or Leland Dawes would be unhappy with her.

It was going to be a busy night. After dinner, they had to put on the first show, in the main lounge, and after that there would be a second, more intimate show in the Pisces Lounge.

Thank goodness sailing night required only casual dress, for she certainly wouldn't have time to change. Another plus was the fact that the shows tonight would be relatively brief, as everyone, including the passengers, would be tired from the excitement and the bustle of getting under way. Tomorrow night would be another matter entirely. There would be the captain's cocktail party, an elaborate show, and the introduction of the cruise director and his staff to the passengers; it would all be formal dress.

After the second show, which tonight featured Leslie Lane, the singer who was sharing a cabin with Betsy Clark, Cassandra would be through for the night, and she intended to make the most of this by going right to bed so that she would be rested for the first full day tomorrow.

She knew that there would be the opportunity to party until dawn. After the second show there would be dancing to the music of the jazz trio in the Nova Lounge, a midnight buffet, and gambling in the casino; but Cassandra knew, from experience, that you couldn't stay up all night and function well the next day, and she intended to give Leland Dawes no opportunity to fault her work.

* * *

As Cassandra walked down the passageway of the Pleiades deck all was quiet. The ship was rolling a bit, but she didn't mind; in fact, she rather liked the rocking motion at night, for she found it conducive to sleep. Back in the cradle, she thought, smiling to herself.

When she let herself into her cabin, she found the light on and a flash of color on her bed caught her attention. It was lavender! Her heart began to race and the hair on the back of her neck prickled as she walked over and picked up the familiar envelope, this time with her name on it.

With dread she opened the envelope and read the brief message: "Cassandra: You made the right decision. A friend."

How had the envelope gotten here? The door had been locked when she let herself in. She thumbed the call button beside her bed. In a moment a rap sounded on the door.

Cassandra opened the door to admit the blond stewardess, Greta. Cassandra held up the envelope. "Did you by any chance put this on my bed?"

Greta's eyes widened. "No, Cassandra. And it wasn't here when I turned down your bed."

"When was that?"

"The usual time, during the dinner hour."

"You *did* lock the door when you left?"

Greta bobbed her head. "Oh, yes, I'm always careful about that." She looked closely at Cassandra's pale face. "Is something wrong?"

"It's not important," Cassandra said absently. "Perhaps the note was left there earlier and got tangled up in the bedding without you realizing it." She ran a hand through her hair and tried to smile. "Don't worry about it, Greta. I'm sorry to have bothered you. Thank you."

After the girl had left, Cassandra stood staring down at the note. She felt violated and, in some indefinable way, endangered. Someone possessed a key to her cabin and could come and go as they pleased. Of course, all cabin attendants had passkeys, but how could it be one of them? No, that wasn't the answer. It had to be someone else. But who?

Cassandra knew that she couldn't ask that her lock be changed. She would have to have a logical reason, and taking such an action would only cast a cloud of suspicion on all the ship's personnel, and she certainly didn't want that.

She went about getting ready for bed. Tired as she was, she doubted that she would get very much sleep this night.

Four

The sharp peal of her alarm brought Cassandra out of a dark and nervous dream where she had been surrounded by evil, threatening figures, whose faces she could not quite see.

She glanced at the face of her ornamental clock with a grimace of distaste. Tired as she had been, she had indeed gotten little sleep. The presence of the note had seemed to permeate her cabin with the chill of the unknown, making her feel vulnerable and frightened.

And now—now she was going to have to face a long and very busy day.

Well, there was no avoiding it. She would ring Greta to bring her breakfast; that and a brisk shower would help.

An hour later, she made her way to the Astral Lounge, where the first meeting of the speakers and staff of the Mystery Cruise was scheduled to take place.

Dawes had assigned her the duty of supervising the activities of the group, and at first Cassandra thought that he was doing this because of her professed interest in the mystery writers, but she had now decided that he had done it because the group bored him and because he resented having on board an activity that he had not initiated and was not in complete control of.

As she entered the lounge Cassandra noticed that most of the guest speakers for the group were already present, including Jake Randle.

Cassandra was intrigued by the diversity of the speakers and was especially intrigued by Roxie Pike. Roxie was a travel agent noted for her penchant for organizing what Ben Lomax referred to as "speciality cruises."

"You'll find her pretty weird, personally," he had confided to Cassandra. "But she does know her business. Last year she organized a Soap Opera Cruise. The speakers were all cast members of the *River Falls* soap opera.

"They showed videotapes of the program and had symposiums where they analyzed the actors and emotions of the characters, and even played some totally new segments, written just for the cruise. She really drew a large crowd for that cruise, much larger than this one.

"Roxie gets kind of bossy, but just be firm with her, and don't let her bulldoze you too much."

Cassandra had been rather touched by Ben's concern, but she had been in her job long enough to not be easily intimidated. Still, she was curious to see just what Ben meant by "weird."

The other nonwriter, aside from Jake, was Todd Breckinridge. Breckinridge owned a bookstore in New York dealing exclusively in mysteries, The Deadly Deed. He made the claim that he had read every mystery novel ever published and boasted that he could find any mystery novel, no matter how long out of print. He was also familiar with old radio mystery shows and had a large collection of them. Every night during the cruise he was going to play over the ship's radio an episode of the old radio mystery serial, "I Love a Mystery," the series that had given Roxie Pike her concept for the cruise. The trip's agenda also included a performance of the popular mystery drama, *Arsenic and Old Lace*. Breckinridge was to direct it, using members of the Mystery Cruise as the cast.

What made Breckinridge stand out in a crowd, though, was his appearance. In his fifties, he was tall and skinny, with the cadaverous look of a John Carradine. Cassandra soon discovered that he was garrulous to the point of utter boredom; the problem was that he only talked about one subject—mysteries.

The writing couple, Bob and Sandra Dean, were warm and friendly people, yet Cassandra was somewhat disappointed to discover that they were not as witty as their books. In fact, they seemed to possess little sense of humor at all.

Alex Dudley, Jake Randle's friend, and his wife, Madeline, struck Cassandra as a nice couple, but she could detect none of the derring-do in Dudley that his famous character, Fargo, possessed.

The writer of the espionage novels looked nothing like what Cassandra thought a spy should look like, and the writer of the romantic suspense novels was close to sixty, tiny and delicate as a bird.

The last writer of the group was the only one who seemed, on the surface at any rate, to fit the image that his work projected. Rhys Carson was the ex-confidence man. For twenty years he had plied his trade profitably, without once being caught. He made the boast that he had never served a day in jail. Then suddenly, he told Cassandra, he "got religion."

"Got religion?" Cassandra asked. They were sitting together, waiting for the group to assemble, and Cassandra had struck up a conversation. "You mean literally?"

Carson laughed; he had an infectious, rolling laugh. "Not religion as such. I always tell people that, to save a lengthy explanation. Actually what happened was, I suddenly realized that I was past the fifty mark, my looks were going, and I was losing confidence in myself." He laughed again. "When a con man loses confidence in himself, he's finished. And looks and charm are a part of the full package. I knew that if I slipped once, if I spent a spell in the slammer, I would never recover. So I decided to look around for another occupation."

Cassandra watched him, intrigued. Carson had lost very little of his charm. He was still lean and trim, with a shock of thick white hair. He dressed flamboyantly, but with a nice eye for colors. She said, "And you decided to become a writer, just like that? From what I've read writers usually have to work at their trade for a long time before they make that first sale."

"Well, I was luckier than most, I guess. I happened to meet up with a literary agent, and he caught fire when he learned that I was a retired con man. He said there was a book in it." Carson grinned slowly. "I've since learned that's a stock reaction from agents. With me it worked. I wrote of my experiences in the trade, he sold it, and I was off and running. I thought that if I could write nonfiction, why not mystery novels? So I dreamed up a character like me, a con man, who always seemed to become involved in murder cases, never mind that I've never been closer to a real murder than the news on the tube. I'll tell you something, dear Cassandra." He put his mouth close to her ear. "I don't want the others to hear, but writing, in my opinion, is like a con game. You simply have to con an editor, a publisher, whatever, into buying what you produce."

Cassandra laughed. "I doubt that most writers would agree with you on that."

"Oh, I'm sure they wouldn't," Carson said cheerfully. "But in my opinion, it holds true . . ."

The sound of clapping hands drew their notice. Roxie Pike was demanding their attention. Roxie was in her forties, a slip of a thing, thin as a reed, and looked frail enough to blow off the aft deck in a puff of wind. But Cassandra had already learned that she had a whim of iron, inexhaustible energy, and a fertile imagination.

"All right, folks," she said in a surprisingly deep voice for such a small woman. "Your attention, please! Our fans will be arriving soon. Now, most of you on the staff have been briefed on what will be required of you . . ."

Jake Randle, who had been standing at the side windows, strolled over, taking an empty seat beside Cassandra. In a low voice he said, "Good morning, Cassandra."

"Good morning, Mr. Randle."

"Jake, please."

She returned his smile, then switched her attention back to Roxie Pike.

". . . there will also be the panel discussions, besides the individual lectures on writing techniques and the like. Mr. Dudley is going to tell us about how he created his character, Fargo. Mr. Randle will talk about what it means to be a homicide detective and what differences, if any, exist between that and being a private detective. And Mr. Carson is going to enlighten us about his life of crime . . ."

Jake muttered to Cassandra, "She sure sounds like a teacher I had in the seventh grade. Looks like her, too."

Cassandra hid a smile behind her hand.

"Mystery quizzes will be published daily in the ship's newspaper. Our writing couple, the Deans, who have written and published numerous mystery short stories, will take plot suggestions from the audience one day and write a complete short story while on stage. That should be of interest to our passengers. And of course, there will be our mystery play performed on our next-to-last evening together, *Arsenic and Old Lace*. And as to that, Mr. Breckinridge informs me that he needs another actress for his cast. I thought, Cassandra, since you are an ardent fan, you would be kind enough to help us out."

"Me?" Cassandra said, startled. "I'm no actress."

Breckinridge said, "You take part in some of the evening shows, don't you, Cassandra?"

"Well, yes, but only in crowd scenes, maybe a little singing or dancing. I seldom have any lines."

Breckinridge gave his wolfish smile. "It's not all that hard, Cassandra. I'll teach you all you need to know."

Roxie clapped her hands. "It'll be great fun, Cassandra. Now, I have made copies of our full two weeks agenda, which I will pass out to each of you."

Jake accepted his and ran a dubious glance over it. "I don't know how all this is going to work out," he mused. "I also got bulldozed into acting in this play, Cassandra. I've never been very much for speaking before a group any larger than two."

Rhys Carson, overhearing, leaned across Cassandra. "Surely you've heard that old saying, 'When you're shy before a group, just imagine that all those in your audience are naked.' You'll be surprised how effective that is at putting you at your ease."

Grinning, Jake glanced around at the gathering, his glance coming to rest on Cassandra. "I'm not so sure. It might cause some embarrassment, considering some of the ladies present."

Cassandra felt herself blushing.

Carson laughed. "It doesn't quite work that way, I've found. Being naked in a group of nudists doesn't turn a man on, you know."

Jake looked at him interestedly. "You've done that?"

"Oh, yes." Carson nodded. "There aren't many things I

haven't tried. Somewhere I read that a good writer must experience all aspects of life before he can write about it."

"Does that apply to murder as well?" Jake was staring at him intently. "After all, that's what most of you write about."

"Oh, well." Carson gave an eloquent shrug. "There have to be exceptions."

"I should hope so . . ."

Jake was interrupted by a handclap from Roxie. "Here comes our group now. Let's make it interesting for them. But before we begin you'll notice on the agenda that some of us are scheduled to meet again this afternoon, in the cardroom. Please try to be prompt."

Once the program was underway, Cassandra left to help with the rehearsal of the evening show. The rehearsal lasted until lunchtime, and when the announcement came over the loudspeakers, she realized that she was hungry. She always ate like a horse when at sea, but she was so active that she never put on any weight.

There was a general exodus from the lounge, and as Cassandra turned to go, she saw Jake Randle approaching.

"I finally tracked you down," he said. "Will you join me for lunch?"

She could not help but smile. "Well, that proves you are a detective, anyway."

"Come on, you have to eat," he said winningly. "Why not with me?"

"Why not?" she said, still smiling.

"Come on then." He took her hand. "It's too beautiful a day to eat in the dining room. How about the buffet?"

They made their way down to the next deck below, where a lavish buffet was laid out on trestle tables. A nice breeze enlivened the air. People were already lined up at the tables.

Jake looked at the lavish spread with awe. "My God, the

food here! If I don't watch it, after a month of this I'll go home weighing thirty pounds more."

Cassandra laughed. "Wait until you see the Nordic buffet in the main dining room on the day before we reach Genoa. That makes this one look like Tiny Tim's supper."

Jake glanced around. "These tables are soon going to be filled up. Why don't I hold one down while you go through the line, then I'll go through? And how about a drink? One thing about taking a lady to lunch on a cruise ship, it's cheap. The least I can do is buy you a drink."

"All right, I'll have a vodka gimlet."

Cassandra stepped onto the end of the line. Out of the corner of her eye she saw Jake capture a table and motion a deck waiter over. She liked Jake Randle. He was personable, bright, with a dry wit, if a bit cynical. Most of all there was an air of competence, of complete self-assurance, about him. In many men this came across as arrogance. Not so with Jake Randle.

When she brought her tray to the table, Jake joined the line for his. She had a sip of her drink and waited until he came back before starting to eat. Curious, she picked up his drink and sniffed it—scotch, and quite strong.

As they ate they discussed the various details of the Mystery Cruise and how it had come about that Jake had joined it. "I'm not sure I made a wise choice," he said wryly. "Oh, not the cruise itself, I'm sure I'll enjoy that. Especially now that I've met you." His look was direct.

Flustered, Cassandra said, "You mentioned something about a month. You're going all the way then?"

He nodded. "Oh, yes. This is my first cruise, and my first vacation in some time. I thought I might as well take advantage of everything offered."

"I'm looking forward to it as well," she said, thinking of her father and the mysterious notes.

"You've never worked this particular cruise?"

"No, not this one." Suddenly she had an urge to tell him

her reason for taking this particular cruise. Jake was a person she felt she could confide in, and he *was* a detective. Maybe he could help her with the mystery of the lavender notes. But she decided to wait, at least until she knew him a little better.

She said, "You're not married?"

"Was. Past tense." He looked at her, unsmiling.

"I'm sorry," she said sympathetically. "I remember reading once that the divorce rate among policemen is one of the highest."

"That's true, but oddly enough, my wife left me for a different reason." Now he smiled slightly. "When *I* quit the department, she left *me*. To her, it seemed, being a cop's wife had a touch of glamour. When I quit, she quit. How about you? I assume you aren't married, either?"

Cassandra shook her head. "No, working a cruise ship is not conducive to a good marriage. Unless both work the same ship, and that might not be a good idea, either."

"I'm glad."

Startled, she said, "Glad?"

"Yes, since I intend seeing as much of you on this cruise as you'll let me, Cassandra."

Taken aback, she said quickly, "Not that I'm not flattered, Jake, but I'm afraid I don't have much time for socializing. The hours we work are incredible. Seven days a week, fourteen and fifteen hours a day."

"But you must have *some* time off," he protested.

"Not a whole lot. My only free time on board ship is after most passengers are in bed. And when we're in port, I get some time off, alternating with the other staff members."

He shook his head. "All work and no play, you know."

"Oh, but I love it. Most of the time, anyway . . ."

"After watching *The Love Boat*, I thought the staff, both men and women, went about happily dating the passengers, taking shore trips, and jumping into bed at every opportunity."

Cassandra was shaking her head. "That's not true. I've watched the program a few times; that ship must run itself. As you say, the *Love Boat* staff spends all their time either chasing or being chased and interfering with the passengers' private lives. The truth is, there simply isn't time for that. Oh, I'm not saying there aren't shipboard romances. It happens, but less often than you'd think."

Jake got a woebegone expression. "You make it sound like I won't be seeing you at all." He brightened. "But you have to eat lunch. Maybe we can do this again from time to time."

"I think that can be arranged," she said solemnly.

"Unluckily, I've already been assigned a table and it's not yours. Can anything be done about that?"

"The line policy is to scatter the officers and staff members among the regular passengers." She hesitated. She could ask to be seated at Jake's table, but if Leland Dawes found out, he would want to know why. Besides, she wasn't sure yet she wanted to sit at the same table with Jake. It would be better if they didn't see each other that much. She said briskly, "I think it's too late to do anything about that, Jake. Now, I have to run, I have a million things to do."

"At least I'll see you at all the mystery functions, since you're the ship's liaison with the group." As she started to get up he reached out for her hand. "I like you, Cass. I think I'm going to like you very much."

Cassandra was suddenly shy. "You move fast, don't you, Jake? We've just met, for heaven's sake!"

His gaze didn't falter. "When I see something I want, I go after it. The winners in this world always do."

She disengaged her hand. "We'll have to see. I think I like you, too, but let's take it slow, okay?"

"Sure, just so long as you know." He sat back, smiling slightly. "I can wait. I've waited this long."

"This long?" She laughed uncertainly. "Less than a day?"

He said simply, "I've been waiting all my life."

The phone in Ares' penthouse suite rang. Ares scooped it up quickly. "Yes?"

"Your call is ready now, sir. Your party is on the line."

Ares waited until the operator was off the line, then said, "Zeus? Is that you?"

"Yes, Ares. What do you have to report?"

"The girl seems to be becoming very friendly with a detective on board."

"A detective?" Zeus said sharply.

"Yes. What they call a private eye. His name is Jake Randle. He's a member of this 'I Love a Mystery' cruise group. He and the girl just had lunch together and they seemed very, shall we say, intimate?"

"Is there any chance that Cassandra has employed him?"

"I have no way of knowing that yet. I couldn't get close enough to hear what they were saying, not without arousing suspicion. But I have learned that Randle was once a New York homicide detective, now working for himself in Florida. I also found out that while the rest of the Mystery Cruise people are disembarking in Genoa, he is continuing on, which is suspicious in itself."

Zeus said, "It's within the realm of possibility that she has employed him. We know that she has very little money, only what she has saved, but she could just be foolish enough to squander it."

"Should we move then?" Ares said eagerly.

There was a brief silence. Then a sigh came over the line like a faint wind. "I suppose we have little choice in the matter. But be circumspect, Ares. Whatever you do, be certain that no breath of suspicion is cast upon us."

"I will be very careful, sir."

"I will leave it in your capable hands then. Is Artemis with you?"

"Yes."

"May I have a word with her?"

"I'll put her on."

With a gloating look Ares extended the receiver to Artemis, who had been listening closely. "He wants to talk to you."

She took the receiver, and said, "Yes, Zeus?"

While she listened without speaking, Ares strode exultantly to the liquor cabinet and made himself a drink, scotch on the rocks. Sipping it, he watched Artemis.

She finally said, "Yes, Zeus, I understand. Good-bye."

She hung up slowly and stared up at Ares unhappily. "So it seems you're to have it your way, after all."

Grinning, he shrugged. "It has to be done, my dear. That is the reason Zeus sent us along on this cruise."

"But this private detective . . . If Cassandra has hired him, he can't find out anything about her father now, not until after Genoa at least."

"We can't afford to wait that long, my dear Artemis. The longer we wait to do anything about her, the more likely the finger might point to us. Anyway, why are we debating? You heard Zeus. He has made his decision and his word is law." He smiled unpleasantly. "And you know what happens to those of us who defy him."

Five

Shriek of a train whistle.

ANNOUNCER. Now join us for another episode of "I Love a Mystery," featuring the adventures of Jack, Doc, and Reggie, specialists in crime and adventure! Tonight they are following the treasure map of P. Y. Ling to the pirate loot of The Island of Skulls! . . . [*Music swells.*] A new Carlton Morse adventure thriller!"

Cassandra, on her bed, absorbed in paperwork, smiled, listening with only half an ear, as Sibelius's "Valse Triste" swelled to a crescendo. Every evening, at six o'clock—a time when most of the passengers would be in their cabins getting dressed for dinner—Todd Breckinridge was broadcasting fifteen-minute segments of the famous old radio show over the cabin radios.

Cassandra was too young to have heard the originals, but surprisingly, she found them not too dated; in fact, they strongly reminded her of the movie, *Raiders of the Lost Ark*. She considered them amusing, and she had noted that they were generating considerable comment among the passengers.

Reluctantly, she returned her attention to her papers. She was working on questions for tomorrow morning's interview with Jake Randle. She had come up with the idea of a daily interview with a different member of the mystery staff, her contribution to the Mystery Cruise. Roxie Pike

50

had welcomed the suggestion with enthusiasm, but unfortunately she had also insisted that Cassandra herself conduct the interviews, which added another hour a day to Cassandra's already overburdened schedule. The interviews were conducted in the Pisces Lounge, on the Promenade deck, from eleven until noon each day. Now, four days out of Fort Lauderdale, Cassandra had already interviewed Alex Dudley, and Jake was the next logical interviewee, since Dudley had been instrumental in getting Jake on the mystery staff.

She was looking forward to the interview with Jake. She'd had lunch with him twice, and she had allowed him to persuade her to go dancing in the Astral Lounge last night. She wasn't free until after the eleven o'clock lounge show was over, and they had danced until well after two. Although she had paid for it with missed sleep, Cassandra had thoroughly enjoyed herself. Jake was an excellent dancer and very good company. She liked him, she had decided; she liked him very much.

She intended to put him on the hot seat during the interview, both to needle him a little and to learn something about him at the same time. She was devising some probing questions . . .

Her attention was drawn again to the radio. She had been following the frantic action only peripherally, but now she listened more closely. Jack Packard was about to rescue two girls imprisoned in a bamboo cage suspended high in a spiderweb of ropes in the center of the Temple of the Jaguar. Edith, one of the girls, was half out of her mind from being imprisoned in the precarious cage for so long and refused to cooperate with Jack's rescue efforts. She paced the cage, muttering to herself. Jack's patience was soon exhausted, and he seized her by the arm.

JACK. You little hussy, you bit my arm! Stop it, Edith. Stand still!

EDITH. I'll bite you—I'll bite you!

JACK. Look, we haven't got all day. When it gets around
Holy Joe has been killed we'll have all the priests
in the joint on our tail—now come here!

EDITH. No! No!

JACK. All right. Then I'll have to do it this way. [*Sock!—
body hits the floor.*] Poor little kid. When you
wake up you'll be out of all this. Maybe knock
a little sense back into your head, too.

Smiling to herself, Cassandra listened through to the
end. At the finish of the closing credits, Todd Breckinridge's
hoarse rumble cut in: "Be sure to listen tomorrow at the
same time for the further adventures of Jack, Doc, and
Reggie."

Cassandra switched off the radio and returned to her list
of questions for Jake Randle.

Word had gotten around about the interviews, and the
following morning at eleven, the Pisces Lounge was
packed. Cassandra was pleased to note that not only were
all the Mystery Cruise passengers present, but as many of
the other passengers as could crowd into the lounge. She
was seated at a table in the center of the lounge, fiddling
with the sound system, with an empty chair for Jake beside
her. At a minute before eleven Jake still hadn't put in an
appearance, and she was beginning to fidget when she saw
his tall figure coming through the crowd.

As he sat down beside her Cassandra leaned over to
whisper in his ear, "I was beginning to think you weren't
going to show."

"I thought about it," he said in a growling voice. "Believe
me, I thought about it. Why I let myself get roped into this,
I'll never know."

"It's in your contract," she said with a smile.

"What contract? I agreed to speak on what I know, not

subject myself to something like this. Roxie tells me that this is all your idea, so I guess I have you to thank."

"The subject of the interview is something you should know intimately," she said composedly. "Jake Randle."

Before he could respond she turned away, rapping on the table for attention. As the crowd quieted, she said into the microphone, "For those of you not members of the Mystery Cruise group, the man on my right is Jake Randle. Mr. Randle is an expert on police procedure, and he is at present a private detective, with his own firm in Miami. For those of you who may think private eyes exist only in fiction, we are going to prove you wrong here today. Mr. Randle, would you provide us with some background on yourself?"

Jake gave her a baleful glare, cleared his throat, and spoke into the mike. "I want to say first off that policemen, most of them anyway, consider anyone with a mike in their hand as an adversary. I have no idea what questions Miss Kanaris intends to ask, but I've been schooled to say, 'no comment,' when a mike is thrust under my nose." He smiled slyly at Cassandra from behind his hand. "As for my background, being a cop sort of runs in my family. My father was a cop, and I have an uncle who is still on the New York force. He's now a precinct captain." His brief smile had a wry twist. "I never made it that far. My father was killed by some hopped-up punk during a liquor store holdup. Despite that, I joined up when I got out of college. I had some thoughts of becoming a lawyer, which would have put me on the other side, since I was thinking of criminal law. But I didn't like what I saw going on in our courts. I was on the force for seven years."

He paused briefly, his eyes turning stony and bitter.

Cassandra stepped into the pause. "Would you care to tell us why you left the police department, Mr. Randle?"

He gave a start. "Why? I stepped on some toes, some very important toes. I resigned. I suppose you could say that I was given a choice, resign or spend my years until retirement on traffic control."

"Whose toes did you step on?"

Jake turned a hard gaze on her. "No comment on that," he said flatly. "Besides, it would be of no interest to anyone here."

Cassandra doubted that, but she decided to beat a hasty retreat. "Why did you decide to become a private detective? Because you'd read mysteries about private eyes and decided that it would be a glamourous profession?"

"Hardly," he said curtly. Then he smiled slightly. "The life of a private cop is nothing like that of a private eye in mystery stories. None that I've read, anyway. As for the reason I became one, it's all I know, at least the only profession where I could make any kind of money. Many ex-policemen go into security work or become guards, bodyguards, even night watchmen. None of those appealed to me, and I would have had to work for somebody else. I had had enough of that, working for the City of New York."

"Do you like your new profession?"

He nodded. "Very much. It's an interesting occupation."

"What exactly do you do? Divorce work?"

"I steer clear of that. That's the sordid side of the business, and I avoid it as much as possible. I specialize in internal security for stores and plants, and also occasionally take on the job of looking for someone: runaway children, runaway husbands or wives, now and then some guy who has absconded with money. Usually the police devote little time to such cases."

"Security work?" Cassandra said with arched eyebrows. "But you just said that many ex-policemen do security work and I gathered that you didn't think much of that."

"What I do is quite different. Some department store, for instance, may suspect that an employee is stealing from them. Or a plant may suspect that an employee is selling trade secrets to a competitor. Another department store may be having problems with shoplifters. That's the kind of security work I'm talking about here."

"How about murder cases? Are you ever involved in homicide investigations?"

"Yes, a couple," he said after some hesitation. "I do some investigative work for defense attorneys in the Miami area."

"Perhaps you could tell us some interesting things about your investigations?"

"I'm afraid not," he said stiffly. "The cases are too recent, and I'm not too pleased with the way some of them turned out."

Cassandra thought that he was being unnecessarily reticent, but she decided not to push it. "But surely you can tell our audience about some of your more interesting investigations while you were a homicide officer?"

"We-ell, perhaps." He caught his lower lip between his thumb and forefinger and worried it for a moment, gazing into the distance. Finally he glanced sidelong at Cassandra, then out at the audience. "Often the details of a murder investigation are sordid, if not outright gory. Are you all sure you want to hear?"

Several people spoke at once, encouraging him to proceed, but Cassandra noted that a few people began to drift out of the lounge as Jake started the story of a murder in a small Manhattan hotel where a man was killed on the second floor landing and his death was first discovered when a passerby on the street outside detected blood pouring down the stairs. "It's amazing how much blood the human body contains . . ." Jake said.

Ares turned to Artemis with a gloating look. "You see, this man Randle and Cassandra are working together."

They were seated together in a far corner of the Pisces Lounge and had listened to the interview intently. Artemis said, "Just because she's interviewing him doesn't necessarily mean that he is working for her. This is all a part of her job."

"Randle is not a mystery writer, he's a cop. All this is merely a front for his real purpose in being aboard. She has hired him, you can be sure of it."

"Perhaps." Artemis shrugged slightly. "What are your plans?"

"I'm working on one," he said smugly. "There is plenty of time, over ten days yet. The closer we are to Genoa, the better."

At the interview table at the front of the room Cassandra asked, "We have time for a couple of questions from the audience. Anyone have a question for Mr. Randle?"

Several hands went up, Cassandra nodded to a man in the front row.

"You mentioned that you got in bad with the New York police when you stepped on some important toes. I know Miss Kanaris asked you but . . ." The questioner grinned. "I'm from New York and I'd sure like to know whose toes."

"I'm sorry, I can't go into that," Jake said tightly.

Cassandra nodded to a woman who had her hand up. The woman said, "I've been thinking of writing a mystery novel. That's why I'm along on the 'I Love a Mystery' cruise. Do you have any advice for new writers?"

"Since you're of the female persuasion, you might use a woman private eye as your heroine. I haven't read too many of those. In fact, I've never met one in real life, although I suppose there are a few around. In this day of women's liberation, it's high time some were getting into the profession." Jake grinned as laughter swept the room. "Seriously, I think you should check with one of the bona fide mystery writers. They could advise you far better than I can, I'm sure."

The bell for lunch sounded over the intercom system, and the audience began to stir. Cassandra said, "That's all for today, ladies and gentlemen. Tomorrow at this same time we will interview our writing couple, Bob and Sandra Dean. I'm sure it will be an interesting session. Now, how about a round of applause for Mr. Randle?"

There was a burst of applause, which Jake acknowledged with a dip of his head, his face wearing a laconic smile, as the passengers began to move toward the exits.

Cassandra said in a low voice, "Did you have to go into such lurid detail, Jake?"

His grin widened, and he raised and lowered his shoulders. "You asked for details. As a famous man once said, if you can't stand the heat, get out of the kitchen."

"You saw some get up and leave. I think you did it deliberately, trying to shock them."

"Most people aren't that easily shocked, Cass. That's one thing I learned early on, people are drawn to the scene of a murder like flies."

"You're too cynical by far." Still angry, she began to gather up her notes from the table.

"I suppose you're right. I guess I wanted to get back at you for arranging this and I went too far." He captured her hand. "I'm sorry, Cass. Forgive me?"

She hesitated for a long moment. After all, it was partly her fault, she supposed; she had wanted to put him on the hot seat. She smiled slowly. "Of course, Jake."

"Then how about joining me for lunch?"

She shook her head. "I can't, Jake, not today. I'm skipping lunch. You're right, this interview thing was my idea, and as a result, it's piled more work on me. I have a million things to do."

He didn't release her hand. "Then how about dancing again? I thoroughly enjoyed last night."

"I did, too, but you know how much sleep I got? It was after two when I went to bed, and I was up at six this morning."

"So I got one more hour than you did and you're younger than I am." He squeezed her hand gently.

"All right, Jake. I'll meet you there as soon as I can get away."

In a penthouse suite on the Solar deck, Aphrodite and Poseidon were conferring.

Aphrodite said, "Have you been observing Ares and Artemis?"

Poseidon nodded. "As closely as I am able."

"They know we're on board, of course?"

"Oh, yes. Ares, with his usual charm, warned me not to interfere. He said we would be sorry if we did."

Aphrodite sighed. "I must say Zeus could not have selected a better pair. Especially Ares. The man's vicious, evil. In my opinion he's a psychopath."

"We've all known that for some time. If you'll recall, that was the main reason we broke away from Zeus and his cohorts. They believe they're above any law, moral, legal, or otherwise."

"Yes, I know." She sighed again. "You're convinced then that they mean Cassandra harm?"

"I have no doubt of it."

"They'll go as far as to kill her?"

"If they think it necessary to attain their ends."

"We must not allow that to happen." She leaned forward tensely. "Do you have any inkling of what Ares plans?"

"No. It's so easy to kill someone on board a ship like this. Find her alone on deck at night, one push over the rail, and she's gone."

Aphrodite shivered. "We must prevent it, Poseidon!"

"All we can do is watch, wait for Ares to make his move, and try to anticipate it."

As the band stopped Cassandra collapsed into Jake's arms, laughing. "I think I've had it for tonight, Jake. I'm exhausted. Also . . ." She giggled. "I think I've had a little too much to drink."

It was permissible for the officers and staff members to drink, but any excess was frowned upon; and several of the ship's officers were also in the Astral Lounge. Cassandra knew that she had to watch herself; one more drink and she'd probably be out of it. For a little while tonight she had let everything slip from her mind, everything but Jake and the music. She couldn't remember when she had enjoyed herself so much.

Jake held her briefly, close in his arms, and she inhaled the male scent of him. His slender body was well-muscled, and there was no excess fat on him. A tide of desire swept through Cassandra, dizzying her senses.

She felt bereft as he stepped back, still holding her hand. "I guess it is getting late, I'd better see you to your cabin."

As they started to leave Jon Slezak, the leader of the band, called out, "You're some dancer, Cassandra! It's always a pleasure to watch you."

Turning, Cassandra blew him a kiss, absurdly pleased at his praise. Just outside the lounge they caught an elevator going down to her deck. They were alone in the small elevator but stood close together. Jake's arm was around her shoulders.

As they started down he tipped her face around to his, his big hand cupping her chin. His eyes were soft and glowing, and Cassandra's breath left her in a rush as she anticipated his kiss. She had no thought of resisting. Instead, she leaned toward him. As she felt the touch of his mouth a tingle went through her, and she pressed against him, returning his kiss freely.

She didn't notice the elevator come to a stop, or even hear the doors sigh open, so caught up was she in the sensations his kiss had aroused in her.

He broke the embrace, stepping back slightly. He said huskily, "We're here, Cass."

"Oh! I didn't realize," she said dazedly.

"Which way's your cabin?"

"Down this way." Stepping out of the elevator, she motioned, and he followed her down the passageway.

As she stopped before her door, Jake took her by the shoulders and turned her toward him. She raised her face for his kiss, then moved against him in sweet abandon. They swayed, locked together. Cassandra could feel his throbbing response against her belly, and a weakness invaded her.

A low whistle startled them and they drew apart. They looked sheepishly at the man coming along the passageway. He rolled his eyes at them as he passed, going into a cabin two doors down.

"Cass . . ." Jake drew a shaky breath. "May I come in? Do you share a cabin with anyone?"

"I have my own cabin," she said in a low voice. Her thoughts were a-tumble, her need fighting a battle with caution, and then she murmured, "Yes, Jake. Please come in."

She had her key out, fumbling with the lock. With a smile he took the key from her. His own hands unsteady, he finally unlocked it.

Cassandra flicked on the light and stepped inside, her glance going at once to the bed. She gave a sigh of relief. There was no lavender envelope!

"What is it, Cass? Were you expecting someone to be in here?"

"No, no. I was just . . ." She broke off. "I'll tell you about it some other time."

She turned to lock the door, and as she faced around again, he was waiting for her, his arms open. She went into them without hesitation.

"Cass, I want to say something. I've heard about shipboard romances, how they usually end when the cruise does. I don't want this to end like that."

"Jake, let's not make any rash promises, okay?" She reached out to touch his mouth with her fingertips. "It's too soon. Let's wait and see how it goes, okay?"

He smiled slightly. "I've also heard that relationships happen quickly on board a ship. That certainly seems to be true."

"Yes, I've noticed that," she said with a nod. "And that may be the reason they go awry when the cruise is over."

"Have you . . . ?" He shook his head sharply. "I was about to ask if you knew that from personal experience, but it's none of my damned business."

As she opened her mouth to speak, he closed it with his. The kiss this time was gentle, undemanding, but even so she experienced the now-familiar leap of response.

Paradoxically, she felt suddenly shy. She stepped away from him, moving aimlessly about the cabin. "I don't have anything to drink in here."

"I don't need a drink, Cass. Do you?"

She laughed uncertainly. "No, I've already had too much."

"Cass . . ." He caught her arm and stopped her wandering. "If you'd rather I go, I will."

"No!" She turned into him, clinging fiercely.

He held her close. "It's just that you seem so nervous. I would've thought, considering your job, that you would have experience. And I don't mean that in a derogatory way."

Hiding her face against his shirt, she murmured, "But this is different."

"You feel that, too?"

She nodded.

He tipped her face up and kissed her. Without another word he stepped back and began removing his clothes, folding each item neatly across the seat under the porthole.

Cassandra began undressing as well, but she couldn't

help turning her back. What *was* wrong with her? Jake was right, she certainly wasn't all that innocent.

Nude, she raised the covers and slipped under. Except for the expensive suites, there was no such thing as a double bed on the ship, and the narrow beds weren't made to accommodate two people. Finally, she looked at Jake, just as he straightened up from removing his shorts. He was well-made, with broad shoulders and a deep chest, matted with dark, curly hair, and a narrow waist . . .

She drew a quick breath at the sight of his erection. The blood thrummed in her veins as he came toward the bed. She moved back against the cabin wall, making room for him.

Slipping in beside her, he kissed her lingeringly. There was a tenderness and solicitude about him that was unexpected, considering the directness of his nature and the state of his arousal.

He was a good lover. He knew where to touch and caress and kiss, to stoke her passion until she was ablaze with wanting him. Behind the gentleness of his touch, she could sense a strength and a ferocity that only needed the proper moment to be unleashed.

The passion of their bodies set up a furnace heat underneath the covers, which soon were thrown back. As his knowing hands stroked her belly and flanks and inner thighs, Cassandra began to tremble. She murmured his name over and over in a guttural voice.

All of a sudden she gasped aloud, her hips arching far off the bed, as his fingers explored the center of her moist heat.

"Jake, please Jake!" Her head rolled on the pillow and she urged him to her with plucking hands.

He rose then and moved between her spreading thighs, hesitated for a long, agonizing moment, and went into her with a plunging thrust.

A shudder ran the length of her body, and this seemed to

be the signal he was waiting for. He moved beyond the restraint that had held him back and began to thrust powerfully. They moved together in a frenzied rhythm. His artful lovemaking had already brought her close to the verge, and she let herself go with a glad cry. She reached up for his head and brought his mouth down to hers, parting her lips to accommodate the dart of his tongue.

Then the first mighty spasms of ecstasy seized her and her lower body left the bed, cleaving to him, holding him immobile and off the bed as she shuddered again and again, moaning softly deep in her throat.

As she collapsed back onto the bed Jake did not slacken his driving rhythm. Within seconds, to her vast astonishment, Cassandra felt tension building in her, again, and she began to move in conjunction with him, Jake groaned softly, his rhythm quickening, as she rose to meet him, and this time their passion broke together.

A few moments later Cassandra said breathlessly, "All I can say is wow! And that seems inadequate."

"I know, Cass, I know." Lying beside her, he pushed the damp hair out of her eyes, and kissed her forehead tenderly. "I can't remember when it was ever quite like this for me. You see now why I don't want this to go the way of other shipboard romances? I told you yesterday that when I saw something I wanted, I went after it. Now I'll also add that I keep it."

She made a sound of protest. "You make it sound so . . . so possessive."

"Oh, no, I didn't mean it that way. But I do love you . . ."

"Sh-h, not now, Jake." She put a finger across his lips. "We'll have almost a month together. Let's not spoil it by getting too serious in the beginning. Let's wait and see how it goes."

She thought again of telling him about her father, the reason for this journey and the notes, and that she didn't want to get too emotionally involved until the search was over, one way or another. Yet it was far too early to confide so much to him, even if he was by profession a cop and might be able to help her cope with the threat she felt implicit in the notes.

Cassandra had learned early to rely on her own resources. Her mother had never been much help with any problem that arose, and Cassandra had learned to cope. After all, this problem was hers, not Jake's, not anyone else's. To ask for help, at least now, would be an admission of failure—or so it seemed to her— and she had never admitted failure in her life.

Jake was speaking. She said, "I'm sorry, Jake. I was woolgathering. What did you say?"

"I said, we're going to see as much of each other as possible, aren't we?"

She laughed softly, touching his cheek. "Greedy, aren't you?"

"When it comes to you, yes."

His head swooped down, his mouth finding hers, and she wrapped her arms around him, holding him close.

Six

Cassandra, smiling, put down the copy of the script of *Arsenic and Old Lace* and reached for her coffee. The script had been delivered that morning by Roxie Pike, while Cassandra was getting dressed, and this was the first time she had found a minute to look at it.

It was now ten-thirty, and Cassandra was taking advantage of a short break in her schedule to rest in the small Lunar Lounge, which was usually deserted at this hour.

The coffee was good, sweet and white, the way she liked it, and she realized with some surprise that she really felt in pretty good shape, despite the fact that last night, again, she'd gotten only a few hours sleep. This thought, of course, led her to thinking of the reason for her lack of sleep, and her cheeks, as well as more intimate places of her body, grew warm.

Engrossed in her thoughts, Cassandra was startled when the door of the small lounge swung inward and then felt a flash of annoyance. She was enjoying her thoughts and didn't wish to be interrupted, but when she saw who was coming through the door, her annoyance vanished, to be replaced by a deeper flush, this time of pleasure. It was Jake.

His face lit up when he saw her. "There you are! I've been looking everywhere for you. I thought I'd never find you."

Feeling absurdly pleased, Cassandra found herself grinning at him like an idiot. She forced composure on herself, and said lightly, "That doesn't speak very well for your skills as a detective."

He slid into the booth beside her, moving close so that his leg touched hers. "I wish the bartender weren't here," he said, a teasing gleam in his eyes.

Cassandra found herself grinning again. "And why is that?"

"Because, if he wasn't, I'd show you how glad I am to see you."

"You mean that your way of showing me would be something that could not be properly done in public?"

The gleam in Jake's eyes was wicked now. "You can bet your pretty little bippie it would." Reaching down, he gave her thigh a squeeze.

The touch of his hand made Cassandra want him, and she wished that right here and now, they could be together.

"Are we having lunch?" Jake asked.

She shook her head. "I can't, Jake. Wish I could, but we're putting on one of the big shows tonight, *Finian's Rainbow*, and we start rehearsal right after lunch, and in a few minutes I have to conduct the interview. I'm skipping lunch today."

"Tonight then?"

She shook her head again. "I'm sorry, but I can't, Jake. I only got two hours sleep last night, and not too much more the night before. Pretty soon it'll start to show, and my work will suffer." When she saw his woeful expression, she covered his hand with hers. "I really am sorry."

He fixed his gaze on hers, and his expression became serious. "But you're not sorry about last night, are you? Because if you are, I'll jump overboard."

Lowering her voice, she said, "You won't have to do that, Jake. I'm not the least sorry about *that* part of last night."

His hand turned under hers, clasping it in a grip that was almost painful. "I'm glad of that, at least. Well, I can't say you didn't warn me—about how busy you were, I mean."

She sighed. "I did warn you, yes."

Seeing the playscript, he reached for it. "What's this?"

"The script of the mystery play Roxie's putting on. Don't you have a part in it?"

Riffling through the pages, he nodded. "I do, yes, but Roxie said that she was short of scripts at the moment. She's having more copies made, and I'll have one before the day's out." He grinned. "Can't you just see me as an actor?"

"Well, I don't know." She smiled. "You *are* rather good-looking."

He returned the script. "I tried to get out of it, but Roxie said that it was part of my duties as a lecturer."

"What part are you playing?"

He shrugged. "Mortimer. The lead, no less. How about that?"

"Then we'll be playing opposite each other!" she said in delight. "Roxie asked me to play Elaine, the ingenue. I don't know who's playing the other roles, except that Todd Breckinridge, as well as directing, is playing the Jonathon part, the role Boris Karloff played in the play."

Jake looked at her in astonishment. "You're too young to remember that movie, Cass. Why, it must have come out in the forties, or the thirties."

"You're forgetting the wonders of television. In fact, I saw it on The Late, Late Show not too long ago. It was a delight."

"That it was, a great movie," he said absently. He grew pensive. "So, I won't see you this afternoon or tonight?"

The thought made her feel sad. "Well, you'll *see* me. At the run-through of *Arsenic*."

"There will be dozens of people there," he said in a grumbling voice.

"Tomorrow morning," she said, "let's have breakfast together. My day starts a little later tomorrow, and I'll have time for a regular breakfast in the dining room. I warn you though, that I intend to pig out. It won't be a pretty sight."

His smile warmed her like the sun. "I'll chance it," he said, taking her hand again.

Suddenly she thought of the time, and looked at her watch. "Oh, good heavens! I've got to get going, or I'll be late for my interview."

His hand on her arm stopped her from rising. "Cassandra, before you go, I think you should know something."

Feeling at once apprehensive and excited, Cassandra tried to pull her arm free, but he held it firmly. "Maybe you'd better not say it, Jake."

"But I want to," he said quietly. "I never thought I would say this to a woman again, but . . . You must know that I'm in love with you."

His words, spoken softly, had a profound and unsettling effect on her. "You mustn't say that, Jake!"

"Why not? It's true."

"Because it's too soon. You can't feel something like that this quickly. I mean, love at first sight . . . Well, things like that simply don't happen in real life."

"You're spooked, I can understand that. I probably shouldn't have spoken so soon, but I keep having this feeling that our time is in some way limited, and I wanted you to know. I'm sorry if I upset you, Cass."

"I'm not upset," she said, avoiding his gaze; but she knew that she spoke a lie. How could she feel two such conflicting emotions at once—elation and apprehension?

Cassandra found herself unable to sleep that night. It had been close to midnight when she had finally got to her cabin, undressed, and taken a hot bath. Stretching out on her bed, she had expected to go to sleep at once, but now she was wide awake, staring up into the dark, her mind overactive.

She missed Jake, dammit! It was ridiculous, but there it was. They had spent one night together, actually only a few hours, yet she yearned for him; her treacherous body ached for him. She couldn't stop herself from thinking of last night, going over every intimate detail vividly. Naturally, this only made matters worse.

She sat up in bed, knees drawn up, her arms wrapped around them. Was she in love with Jake Randle? He was a good lover, true, but other men she had known were good lovers, and she had never lost any sleep yearning for them when they weren't in her bed.

"You seem to have it bad, kiddo," she said aloud.

With a sound of exasperation she got up, put on a pair of slacks, a pullover sweater, and comfortable shoes, and took the elevator up to the Promenade deck. The clock by the elevator gave the time as two o'clock. She laughed to herself. She wouldn't dare tell Jake that she hadn't slept after all!

Even at this late hour the Promenade deck wasn't completely deserted; she knew from experience that people could always be found on deck, no matter what the hour.

She found a spot by a steel stanchion, a lifeboat overhead shadowing her from the full moon. It was a clear, beautiful night, the moon very bright, paling the distant stars to diamond pinpoints. The ship was rolling slightly, shallow swells passing under her in rhythmic procession. Gazing down, Cassandra saw that they were being shepherded by a school of flying fish, forming silver, glinting arches as they leapt out of the water, sailing for a few feet, then returning to the water with a faint splash.

Cassandra watched them, touched by their beauty, but her thoughts were on Jake Randle. She had met a few men who attracted her physically, and the very few sexual encounters she had experienced had been pleasant enough, but she had never come close to being in love. There had as yet been no man who had stirred thoughts of marriage, no

one she had thought of living with and having children by;
but now she was thinking of Jake in that context. Why did it
have to happen now?

She sensed that if she had met him at any other time, she
would have welcomed this chance. But not now, not when
she was engaged on a quest. It seemed to her that this was a
crucial point in her life. The search for her father was
assuming more urgency with every passing day, with every
mile that she traveled toward Rhodes. She had to *know*,
one way or another, whether Jason Kanaris was alive or
dead.

"Such serious thoughts, kiddo," she whispered to herself, and laughed. She heard the thudding footsteps of a
jogger behind her and started to turn to go back to her
cabin, but as she did so a hard body collided forcibly with
hers. Off-balance, she was thrown hard against the top
railing; her feet were knocked out from under her, and she
began to topple toward the water far below.

At that moment the ship rolled, and she was falling free.
A scream was torn from her. Frantically she turned,
twisting half around, her fingers clawing for purchase. At
the last moment she managed to catch the bottom rail with
both hands, but she still swung sickeningly out into space,
brought up short by only her hands, gripping the railing.
Her grip was almost torn loose, and her arms felt pulled
from their sockets. She was hanging with her back against
the side of the ship now, an awkward position from which to
pull herself back up, and the railing was slippery from the
spray. She knew she couldn't hold on very long. She hung
there, swinging back and forth. If she went into the ocean
this late at night, the odds were small that anyone would
see her, and once she was in the water, the ship would sail
serenely on.

Instinctively, she cried out for help, but the wind ripped
the words away. Desperate, she exerted all of her strength
and managed to pull herself partway up, but in doing so she

forgot about the rail, and her head banged into the hard metal. Pain burst in her skull, and she dropped full-length again, just managing to retain her precarious grip on the rail.

And then, just when she thought her strength was gone and she would slide into the sea, strong hands gripped her right wrist, and a deep voice said, "I have you, my dear. Just hang in there, and I'll have you safe in a second. When I shout, let go of your grip with your left hand and let yourself go lax. I'll heave you up over the top rail. You may get bruised a little, but you'll be all right. Trust me."

Craning her neck back and up, Cassandra could see the white blur of a face leaning over the top rail. The man's grip tightened painfully around her wrist. He shouted, "Now!"

Cassandra let her left hand fall away and relaxed as much as possible under the circumstances. It passed through her mind that it wouldn't be easy to swing her full weight up and over the rail, yet she felt that she had to trust the warm, deep voice.

Then she was being hoisted up, bumping the iron railings as she went, but within a few seconds, her head and shoulders were above the top rail. A strong arm wrapped around her, underneath her arms, and then she was over, her feet planted solidly on the deck.

She collapsed against a broad chest, weak with relief. Now that it was all over, now that she was safe, she realized just how close she had come to death. She couldn't possibly have held on much longer, and she would never have been able to find the strength to haul herself back onto the deck.

She could smell the odor of cigars on the jacket of her rescuer as he patted her paternally on the shoulder. "You're safe now, my dear."

Cassandra stepped back in order to see him and almost fell from weakness. He caught her arm and steadied her. In the light from the windows behind her Cassandra could see her rescuer's face clearly now. It was a strong face, deeply tanned to an almost mahogany color and adorned with a shock of thick, graying blond hair and blue eyes. He was a big man, well over six feet, with broad shoulders and strong arms. He looked to be in his late forties. Cassandra couldn't recall seeing him before, but she was far from familiar with all the passengers yet.

"I do thank you," she said shakily. "I'm Cassandra Kanaris, the assistant cruise director."

He nodded gravely. "Yes, I know. I've seen you bustling about. I'm Eric Johanson."

The name struck a chord of memory. "You're in one of the penthouse suites."

Again he nodded. "That is correct, my dear." He smiled suddenly, even white teeth flashing, and his blue eyes became merry. "I couldn't sleep and was strolling on deck."

"It was fortunate for me you were. You probably saved my life." She shivered, looking back along the deck in the direction the jogger had taken. "Did you see the person who bumped into me?"

Something flickered in his eyes, but he said, "I'm afraid not. I heard your shout, and . . . You mean someone knocked you over the rail?"

"I was leaning on the rail. I was having trouble sleeping, too, you see. I was turning away, to go back to my cabin, when a man came jogging along the deck. We collided, and I went over."

"But why didn't he stop? He must have realized what had happened."

"I don't know. Maybe he didn't," she said slowly. For the first time she considered what had happened. Perhaps Johanson was right; the jogger had hit her hard enough to knock her overboard, so he must have been aware of the collision. Why hadn't he stopped, either to apologize or to see if she was all right? Could it be possible that it wasn't an accident? Had the jogger deliberately collided with her, hoping to knock her overboard?

She shivered, hugging herself, and Johanson spoke. Cassandra had almost forgotten about him. "I'm sorry, I was being rude. What did you say?"

"It's so easy for a fatal accident to happen on board a ship like this, especially late at night," he said. "Or do you suppose it could have been done on purpose?"

It was upsetting to have voice put to what she had just been thinking. She said quickly, "But that's ridiculous!"

"Perhaps, but then one never knows. Is there anyone on board that you know of who might wish you harm?"

"Of course not!"

He looked at her for a few moments, until she became uneasy under his scrutiny. "I would suggest, Miss Kanaris, that you exercise a little care. Don't stroll at night on deck. Not alone, at any rate. Stay away from the railing unless there are other people about. As the saying goes, it wouldn't hurt."

She smiled with an effort. "I'm sure it was just an accident, Mr. Johanson, but I'm grateful for your concern. And again I thank you for saving my life. If you will excuse me now, I think I'll go to my cabin."

The man called Johanson watched her walk away, head erect, shoulders back. He took out a Macanudo cigar and lit it. She must have been truly shaken by the incident, yet she controlled it very well. Such a splendid woman, he thought: courageous, spirited, and truly lovely. What a pity it would be if anything happened to her!

Artemis said, "I thought you were going to wait until just before the ship reached Genoa?"

Ares paced the floor of the penthouse suite, sipping a dark scotch. He shrugged. "I happened to be on deck when I saw her come up. The opportunity was simply too good to pass up." He smacked his palm against the bulkhead. "It would have worked, too, if that damned Poseidon hadn't interfered!"

"Now she'll be on her guard."

He shrugged again. "So what if she is?" He grinned unpleasantly. "That'll just make it more interesting."

"Zeus warned you not to arouse her suspicions."

"Zeus isn't here, I am. I have to do it my way."

"No, you just couldn't wait. You're an evil man, Ares. If a day passes without you doing harm to someone, you're unhappy."

He wheeled on her savagely. "Just shut up, Artemis." He took a threatening step toward her. "The day isn't over yet. I just might take my frustration out on you; did you ever think of that?"

Her head went back. "I'm not afraid of you, Ares." But there was a faint tremor in her voice.

"You should be, you should be. You know me well enough by this time."

They were well into *Arsenic and Old Lace*, at the point where Mortimer, played by Jake, comes on-stage for the first time. Cassandra was also in the scene, as Elaine Harper, as was June Hays, one of the Mystery Cruise passengers, who was playing Martha Brewster, one of Mortimer's two aunts.

Mortimer, entering, speaks to Elaine, then crosses down toward Martha, placing himself between Martha and Elaine. In so doing, he pats Elaine familiarly on the rear.

Cassandra, despite the fact that she was expecting this familiarity, couldn't help jumping.

In the front row of seats in the theater, Todd Breckinridge erupted, waving his copy of the script. "No, *no*, Cassandra! You're not supposed to show any awareness. You must act as if nothing had happened, so the audience will realize that you and Mortimer are already on intimate terms."

He jumped up onto the stage and planted himself in her spot. "Go through it again, Jake, and pat me on the butt."

Jake looked at him askance. "I'm not of that persuasion, friend."

Cassandra hid a smile behind her hand, as Breckinridge waved his script again. "Just *pretend* that I'm Elaine."

"That much of an actor I'm not," Jake said with a poker face.

"Cops! They always have to play it tough, to keep their macho image intact," Breckinridge growled. "I don't know why I cast you as Mortimer. You'd been better typecast as Brophy, the cop."

Jake said, "And here I thought you were casting me as the hero because of my good looks and charm."

This caused a ripple of laughter to run through the group.

Breckinridge waved his hands in disgust. "Why did I ever saddle myself with this thankless task?"

"Because you're a frustrated director, Todd," Roxie Pike said.

Rhys Carson spoke up. "After all, we *are* amateurs, Todd. And as such, I think we're all . . ." He assumed his role as Teddy. "I think we're all doing just bully."

Ignoring him, Breckinridge stepped aside. "All right, Cassandra, assume your position, and we'll run through it again. Only this time, for heaven's sake, don't show any reaction!"

Still struggling to control her laughter, Cassandra resumed her position, holding her script in one hand and reaching up with the other to adjust the outlandish, wide-brimmed hat that Breckinridge had insisted she wear for the role—"We don't have much in the way of costumes, Cassandra. At least the hat will make you stand out."

Too much so, Cassandra thought; the hat made her look ridiculous.

As Breckinridge returned to his seat Jake whispered in her ear, "Now with you I'm not acting. Just wait until we have our first stage kiss."

"Now behave, Jake," she said. "Give poor Todd a break."

"Poor Todd indeed. He takes himself too seriously."

They resumed rehearsal, managing to read through the rest of the first act without Breckinridge throwing another tantrum.

"All right, people," he said glumly. "That's all we have time for today." He added grudgingly, "I don't suppose it went too badly."

Carson bowed mockingly. "We are grateful for the fulsome praise, sire."

Breckinridge grunted. Then, as though he felt he could relent now that rehearsal was over, he grinned, waving his hand. "Get along, all of you. You're coming along fine. We'll all get a standing ovation."

"If anybody comes, aside from the Mystery Cruisers," Jake said to Cassandra as they started away. "We *are* amateurs, no denying that. So who wants to see a bunch of amateurs?"

"You may be surprised. Some people prefer an amateur production to a professional one."

"Who, sadists? People coming to see us make asses of ourselves?" Before closing the stage door he looked around the cramped backstage area with displeasure. "And it's so damned cramped back here. How we are all going to manage back here, I don't know."

"Count ourselves lucky," she said. "On most cruise ships this is a movie theater, with nothing but a movie screen and a small strip of stage, no wings at all. And no stage door exits. But when they renovated the *Star*, adding the penthouse suites, they also enlarged the stage area and added wings."

"Yeah, lucky us," Jake said dourly, as they started along the passageway.

Cassandra didn't respond, her thoughts turning again to the incident on the deck last night. From time to time, all morning, she had thought back to that frightening moment, when she had hung helplessly out over the sea.

And each time she thought of it, she debated whether or not she should confide in Jake. It would be a great relief to be able to talk to someone, and yet she still wasn't certain she was ready to dump her problems on him. Besides, he might laugh at the idea that anyone should be trying to kill her.

Jake said, "You seem quiet all of a sudden, Cass. Anything the matter?"

"Not a thing." She turned a bright smile on him.

He gave her a searching look, and she realized he sensed something was troubling her. She was beginning to learn Jake had far more sensitivity than a policeman was traditionally supposed to possess.

Before he could speak, she said, "You mentioned something about us going ashore together somewhere along the way. Well, I've been able to get the whole day off when we reach Madeira. I hear it's a really lovely island. Shall we spend the day together?"

"I'd like that, Cass." He gave her hand a squeeze. "I'd like that very much."

With the incident on the deck fresh in her mind, Cassandra was very cautious during the next few days. She found herself seeking the company of other people during the times when she might have been alone. And she found that she felt a real aversion to going on deck; although the last was no real problem, for they had run into some rough weather, and the driving rain and high seas had made it necessary to rope off the decks so that the passengers would not be tempted to use them.

Many of the passengers, including Jake, were seasick the whole time. When Cassandra saw him, the second morning of the storm, he was pale, and embarrassed about his condition.

"I've never been so miserable in my life," he muttered. "I've always heard the expression, 'I'd rather be dead,' but I didn't know what it meant until now. If this is what cruising is like, forget it."

It was a plaint Cassandra had heard countless times before, and she could only offer sympathy. "Beyond that, Jake, there's nothing much I can do. You can only live through it, and believe me, you will, no matter how you may feel right now." She kissed him on the cheek. "The best thing for you to do is go back to your cabin and your bunk, take the medication Dr. Abramson gave you, and think about our shore excursion on Madeira."

"On land, thank God! So long as I can set foot on solid ground again, I'll be forever grateful."

Aphrodite said, "I'm delighted that you were able to save Cassandra, Poseidon."

Poseidon shrugged slightly. "It was mostly a matter of luck. It was fortuitous that I was there at the precise moment that Ares pushed her, but I cannot be present every minute of the day. At least we can hope that this has alerted her, so she will be more on her guard from now on."

"If only we could turn that wicked man over to the ship's officers, so they could slap him into the brig, or whatever it's called!" Aphrodite said angrily.

"That would be most gratifying, I agree." Poseidon smiled gently. "But that is against the rules of the game. We are never, under any circumstances, to call in outside assistance."

"But this is a different matter, Poseidon. Cassandra is not one of us. We have no right to endanger the life of an outsider."

"You know that has no bearing, my dear. And besides, who is to say that she *is* an outsider?"

"I know, I know." Aphrodite sighed heavily. "But as you say, we cannot protect her all the way. What if she goes ashore? Maybe in Funchal, on Madeira?"

"I will continue to watch Ares closely. If Cassandra does

go ashore and if Ares follows her, I will go along. There is one positive factor. Now that Cassandra has met this detective, Jake Randle, perhaps he can offer some protection. He seems a competent individual."

"But is he, is any mere mortal, a match for Ares?" Aphrodite said glumly. "I very much doubt it."

Seven

Cassandra's first impression of Madeira was one of steep mountains, picturesque architecture, and flowers, flowers everywhere. It truly was, as the brochures claimed, a garden island.

She and Jake had agreed that they would take a taxi tour instead of the ship-organized excursion. On the regular bus tour, Cassandra knew, they would have no privacy; since she was assistant cruise director, she would be looked to for advice, conversation, and supervision.

She also knew from experience, that the best way to see many ports was on your own. On the organized tours, because of the number of people involved, there was considerable regimentation and lots of time was wasted in getting forty or more people on and off the buses at each stop. Invariably, there was someone, or several someones, who overstayed the allotted time at a certain spot and thus kept the rest of the group waiting.

Of course, there were some places that did not have reliable taxi service, or places where the fares were prohibitive, and in those places, organized trips were the best bet; but Funchal was a relatively small port, with adequate taxi service, and she was looking forward to being alone with Jake, away from the *Star*. After all, the only time they had really been alone had been in her cabin, and there they had been making love. She had felt it would be wise to see how they got along during a whole day together.

There were a number of taxis waiting on the dock, all of the drivers clamoring for the attention of the passengers streaming off the ship.

Jake, now feeling fine again, smiled and squeezed Cassandra's hand. "I'll find one who speaks English."

She nodded. "I'll give you a little tip, Jake, don't simply ask them if they speak English. Most of them understand enough to say yes to that, but often that's the *only* English they know."

Jake laughed. "I didn't realize you had a suspicious nature."

She shook her head. "It's not suspicion, just experience. Trust me."

He gave her a warm look. "I do, I do. I just want you to return the favor."

He turned away, to speak to the drivers, and Cassandra watched him, admiring the way he looked and moved. He was a good-looking man, there was no denying that.

In a moment he returned with a tall, pleasant-looking young man who smiled at her, showing perfect teeth, and said in very good English, "I am Roberto. I can show you whatever you wish to see."

"We'd like to see some of the countryside," said Cassandra. "We'd like to get some idea of what the island and the people are like, and we've heard about the sleds and the sled rides down the hill. We'd like to do that."

Roberto smiled widely. "No problem. I can take you up

into the hills, show you the villages and the farms, and to the place where they grow the orchids, then back to where they ride the sleds. You will enjoy it. Madeira is very beautiful." He bobbed his head rapidly. "Okay?"

Cassandra looked at Jake. "Okay?"

He nodded. "Sounds good to me."

As the small, European-built car began to climb the narrow road leading up into the mountains, Cassandra felt Jake take her hand. Feeling peaceful and relaxed, she looked out the window, down onto the red-tiled roofs of the picturesque city spread out below. It had taken only a few moments for them to climb to a considerable height.

Jake, peering past her over the edge of the road, whistled softly. "It certainly is precipitous. These mountains seem to go almost straight up. But it's so beautiful! The air is clear, the sky is so blue. And the climate's comfortable."

Overhearing him, Roberto turned to give Jake a quick, smiling glance, then immediately turned his attention back to the road. "We have an agreement with the saints," he said. "They have agreed that it will not rain during the day, only during the night. That way everything is kept fresh and fertile, and we are not inconvenienced."

"Sounds like an ideal arrangement," Jake said, winking at Cassandra.

During the next two hours, Cassandra felt her tension and apprehension drain away as they drove upward along neat country roads, lined with blooming shrubs and trees. They saw thatch-roofed huts and steeply terraced farms that ornamented the mountainsides with their furrowed patterns; they saw peasants wearing knee-high boots and unusual knitted caps—which looked to Cassandra much like those she had seen on Indians in the Andes—leading placid milk cows along the roadside. Cassandra, a confirmed snapshot nut, took pictures of everything.

"Where are they taking the cows?" she asked Roberto.

The young driver laughed and slowed the car until they

were barely moving. "For a walk. You see how steep is our terrain. It is too steep, and too much cultivated, for us to let our cows roam, so the animals are kept in little huts, like that one there with the grass roof. Still, they must have exercise, and so their owners walk them along the road. For their health."

The sound of a klaxon startled Cassandra, and she glanced out the window to see a small man operating some kind of a bicycle-powered cart, moving up alongside the car. In the cart portion of the vehicle, which was in front, lay approximately half of a very large fish.

"A tuna," Roberto said to her unasked question. "It is a fish vendor."

While they watched, a woman wearing a long, heavy-looking dark skirt and a colorful apron came out of one of the thatch-roofed cottages and waved the fish vendor to a stop. After some voluble conversation, the vendor took out a large knife and cut off a sizable chunk of the fish, which the woman placed in a basket.

"The people up here do not change," Roberto said. "They live much as they have for hundreds of years. Of course it is different down in the city. There, things are more modern. Now, if you wish to ride the sledges, we will go back. You will enjoy the sledges. They are an unusual thing."

And indeed they were. Cassandra had read about the sleds, or sledges, of Madeira in a travel article. In earlier days the sleds had been used to haul goods and supplies up and down the steep, narrow, stone-paved streets. Now they offered exciting rides for the tourists.

Cassandra was captivated by the sleds, but somewhat nervous about their safety, as they were made from a rather light, wickerlike material. The attendants—there were four for each sled—were clad in neat white pants and shirts, two held ropes behind, and the other pair in front.

As Cassandra stepped into the sled she took Jake's hand.

"I don't know about this," she said dubiously, gazing down the street, which swooped away beneath them at a frightening angle.

"Too late now," he said cheerfully. "We're committed."

With that, the two men at the lead ropes began to pull, and the sled began to move, slowly at first, and then gaining speed. Soon, the high stone walls on either side of the street were moving by rapidly, and Cassandra could only hope that the two men on the rear ropes, who looked very small, were strong enough to control the sled.

And then the attendants jumped on the sled runners, and the wicker contraption was sliding rapidly down the smooth cobblestones.

It was exciting and invigorating, and Cassandra, holding Jake's hand, and gazing at the houses speeding past, laughed aloud with pleasure.

After the sled ride, Roberto drove them back to Funchal, where they had an excellent lunch in a sidewalk cafe, finishing it off with a glass of Madeira wine.

It was a marvelous day, and Cassandra realized that for hours she hadn't thought once about her problems.

It was then that she noticed the taxi, which had stopped opposite them on the street. In the taxi was a lone passenger, a man, whose face seemed vaguely familiar. The man was looking toward them, and Cassandra had the feeling that he was looking *at* them. Now why would he be doing that?

Cassandra, staring into the sun, tried to get a better look at his face. It was a hard face, she decided. Rather cold and cruel looking. Youngish. Maybe forty or so. It must be one of the *Star* passengers.

The man's apparent study of them made her uncomfortable, and suddenly she thought of the lavender notes and the deck incident, and she looked quickly at Jake, to find him smiling fondly at her.

"I tell you what," he said confidentially. "This is a beautiful place, and I've had a wonderful day, but I'd like to make a suggestion. Let's go back to the ship, babe."

She stared her surprise. "We don't have to be back to the ship until five. We sail at six."

"But after five you'll be busy, right?"

She nodded. "That's true. But I still don't see . . ."

"Yes, you do." He captured her hand. "We've had a part of one night. The rest of the time you've been busy, or I've been down with *mal de mer*. If we get back early enough, we'll be able to spend some time in your cabin. What do you say?"

Cassandra felt her body go warm, and she knew that she was blushing. She bobbed her head, and whispered, "Right, Jake."

"So let's get the show on the road."

He got up, leaving a generous tip for the waiter, and they went out to hail another taxi, locked hands swinging between them.

They got back to the *Star* shortly after three and went directly to Cassandra's cabin.

"It was a nice day, Jake. Thank you."

"Yes, nice," he said, cupping her face between his hands and tilting it up to his. "But this is even nicer."

Cassandra sighed, her eyes fluttering closed, and let the sensations started by his kiss take her. In an amazingly short time they were undressed and on the bed together. This time, Cassandra noticed, Jake hadn't bothered to stack his clothes neatly, and she experienced an absurd pleasure at the fact that she had been the cause of this forgetting what she now knew was his almost compulsive neatness.

She felt herself responding strongly to his intimate caresses, and soon her body was a single, heady pulsebeat of desire. As his hands stroked the insides of her thighs, Cassandra opened to him.

"Now, Jake! Oh, yes!"

As he went into her she felt the first quiver of an orgasm, and she cried out, cleaving to him, shuddering again and again. Jake continued to drive into her, his tempo quickening. Cassandra went lax as her final spasm of pleasure ceased. She reached up to cup her hands behind his head, bringing his mouth down to hers. To her amazement, at the first touch of his warm mouth, she felt her passion renewed; and she adjusted her rhythm, rising and falling with him.

He tore his mouth away, a guttural sound coming from deep in his throat. His head went back, and his body went rigid. As she felt him begin to throb inside her Cassandra's pleasure also peaked again—her second orgasm within as many minutes. This was the first time she could recall this ever happening to her.

When he finally lay quiescent, his head cradled on her shoulder, Cassandra murmured, "Yes, that *was* nice, darling. Very nice indeed."

He raised his head to gaze down into her eyes, his own eyes holding a glint of mischievous humor. "We must do this more often."

"Maybe it won't be that hard to arrange," she said with a grave face. "I also managed to wangle shore leave when we're docked for the day in Barcelona."

He frowned at her. "Why didn't you mention this before?"

"I wanted to wait and see how today went first." As his frown darkened, she added hastily, "Well, how was I to know? We could have bored each other to tears. It'll probably be the last free day I'll have for some time. After we leave Genoa, the Mystery Cruise is over, and I'll be expected to help shepherd the passengers on most of the other shore excursions."

"Well, I suppose I could always book your tours, as much as I hate tourist groups." He sat up against the head of the bed, a thoughtful expression on his face. "Do you like kids, Cass?"

She gave him a startled look. "Of course I like kids! What kind of a question is that?"

"Beverly and I talked about having children, but decided to wait for a few years. By that time, of course, we'd gone our separate ways. Oh, I'm not saying that it would have saved our marriage, having kids. Likely nothing would have, so I'm just as glad we didn't."

"So what are you saying?"

"I'm saying that I see no reason why we couldn't have a whole passel of kids." He grinned at her. "I was an only child, and I always wished I'd had brothers and sisters."

"Now just hold it right there, Buster! You're rushing things again. I told you I wanted some time."

"But after today, I thought maybe you'd come to a decision, the *right* decision."

She had to laugh. "You never let up, do you?"

"I'm a very stubborn fellow, babe."

He reached out for her, and in a moment they were rolling back and forth on the narrow bed, laughing like idiots.

In Barcelona, Jake rented a car, a small Renault, instead of hiring a taxi. "The way most of these cab drivers drive scares the holy shit out of me."

"It's not only the taxi drivers," she pointed out.

"True, but at least I'll be behind the wheel and able to watch out for the other wild drivers."

Barcelona was a lovely city, old and modern at the same time. It was also a city of cathedrals, some of the most beautiful in the world.

They were both suitably impressed by the unfinished Templo Expiatorio de la Sagrada Familia, the oddly modern-looking cathedral with its fantastic "sand castle" architecture and decoration of organic inspiration. Jake leaned against their rented car and gazed up at the soaring towers, the strange stone branches and convolutions, with the closest thing to an expression of awe she had ever seen on his face.

"Now that," he said, "is something else. It's worth seeing."

Cassandra nodded. "It's like a fairy-tale castle. Beautiful and strange." She motioned with her camera. "Cross the street, Jake, and stand in front of it. I want to take your picture, with the temple in the background."

"Aw, hell, Cass," he said in disgust. "Do you have to?"

"Yes, I have to. Now go on, don't be difficult."

The narrow street was crowded with cars and motorbikes, and Jake had to dodge his way across. Cassandra backed up as far as she could, camera poised, waiting for a break in the traffic.

Finally the signal at the corner changed and the traffic cleared. She aimed her Olympia camera at Jake, trying to get as much of the church background into the picture as she could. Just as she snapped the camera, a taxi drove between her and Jake.

"Damn!" she muttered under her breath and lowered the camera, glaring at the cab.

There was one passenger inside, a man, who was looking back through the rear window. The face was familiar and she flashed on the other day on Madeira. For a reason she couldn't fathom she swung the camera around and snapped a picture of the man, who ducked back out of sight too late. She was sure he was the same man she'd seen in the cab parked across the street from the sidewalk cafe where they'd stopped for lunch in Funchal. Later, she had searched for that face among the passengers, but she hadn't seen anyone resembling him on board, and the incident had slipped her mind.

"Hey!" Jake shouted across the street. "If you're going to

take my damned picture, do it. I'm not going to stand here all day!"

She turned back to Jake and raised the camera. Just as she started to depress the button, Jake made a horrible face, wiggling his hands at his ears.

"Darn you, Jake Randle. "I've already wasted two pictures on that taxi. Now behave!"

He laughed and posed naturally while she took a couple of quick pictures. As Jake crossed the street to her Cassandra was reassured by the sight of him. Surely she could trust him. Why not tell him what was on her mind?

As he took her arm to help her into the car, she said, "Jake, I think someone is following us."

He looked at her curiously. "Why should you think that?"

"Well, you know the other day in Funchal, when we stopped at that cafe for lunch, and a cab stopped across the street for a few minutes?"

"No, I don't remember anything like that. But what about it?"

"A cab passed along the street as I started to snap your picture just now. I'm sure that the passenger riding in it was the same man I saw in the taxi on Madeira."

He gave her a skeptical look, then automatically swiveled around to look up the street. The taxi, of course, was no longer in sight. "Was it someone you knew?"

"Well . . ." She hesitated. "He *looked* familiar. I'm sure I've seen him somewhere before."

"A cruise passenger, perhaps?"

"I think so, but I'm not sure."

He shrugged. "Probably just a coincidence, anyway. It's surprising how much coincidence figures in life. I learned that early on in police work." His look became intent, searching. "Is there any reason why anyone should be following you?"

She hesitated for a moment, then said slowly, "None that I can think of." Silently she scolded herself. That had been an opportunity to tell him what had been happening to her, and she had backed off, again.

"You know what I think?" he said with a slight smile. "I think you've been working too hard and your imagination is playing tricks on you, babe. If some guy is following you, it's because you're a good-looking broad, Cass." He was grinning openly now. "He's probably trying to figure out a way to make a move on you."

"You're laughing at me!"

He sobered. "No, I'm not. At least not in the way you think." He put a hand on her arm.

"And don't call me a broad!" She flung his hand off. She had been right not to tell him!

"Cass," he said gently. "That doesn't mean anything. It's a habit that's hard to break. I'll try not to do it again. Forgiven?"

His eyes were warm and tender, and looking into them, Cassandra felt her anger beginning to dissolve. She tried to smile. "You know that women nowadays consider 'broad' a degrading name."

"You're not a broad to me." He held his hand up, then placed it over his heart. "I swear, never again."

She smiled then, with all her heart. "Okay," she cried gaily. "Let's get in gear, Mr. Randle. We have a lot to see yet."

They spent a busy day, with Cassandra taking pictures by the dozens. Over a late lunch at an outdoor cafe off one of the many plazas, Jake grumbled, "You're a camera nut, you know that? You've got enough pictures of me to make up a full album."

"That's exactly what I'm doing, making a Jake Randle album. What is it you cops call it, a mug book?" She smiled mischievously. "I'll call it my Jake Randle mug book, something to show to my grandchildren."

"*Our* grandchildren," he said gravely, and covered her hand with his.

"Now there you go, premature again."

"I figure I should remind you now and again. Wouldn't hurt."

"Well, at least you're not premature in bed."

"Why, Cass!" He began to laugh. "A bawdy joke. I can't believe my ears."

Heat rushed to her face, and her glance slid away. She mumbled, "It just slipped out."

"Now *that* I won't touch with the well-known ten-foot pole." He got his laughter under control. "But I think I like you a little risqué. It shows . . . Well, it reveals a whole other side of you. I'll bet you don't often do that."

Cassandra couldn't recall ever making such a remark to a man, but she wasn't going to give Jake the satisfaction of knowing that.

Their last stop of the day was on Montana de Montjuich, from where, beside the lovely monument to the sardana, the traditional dance of Barcelona, they could see the whole city of Barcelona spread out below them. They could even see the *Star* at her dock. They went through the ancient castle and the historical military museum, and Cassandra finished another roll of film before Jake began to pressure her to return to the ship. "I want some time with you before we sail and you have to go back to work," he said.

She was pleasantly tired, and agreeable. "It's been another lovely day, Jake," she said in the car, as they started back down the hill. The road was quite steep going down, with side streets entering at intervals. She placed her hand on his knee.

He gave her a quick glance, eyebrows arching. He growled, "How can I watch where I'm going, when you're doing that?"

"What am I doing?" she asked innocently.

"You know very well what you're doing . . ."

He glanced back at the road just as a van truck came shooting out of a side street on their left, headed right for them. Jake shouted explosively, "What the hell!"

He slammed on the brakes, wrenching the wheel hard to the right. He was too late. The high bumper of the truck thumped into the left side of their car, just in front of the driver's door. Cassandra was thrown violently forward when Jake stepped on the brakes, the dashboard striking her head a stunning blow. Then as the tiny car was forced off the road, she was thrown against the door.

Jake was desperately fighting the wheel, but the car was out of control. It plowed through a patch of flowers alongside the road, bumped along for a few more yards, and then rammed nose first into a tree and came to a shuddering stop. Cassandra had time for just a glimpse of the boxlike truck straightening out and roaring on down the hill, before the car door on her side was wrenched open, and she was thrown out onto the ground.

Still conscious, she was aware only of a blazing pain in her head. Then she heard Jake's urgent voice. "Cassandra! Are you all right?"

She managed to raise her head and blink dazedly up at his face. His features were paper-white, made to appear even more so by a zigzag streak of blood running down his cheek from a cut on his forehead. She whispered, "I . . . I think so, except for my head. I struck it on the dash."

"I can see that; you're bleeding." Tenderly, he fingered the lump on her forehead. "It doesn't look too bad, but there's always the chance of a concussion. Nothing broken?"

She struggled to sit up, gingerly flexing her arms and legs, as Jake helped prop her upright. Glancing around, she saw a crowd had already gathered around the wrecked car.

Jake said again, "Nothing broken?"

"Everything seems all right."

"That screwball! He came right out of nowhere. I don't

think he was even looking. He must have been drunk. But I managed to get his license number, so I can turn him in to the police." He eased her back against a nearby tree trunk, and stood up. "We have to get you back to the ship, and to the doctor. I'll see if I can hail a cab."

He walked over to the street, where the traffic was now at a crawl, as the drivers all slowed to gawk at the accident. Cassandra was all right now, except for the throbbing of her head. Could it have been an accident, or done on purpose? Despite Jake's earlier remark about coincidences, it seemed a really remarkable coincidence that she had had two brushes with death within a few days time.

Before she could pursue it, Jake was back. "I found an empty cab. We'll take it down to the dock, and I'll put you on board, so you can get medical attention, then I'll have to report this to the police and the car rental company."

Dr. Abramson pronounced Cassandra all right except for a few bruises and the contused head; X rays showed no signs of a concussion. "Of course, we can't always be one hundred percent positive about something like this," he said. One of the two doctors on board, Dr. Abramson was the oldest by a few years, and not the womanizer that his younger colleague was. "But you should get a lot of rest for a day or so."

Cassandra was shaking her head and bit her lip as a lance of pain shot through it. "You know I can't do that, Doctor, I have too much to do. Mr. Dawes doesn't approve of female assistants and this would only serve to confirm his judgment that women aren't physically up to the job."

"Well, at least lie down for a while. You have a couple of hours before we up anchor. If the headache doesn't go away"—he grinned—"as we doctors say, take two aspirins and call me tomorrow."

In her cabin Cassandra took the aspirins and stretched out on the bed. She went to sleep at once. She came fully awake with a start at a knock on the door. She called out, "Who is it?"

"It's Jake."

"Just a minute."

She had removed only her dress and shoes before lying down to sleep. Quickly, she stood up and put them back on. It wasn't until then that she realized that her headache was gone. Gingerly, she touched the swelling on her forehead. Under the bandage that Dr. Abramson had applied, the lump was tender to the touch, but otherwise she seemed all right. She unlocked the door and let Jake in.

He looked at her in concern. "Are you okay?"

"I'm okay, Jake." She gave a shaky laugh. "Except for a few bruises and this lump on my head. What did you find out?"

"Not a great deal," he said with a shrug. "I found out that the truck was stolen, only an hour before it ran into us. The car rental agency gave me a hassle, but fortunately a good samaritan, who saw the truck come out of nowhere, reported to the police station, stating that the accident was in no way my fault; so that got me off the hook, finally, with the rental people."

He crossed the room and dropped down onto the couch with a sigh. "Whew! It's been a day. You know something, Cass? That was a close call we had. If the driver's aim had been a little better and he had hit the rental a little farther back instead of where he did, it could have been totaled, including us."

She sat down beside him, then did a double take as his words penetrated. "You said, the driver's aim, Jake. That makes it sound deliberate."

He never took his gaze from her face. "Maybe it was. I've been thinking about it, and it strikes me that it might well have been. You said earlier that you'd had the suspicion that someone was following us."

"But that would mean that someone was deliberately trying to kill us!"

"That's exactly what it would mean, yes. Can you think of any reason for that?"

"Of course not!" She hesitated. "How about you? If I'd been killed in that accident, so would you. He came at us from your side, Jake."

"If someone had it in mind to kill you, I doubt they'd have any qualms about killing me to get at you." He leaned forward slightly. "There *is* a reason for someone to harm you, isn't there? You've as much as admitted it. Tell me!" He smiled tightly. "After all, such things are my business."

"Not a reason to kill me, not that I'm aware of, but some strange things have been happening to me," she admitted.

"Such as?"

She told him then, about the notes, about the possibility that the incident on deck had been a murder attempt.

When she was finished, Jake leaned back for a few moments in silent thought, catching his lower lip between his thumb and forefinger and worrying it. Finally he looked over at her. "The notes, you still have them?"

She nodded, got up, and retrieved one of her bags from under the bed. She opened it, and got the notes out from a rip in the lining where she had secreted them. Coming back to the couch, she said, "I really don't know why I saved them."

"I'm glad you did." He took them from her and studied them closely, the envelopes and the notes. "The first thing that strikes me is that there's nothing overtly threatening about these notes, Cass."

"I realize that, but . . ." She shivered. "Yet someone broke into my apartment in Los Angeles, and into my cabin here, in order to leave them. And they're, well, mysterious. How does the writer know so much about me? That's what makes them so scary. There's someone out there, maybe on this ship, someone I don't know, who knows about me, about my father, whose clear purpose was to lure me into taking this trip to the Greek Isles."

He nodded thoughtfully. "I can see why that might be a touch upsetting." He studied the handwriting again. "These were written by a woman, I'm sure. Whatever good that does us."

"Would it be possible to get any fingerprints from the paper?"

"Not likely, not after you've handled it, and God knows who else. Fingerprints are vastly overrated, anyway, by the press, by fiction writers. In the first place, the person who left these notes might never have been fingerprinted, and this type of material doesn't take good prints. Besides, Cass, I think we should concern ourselves in the other direction, with whoever might be trying to kill you, if such is the case."

"You think the two things aren't related?"

"I'm not sure. This guy you saw following us, have you put a name to his face yet?"

At the negative shake of her head, he said, "Then you should concentrate on trying to spot him. Dammit, babe, I wish you had told me about all this before! I could have been more alert."

"I thought of it, but I didn't know you well enough, and then I was afraid that you wouldn't take me seriously. You know how you acted when I suggested we were being followed."

"I'll take you seriously from now on, Cass, I promise." He took her hand and drew her into the circle of his arms.

Cassandra let him pull her close, grateful for his warmth and strength. Not only did his embrace give her great comfort, it provided a feeling of security. For a moment a wave of weakness rolled over her. Why not give up the search for her father and remain in this man's arms forever? It was clear now that someone was trying to thwart her search and was not above using any means to succeed.

But no, she couldn't give up! Giving up now would be a failure that would haunt her for the rest of her life. She made a sound deep in her throat.

"What is it, babe?" Jake tilted her face up to gaze down into her eyes. Their faces were so close, Cassandra could see herself reflected in his warm brown eyes.

She shook her head back and forth. "Nothing. Just hold me, hold me tight!"

Zeus' displeasure was evident in the icy timbre of his voice on the phone. "You disappoint me, Ares. I would have expected more guile from a man of your caliber, more finesse. To use a stolen truck as an instrument to kill is the means a stupid thug would employ."

"It was an improvisation, done on the spur of the moment." Ares heard the defensive note in his own voice, and he despised himself for it. He was not a man given to defending his actions. "But if it had succeeded, I would have eliminated both the girl and the detective. To do it that way, off the ship, I calculated that it would arouse less suspicion. It would have been thought nothing more than a hit-and-run accident."

"But what you have suceeded in doing is putting the whole project at risk. The others had warned me that your penchant for violence would bring trouble to us. Artemis told me that you also followed the girl on Madeira. What if she saw you?"

Ares swiveled his head around to glare at Artemis across the cabin from him. "She has been reporting to you then?"

Artemis smiled composedly at him, and Zeus said, "You know that is the procedure, Ares. That is the reason we almost always work in pairs, so each can keep me apprised of the actions of the other." The voice of Zeus changed perceptibly. "How long before the ship departs?"

Ares gave a start of surprise, sensing what was coming. He said warily, "Within the hour."

"Then you will leave the ship there, in Barcelona."

"But I have not yet carried out my mission," Ares said in dismay.

"The girl is not stupid, Ares, even if you are. The chances of her having seen and recognized you are high. You will leave the ship at once." The fury in Zeus' voice curled and snapped like a lash.

"But I have not lost a game yet!"

"You have failed." There was a moment of deadly silence. "Are you defying me, Ares?"

"No, of course not," Ares said slowly. "If that is what you wish, I will obey."

"That is my wish. I will send one of the others to join the ship as soon as possible. Now, I wish to speak to Artemis."

Trembling with fury, Ares held out the receiver, and said in a tightly controlled voice, "He wishes to speak with you, Artemis."

Eight

At midmorning the next day Cassandra went in search of Jake and found him in the theater with the rest of the mystery speakers. The audience was still filing in and Jake was standing on the stage chatting casually with Alex Dudley.

Cassandra went up the short steps and plucked at Jake's

sleeve. He turned to her, his face lighting up. "Cass! How are you today?"

"I'm fine . . . Jake, can we talk privately for a moment?"

He frowned, with a quick look at his watch. "Our panel's about to begin, Cass. We're only waiting for the crowd to gather."

"Please, Jake. It's important, and it'll only take a second." She glanced at Alex Dudley. "I don't mean to be rude, Mr. Dudley."

Dudley grinned. "Think nothing of it, Cassandra. If a pretty creature like you wanted a word with me, I'd say to hell with any panel!"

"Careful, Alex," Jake said with a grin, "don't let Madeline hear you."

Cassandra had already gone down the steps to the theater floor and stood looking back over her shoulder expectantly.

Jake caught up with her. "What's up, babe?"

"Let's go out into the passageway so we won't be overheard."

Outside the theater, she drew him around the corner, and then turned to him excitedly. "I think I've found out who the man was I saw following us. In fact, I'm sure of it."

"So who is he?"

"A passenger by the name of Ian Macomber. He had one of the penthouse suites."

"How can you be sure?"

"Well, I felt fairly certain that he was a passenger, and so I spent a couple of hours last night going over the pictures taken by the ship's photographers. Now, some of the passengers don't like being photographed, but it's almost impossible to avoid it completely. Claude manages to catch them all sooner or later. And I finally found a picture of the man who was following us."

"How did you get his name?"

"The picture was taken at his dinner table, and it showed the table number. Also, remember when I was taking pictures of you in front of the cathedral in Barcelona? Well, the man who was following us was in a taxi that drove by, just as I told you. I took a picture of him. I asked Claude to develop it, and it came out nice and sharp. It's the same man, I'm certain."

Jake caught her excitement. "Then I think the thing to do is confront him . . . Wait a minute. You said *had*, didn't you?"

"Yes." She nodded glumly. "He checked out yesterday, a half hour before we departed from Barcelona."

Jake looked thoughtful. "That does seem rather coincidental. If he was the man in the van, he might believe we saw his face and could recognize him."

She nodded. "That's what I thought. Could we . . . Well, could we report him to the police and have him arrested?"

"Arrested for what, Cass?" He shook his head. "Even if he *was* the man in the taxi, we have no proof that he did anything criminal. All we can swear to for sure is that we thought he followed us a couple of times. That's no crime. And we don't *know* that he was driving the van. As for his leaving the ship suddenly, he could claim a perfectly legitimate reason. A personal or business crisis at home, anything." He shook his head again. "No, if he was trying to harm you, count yourself lucky that he's gone, out of your hair."

"Yesterday, you said there might be more than one."

"*Thought*, not knew. And I meant that the person writing the notes and the one after you might be different people. Besides, now that you've let me in on all this, I'll be keeping a close eye on you." He placed a knuckle under her chin and tilted her face up. "You're precious to me, babe, and I intend to keep you safe and sound . . ."

"Oh, Jake, there you are!" Alex Dudley had rounded the corner. "The panel is ready to go, we're waiting on you."

"Be right there, Alex." Jake smiled at Cassandra. "You coming? It might be interesting."

Cassandra hesitated. She had a million things to do. But then, Dawes had assigned her to watch over the Mystery Cruise, hadn't he?

"Why not?" she said.

Jake winked at her and held her hand until they were inside the theater. There, she took an aisle seat in the back, and Jake went on to the stage. Cassandra watched him, loving the way he walked—head high, his body movements graceful, economical, under tight control.

The possibility that she was no longer in danger brought a feeling of enormous relief, and she felt more relaxed than she had in days. She still had a slight, recurring ache from the bump on her head, but the swelling was reduced, and this morning Dr. Abramson told her that the possibility of a concussion now seemed very remote.

She closed her eyes as Roxie Pike introduced the members of the panel to the audience, and it was only by force of will that Cassandra managed to keep from dozing.

She opened her eyes again as Roxie said, "I think we'll start off with Mr. Randle, since he has had the most experience with investigations. Each member of the panel will give a short, introductory speech, and then we will be open to questions."

Jake rose and stepped to the podium. As he began to talk, Cassandra marveled at how much in command of himself he seemed to be. ". . . first thing an experienced investigator looks for at the scene of any crime is a sign of the perpetrator's M.O." He grinned crookedly. "I'm sure that most of you, the mystery writers at any rate, know that M.O. stands for modus operandi. Every professional criminal has certain things he does the same way in the performance of every crime. No matter how much he may try to avoid this pitfall, there is almost always one thing he does the same way.

"It becomes his trademark, in a manner of speaking. Now, you may think this is a stupid thing to do. And in a way, it is. But a criminal, no matter how hardened, is always in a stress situation during the commission of a crime and has a tendency to repeat certain things.

"That is why it is often difficult to catch an amateur killer—or perhaps I should say a first-time killer. He has no M.O. yet, you see . . ."

A hand descended on Cassandra's shoulder, causing her to start and look up.

Leland Dawes, frowning severely, was bending over her. He whispered, "I want a word with you, Kanaris." He jerked his head. "Outside." He turned and strode toward the exit without waiting for a response.

Irritated by his peremptory manner, Cassandra was at the point of rebellion. Then she sighed resignedly and went after him.

In the passageway he considered her with apparent displeasure. "I've been looking all over the ship for you."

"I didn't hear a page."

"I didn't page you. I had a hunch you'd be here."

"Mr. Dawes, you did assign the supervision of the Mystery Cruise to me."

"But not to the exclusion of your other duties."

"I didn't realize that I'd neglected any of my other duties," she said tightly. "If you think so, please be specific."

He ignored her question and peered at her critically. "You look a little pale and under the weather, Kanaris. I heard something about your being hurt in an accident yesterday."

"It wasn't anything serious." Involuntarily, her hand went to the bump on her head. "I'm fine now."

"I'm glad to hear it," he said with a nod. "Perhaps you shouldn't overdo, take it easy for a day or two."

So you can then claim that I'm not doing my job, she thought angrily. She was coming to a slow boil. "Was there any particular reason you wanted me, Mr. Dawes?"

"Oh, nothing really important. I just wanted to see how you were." He gestured vaguely, turned, and began to walk down the passageway.

She glared after him, seething. Then he took the wind out of her sails. He paused, turning back. "You seem to be doing okay, Kanaris. The passengers have nothing but good things to say about you. Keep up the good work."

With a short nod he continued on, stepping into an open elevator across from the theater.

Deflated, Cassandra stared after him in puzzlement. Was Leland Dawes human, after all? Maybe she had misjudged him. With a rueful shake of her head she started back into the theater, but just inside she saw that Jake was no longer at the podium. Alex Dudley had taken his place, and she changed her mind and went back out.

As she got off the elevator on the Promenade deck she encountered Lisa van Horne, the elderly beauty she had met during embarkation, waiting to get on. "Miss van Horne," Cassandra said with pleasure. "I don't think I've seen you since the day we boarded."

The older woman smiled. "I've been a bit under the weather, my dear—a touch of *mal de mer*—and have been taking most of my meals in my suite."

"I'm sorry to hear that," Cassandra said sincerely.

During the day, in the warm climate, most of the female passengers went about in swim suits, shorts, or sundresses, but Lisa van Horne was dressed as if for dinner, in a long silk, flowered dress, with a regal hat shading her features. She was carrying a book under her arm. Her only concession to casualness was a pair of low-heeled shoes.

She gestured with the book. "This is the first time I've ventured out, so I thought I would do some reading."

"A mystery, I hope?"

"A mystery?" the woman said blankly.

"A mystery novel," Cassandra said quickly. "It would be appropriate."

"Oh, yes, because of the Mystery Cruise. No, I never read mysteries. This is the latest best-seller by Harold Robbins." She began to smile. "At my age most of my sex life is vicarious." Unexpectedly, she gave a burst of rich, bawdy laughter.

Cassandra shook her head. "I really find that hard to believe, Miss van Horne, as attractive as you are."

"How sweet of you, my dear." The older woman patted Cassandra's hand. "I don't say that I don't still enjoy it. It's just that getting it isn't as easy as it used to be."

Cassandra was made somewhat uncomfortable by this sudden revelation, and her face must have mirrored her feelings, for the woman smiled more warmly and patted her hand again. "But it's nothing for you to concern yourself about, my dear. The years have been full and satisfying. I've known a great many men, good, bad, and indifferent, and do not regret a single moment of my life."

"I'm sure you have no reason to," Cassandra murmured.

The elevator doors sighed open again, and Lisa van Horne moved toward them. "Thank you for your concern, Cassandra. You're a nice girl; I've heard nothing but good about you."

Two compliments in one day! Cassandra went on her way with a lightened step. Now that the threat to her life had been removed, she had no reason not to look forward with anticipation to the rest of the voyage.

Her mood of euphoria was broken two hours later when she stopped off in her cabin for a change of clothing. The all-too-familiar lavender note was on the bed.

"Cassandra: Do not relax your guard too much. Because

one is gone, do not think that others will not offer harm. A friend."

She immediately went in search of Jake. She found him seated at the bar in the Pisces Lounge having a drink. She ordered a cola, took him to an empty table across the room, and showed him the note.

Jake frowned as he scanned the note quickly. "One thing the note confirms: apparently the guy who took off in Barcelona *was* after you. Also . . ." He motioned with the note. "Whoever is writing these is on your side, may even be trying to protect you."

"But protect me from whom? And why is all this happening to me, Jake?"

"There you have me. If you haven't a clue, I sure as hell don't." He smiled wryly. "As somebody used to say, it's getting mysteriouser and mysteriouser. But at least the fact that someone else is looking out for you should relieve your mind a little."

She shook her head. "On the contrary. I still feel threatened. Even if whoever is writing the notes is on my side, as you seem to think, it's still an invasion of my space. To think that someone has free access to my cabin frightens me, Jake."

He nodded slowly. "Yes, I can see that, but I don't know what we can do, short of changing the locks, or moving you to another cabin."

"If I did that, I would have to explain, and I hate to even think of that." She shivered.

"Yes, it would be opening a whole can of worms." He squeezed his lower lip in thought. "There's one thing you could do. This guy who left may be replaced in the next port. You could keep tabs on his empty suite, see if anyone moves in there. You can do that without arousing suspicions, can't you?"

She nodded. "Oh, yes, that's no problem. But if anyone

replaces this man, he wouldn't move into the same suite, would he? That would be too obvious."

"You're right, it would be," he said admiringly. "You'd make a good detective, Cass."

"And it's nothing unusual for us to pick up several new passengers at any good-sized port, so there'll be nothing suspicious if new people board."

Jake sighed lugubriously. "It does seem rather complicated, doesn't it? And here I thought I was taking a vacation from detective work."

"I'm sorry, Jake," she said contritely. "It isn't turning out to be much of a vacation for you, is it?"

"Aw, babe, don't say that. I didn't mean that, not really." He covered her hand with his. "It'll keep me in good fettle. Besides, if I hadn't come along, I wouldn't have met you. But there is something else you could do. Can you get me all the information available on our fleeing passenger?"

"That's no problem, either. But what will you do with it?"

"When I was on the force in New York, I had a contact in Interpol. I will get a cable off to him today, requesting any information he can dig up on this guy."

"But what good will that do now, after he's . . . ?"

"After he's flown the coop, as my pop used to say?" Jake grinned. "Maybe none at all, but you never know what overturned rocks may reveal. It can't hurt."

Jake thought it best not to tell her that he also intended to have a check run on her father, Jason Kanaris.

The reception via satellite was not the best, and the voice of Zeus faded in and out. "Artemis . . . hear me?"

"Yes, Zeus, not too well, but I can hear most of what you say. Perhaps it would be better to wait until tomorrow. The reception may have improved."

". . . . cannot wait . . . Too urgent . . . Imperative . . . act at once . . ."

"But Zeus, Ares has only been gone a day," she said. "I

haven't had time to plan anything yet. You warned me to proceed slowly."

"I know, but something has happened." Miraculously, the reception cleared up. "I have just received new information. The detective on the *Star* has initiated an inquiry with Interpol, concerning Ares. That will gain him little, but he has also asked for a check to be made on Jason. That puts us at risk. You must act at once. The girl must be removed before the ship reaches Genoa."

"That soon?" she said in dismay.

"Yes. Even if you put yourself at risk, it must be done."

"I will try, but . . ."

"You will not *try*," Zeus said imperiously. "You will do it, or risk my extreme displeasure. Is that clearly understood?"

"I understand."

"Good! The detective can wait until Genoa, or at least until I can put one of the others on board to assist you. But the girl must be taken care of."

It was the night of the performance of *Arsenic and Old Lace*, and a few minutes before curtain time, Cassandra peered through the curtain at the arriving audience. She was happy to see that the theater was already two-thirds filled. Roxie Pike should be pleased.

Behind her, on the narrow stage, Todd Breckinridge was fussing with the few pieces of furniture that made up the simple set.

Cassandra turned away from the curtain with a smile. Todd had been displaying all the temperament of an old-time stage director. To watch him at work, you would have thought they were opening on Broadway, instead of presenting an amateur production, where the cast were reading from their scripts.

He was finished with the set now and exited through the fake door—supposedly the door to the cellar—that led to the tiny backstage area. Cassandra followed him and literally ran into Jake, who laughed and took her by the arm.

He said, "My God, it's crowded back here!"

She chuckled. "Well, it's primarily a movie theater, after all. It wasn't really designed for plays. How do you like Todd's costume?"

Jake glanced over at Breckinridge, in heavy makeup and a scruffy suit, as Jonathon. Breckinridge was obviously lecturing Claire Thomas and June Hays, the two women who were playing the dotty old sisters, Abby and Martha.

Jake said, "He's really wound up, isn't he? You know, if he tells me one more time to 'really throw myself into the role,' I'm going to throttle him!"

Cassandra shook her head. "He is something else, isn't he?" She adjusted the ridiculous hat she was wearing. "I think I could kill him myself, for making me wear this damn, swear, hat!"

Breckinridge turned away from Claire and June. "Five minutes, people! *Five* minutes! Take your places, everyone!"

The first two acts went well, and there was prolonged applause at the end of both acts. The audience was enjoying it, and they had laughed in all the right places, which Breckinridge had assured the cast was a real compliment.

At the end of Act Two, Cassandra found herself terribly thirsty. She was just heading toward the exit and the passageway beyond, where there was a drinking fountain, when Claire Thomas, who was playing Abby, came toward her.

"Heavens, I'm tired," Claire said with a sigh. "Todd didn't tell me that acting was such god-awful hard work!"

Cassandra smiled. "I know what you mean. My mouth feels as dry as a desert. If Todd asks for me, tell him I'll be right back. I'm going to slip out for a drink of water."

Taking off the uncomfortable hat, she placed it on a

folding chair before heading for the stage door. As she opened it she happened to glance back and saw Claire lift the dreadful hat and put it on.

Smiling to herself, Cassandra went out into the passageway, and made for the fountain, which was around the corner. Turning on the water, she bent gratefully to drink. But as her lips touched the water she was suddenly engulfed in total darkness. The lights had gone out.

Without drinking, she straightened slowly. The darkness was complete, for the theater was on the Starlight deck, far below the waterline.

As she stood there Cassandra felt, rather than saw, someone brush past her, going in the direction of the stage door, and she had to wonder how on earth anyone could see to move.

She could hear voices raised inside the theater and had just about decided to feel her way along the wall in the direction of the sound, when the lights came on again, blinding her with sudden brilliance.

Forgetting her thirst, she headed back for the theater and, as she did so, caught just a glimpse of a figure turning the corner at the end of the passageway. The brief glimpse wasn't sufficient for Cassandra to tell if the figure was male or female, but she did get the impression that the person was wearing pants.

As she started to push open the stage door her foot struck something on the floor, and she looked down to see what seemed to be a pair of sun goggles. Bending down, she picked them up. How strange. Why would someone be carrying sunglasses at night?

The glasses in her hand, she entered the backstage area. Starting toward the chair where she'd left her hat, she noticed that it was gone.

Todd Breckinridge stormed over to her. "Cassandra, have you seen Claire? We have to get the next act underway, and we can't find her anywhere. That damned blackout!"

"The last time I saw her was right here, just after the second-act curtain. She was trying on my hat, and she must have taken it with her."

"Well, where is she? The audience is getting restless."

"Maybe she's in the ladies' room."

Breckinridge's face brightened. "Would you check, Cassandra? Please?"

Cassandra nodded, and set off at a trot for the ladies' room, which was located near the drinking fountain. But the ladies' room was empty, and Cassandra returned to the backstage area to find that the others had been as unsuccessful as she in finding Claire.

Filled with a persistent but unfocused sense of apprehension, Cassandra watched Breckinridge fume, as the others stood around watching helplessly.

Finally, Breckinridge turned to June. "All right, we'll have to continue without her, we have no choice. We can't keep the audience waiting all night. Maybe she'll show up before we get too far into the act."

"But how can I go on alone?" June wailed. "I can't speak my lines to the empty air!"

"Here." Breckinridge snatched her script out of her hand and began marking furiously with a pen. "We'll just change the lines a little. You're the first one to enter, anyway, and your first line is spoken to Jonathon and the doctor, offstage. Then, you simply omit these lines"—he marked angrily, pen slashing—"and you take what should be Abby's line, as she closes the window seat."

He looked up. "Dammit! That window seat is supposed to be open, so that the audience can see that it's empty! Well, June, when you go on stage, you'll open it first, then close it, while you speak Abby's line. Then we'll just skip to where Mortimer enters. After that, you'll just have to say both your lines and Abby's. Maybe, by that time, Claire will get her ass back here.

"There!" He thrust the altered script into June's hands,

and gave her a slight push. "Don't be afraid, dear. It will work out. Just act as though nothing's wrong."

"Easy enough for *you* to say," June muttered. "But I'll try my best."

Cassandra and Jake, who had come up to stand beside June in the wings, watched as the curtain was pulled to show the setting for the last act. The scene was again the living room, and it was empty. The fake door, representing the door to the cellar, was open, and through it came the backstage voices of the characters, Martha, Jonathon, and the doctor, raised in argument.

Then Martha, supposedly coming up from the cellar, walked onstage and spoke her line, shouting it back through the open door.

Cassandra watched her sympathetically. June looked very nervous, and her knuckles, where she clutched her script, were white. Still, she went doggedly ahead, with only a slight hesitation, crossing toward the closed window-seat box.

As she approached it June spoke the line that should have been Abby's and lifted the side of the makeshift window seat so that the audience could see into it.

As June raised the wooden side, her gaze upon her script, there were a few titters of laughter from the audience, and Cassandra, who had been studying her own script, glanced up, mystified.

Why were they laughing? There was nothing funny happening at the moment. And then she saw June standing as rigid as if she had been cast in cement, staring in frozen horror at the window seat, which wasn't empty at all.

Cassandra felt herself go as still as June as she tried to make sense out of what she was seeing, and then June screamed, a terrible sound that seemed to come from everywhere and nowhere. Immediately, Breckinridge lowered the stage curtain.

Cassandra was only seconds behind Jake, as he ran

onstage. She was right beside him as he knelt to look at the contents of the window-seat box, and then she wished she was not, for inside the narrow seat, folded and crumpled in an impossible position, was Claire Thomas, her face twisted in agony, her eyes open and unblinking, with Cassandra's hat crushed down upon her head.

Nine

Even before Jake touched Claire's throat, feeling for a pulse, Cassandra knew that the woman was dead, and Jake's words only confirmed the fact.

He looked up at Breckinridge, who was standing white-faced behind him. "She's dead. I think you'd better make some sort of an announcement to the audience, Todd. No need to tell them what's really happened, just say that one of the cast has been hurt in an accident and you can't continue. Then you'd better notify the captain."

Breckinridge, for once wordless, nodded silently, and turned away.

Jake rose and shook his head. "Damn!"

Cassandra took his arm and fixed her gaze on his face so that she wouldn't have to look at what lay in the window seat. She felt shaken and nauseated.

Jake looked down at her sympathetically. "I'm sorry you

had to see this. A homicide is never a pretty sight, and when it's someone you know . . ."

"It was murder?" Her voice was muted.

He shrugged. "I don't think she got there by herself."

Cassandra shot a quick, involuntary glance at Claire's body, seeing again the awful hat, brutally incongruous now, atop Claire's white and lifeless face. As she did so an idea occurred to her that made her grab Jake's arm in a grip that caused him to grunt.

"Hey! What's the idea?"

"Jake," she whispered, "I think what happened to Claire, was meant for me."

His head snapped around. "What?" As she started to speak again, he added, "Wait," and led her to the other end of the stage, away from where all the members of the cast were gathered, staring down at the dead woman in horror. Todd Breckinridge's voice could be heard on the other side of the curtain, talking to the audience.

Jake said, "Now Cass, what did you mean?"

"Well, during the intermission, I went out into the passageway for a drink of water. I left my hat, the one Todd insisted I wear, lying on a chair, by the stage door. Claire was there. As I stepped outside, I saw Claire trying it on. Not only that . . ." She drew a shuddering breath. "When the lights went out, I felt someone brush past me in the dark, going toward the stage door. And after the lights came back on, I saw someone running around the far corner of the passageway."

Jake pinched his lower lip between his fingers and worried it. "Then you think someone slipped into the theater and killed Claire, believing she was you, because she was wearing the hat?"

She nodded quickly. "That's the way it looks to me."

He sighed, frowning. "This someone you saw, a man or a woman?"

"I don't know. I only caught a quick glimpse and didn't

think it was important at the time. I'm almost sure that the person was wearing pants." She was thinking back. "I have the feeling that it *was* a woman, but I can't tell you why I think that."

"One thing I don't quite understand," Jake said. "I haven't heard yet what caused the power failure, but I think it's a safe assumption that the killer somehow managed to turn the lights off. But how could he, or she, see well enough in the dark to get in and out of the theater, and kill Claire, even assuming that she was mistaken for you?"

Cassandra remembered the glasses she had found, and dug into her jacket pocket for them. "I found these just outside the stage door, where the killer could have dropped them."

She held them out, and Jake took them, examining them closely. "That explains part of it," he said with a nod. "These are infrared glasses. They enable the wearer to see in the dark, at least well enough to distinguish objects, if not a person's features too well. Whoever did this had all the right moves planned out, except they knocked off the wrong victim."

Cassandra glanced across the stage with a shudder. "Poor Claire."

"Poor Claire, yes, but also lucky you." He took her hand and squeezed it gently. "The hell of it is, babe, your luck can't last forever . . ."

There was a commotion at the far end of the stage as two men in uniform came out of the wings—Captain Helsing and the chief purser, Andrew Perrin. Captain Helsing was a man in his early sixties, short, slightly plump, with a sea-weathered face. Cassandra knew he was the most respected captain on the Nordic Lines, yet she had to wonder if he wasn't out of his depth here, investigating a murder.

"Jake . . ." She clutched at his hand. "What are we going to tell them? I mean, about the possibility of the murderer mistaking Claire for me?"

He weighed the question carefully, his thoughtful gaze on the new arrivals now conferring with Todd Breckinridge, who had finished his little speech out front. Jake finally said, "Nothing. After all, it's really only an assumption, perhaps a damned good assumption, but we have nothing to back it up. The same thing applies now as it did earlier, Cass, when you didn't want to tell anyone on board ship about what had been happening, because of the problems that would have come down on you."

"Yes, that went through my mind. But don't you, as a law officer, have to report what you know?"

"I'm not a cop anymore, remember?" He smiled grimly. "I'm a private investigator and as such I have a right to a certain confidentiality as concerns a client. Not to the point where I'd impede an investigation, but I hardly know enough to do that, do I? I haven't even received a response from my guy at Interpol yet."

"But I'm not your client, Jake."

"Give me a dollar and you will be." His gaze became intent. "There is one thing you must consider carefully, however. You're in danger, Cass. I don't think there's any longer any doubt of that, considering what's happened here tonight. If you confide in the captain, he can provide you with far more protection than I can."

"How? By locking me in my cabin and posting a guard at the door?" She shook her head. "No, I don't want that to happen. The captain might even demand that I leave the *Star* in Genoa, especially if he believes that my presence on board in any way endangers the other passengers, and I certainly don't want that. If I had to leave the ship now, it would make it that much more difficult to look for my father."

Jake's glance had gone to the captain. In a low voice he said, "Quick, give me a dollar. I think he's coming over here."

Cassandra found a dollar in her purse and folded it into

his hand, then turned as Captain Helsing walked over to them.

He inclined his head gravely. "Cassandra. A terrible thing, this." His English was excellent, with just a touch of Scandinavian accent. "I was never much in favor of these special cruises."

"Oh, I hardly think you can blame this on the Mystery Cruise, Captain," she said quickly.

"Perhaps not, but I have been a captain of the line for ten years," he said heavily, "and nothing like this has ever happened. True, I have had to cope with crimes of various sorts, pilfering, confidence men on board, even a few deaths, but all natural except for one suicide and one woman overboard during a storm. But murder!"

"Captain Helsing," Cassandra said, "this is Jake Randle, one of the Mystery Cruise speakers."

"Ah, yes." Captain Helsing studied Jake out of faded blue eyes. As the two men shook hands, he added, "You are the policeman, I believe."

"A private detective, Captain."

"I must confess, Mr. Randle, that I am at a loss as to how to proceed with this. We are still a good distance from Genoa, where I can turn this over to the proper authorities. You have had some experience with homicide in your work?"

"Yes, of course."

"Then perhaps you could take charge here?" the captain said hopefully. "There is a fund for such matters, and I could pay you a reasonable fee."

Jake shot a glance at Cassandra. "I'm afraid I couldn't do that, sir. But I would be happy to advise you, and help you, in whatever way I can. No fee involved."

Captain Helsing sighed heavily. "I would be grateful for any assistance, Mr. Randle."

"To begin with you might like to see these." From his

pocket Jake took the infrared glasses Cassandra had found and held them out.

The captain took them and peered at them closely. "What are these and what connection do they have with this affair?"

"They're infrared glasses. As you of course know, the lights went out here and we were in the dark for at least five minutes."

Captain Helsing was nodding. "Yes, I know. But what do the glasses mean?"

"They're used for seeing in the dark."

"Ah! Then that explains how the murderer was able to find his victim!" He handled the glasses gingerly. "But shouldn't we worry about fingerprints?"

Jake shrugged. "It's too late for that. Anyway, from the clever way this was planned, it's likely the perpetrator wore gloves. I would suggest that you put the glasses in your safe, Captain, until we reach Genoa."

The captain nodded. "Do you have any other suggestions, Mr. Randle?"

Lip caught between thumb and forefinger, Jake gazed at the body in the window seat. "I'm not too familiar with ships. I know you have two doctors on board, but can they perform autopsies, or do you even have facilities for that?"

"Not really. In the event of any death not from natural causes—which must be certified as such by one of our two doctors—we keep the bodies in cold storage until we reach the next port." He looked sidelong at Cassandra. "Why do you ask, Mr. Randle?"

"Well, we still don't know the cause of death. There is no blood, no visible wound, which pretty much rules out a gun, a knife, or a blunt weapon. I suspect some kind of a quick-acting poison, probably by injection. I thought it might be advisable to have one of your doctors examine the victim before she is moved, to see if the means of death is detectable without an autopsy. Also, it might be a good idea to have your ship's photographer take some pictures before the body is moved."

"Excellent suggestions." The captain nodded in approval. "I'll see to it right away."

The captain crossed over to the purser, and Cassandra moved to Jake's side. "I'll bet you were a good cop, Jake."

He blinked. "What?"

"I've been watching you and listening to what you told Captain Helsing. You know what you're doing."

"Flattery will get you anywhere," he said with his crooked grin. His glance went past her. "Is that the doctor?"

She looked around. "Yes, that's Dr. Abramson."

"Let's go see what he finds out."

Dr. Abramson was kneeling before the window-seat box, carefully examining the dead woman. After several moments, he said, "Ah, that's it!"

As he stood up, Jake said, "What did you find, Doctor? A needle mark?"

"Who are you?" the doctor said grumpily.

Cassandra said hastily, "Dr. Abramson, this is Jake Randle. He's a member of the Mystery Cruise. He's a private detective and was once a New York homicide officer."

Dr. Abramson grunted. "A private dick, eh? Never met one in real life. But you know your business, young man. A needle went into her, right into the area at the back of her neck, where the nerve ganglia leads up to the brain." He knelt again, gently turning Claire's head until the back of her neck was exposed. "There, see?" He pointed with a long forefinger.

Bending down, Cassandra could see a tiny hole.

Still kneeling, Dr. Abramson looked up at Jake. "How'd you arrive at your conclusion, young fellow?"

Jake shrugged. "There were no overt signs of violence."

The doctor's eyes showed a glint of admiration. He got to his feet with a grunt, brushing his hands together. "You must have been a fair cop. Care to make another guess, as to what substance was used?"

"It could be any number of things, but it had to be fast-acting, like curare. From all appearances she died almost instantly. She certainly made no outcry or struggle. The lights were out for only five minutes or so, and the killer had to make his injection, then stuff her into that box, and make good his escape, all within those few minutes."

Dr. Abramson nodded. "We won't know for sure until an autopsy is performed, but I'd say you're probably correct." He turned to Captain Helsing. "Captain, I suppose we should place her in the freezer now."

The captain said sadly, "Yes, that would seem to the proper procedure. I'll have a couple of the men down to assist you, Dr. Abramson."

The two men walked off, talking in low tones.

Cassandra said, "Jake, you said 'he.' Do you have any reason to think it was a man?"

"Not really. It's a habit you get into on the police. When the sex of the criminal is unknown, you always use the male pronoun, since it usually *is* a man." He grinned faintly. "In spite of women's struggle for equality, the criminal area is one place where they haven't quite caught up, though they may do it yet!"

Before she could frame a reply, Cassandra's gaze fell on the dead woman, and she felt a deep shame. They shouldn't be engaged in light repartee, with poor Claire dead, the victim of an attack meant for Cassandra herself.

She shivered and took Jake's hand. "Let's get out of here."

"I'm all for that."

In the elevator going up, Cassandra said, "What do you think will happen next?"

"Not very much, I should imagine. Not until we get to Genoa. You heard the captain."

"That's what I meant. Do you suppose the police will hold the passengers for prolonged questioning? Most of the departing passengers have planes to catch, probably with limited time. The *Star* is only in Genoa for a day and a night, before we sail again. Do you suppose they will hold us up?"

"The Mystery Cruise members may get hassled a little, since Claire was one of them. As for the ship and the rest of the passengers, I doubt they'll be questioned a great deal. It would be quite a chore interrogating five hundred people." He laughed. "That would be something, wouldn't it? Five hundred suspects! Even more, if you include the staff and crew."

"Jake . . ." She tightened her grip on his hand. "You're a member of the Mystery Cruise. Do you suppose they'll hold you over when we reach Genoa?"

"Not if I can help it." He looked thoughtful. "But I suppose anything is possible. Anyway, let's not borrow trouble. I do want to cooperate with the Genoa police as much as possible, learn whatever I can about the results of their investigation. In most countries the local police extend common courtesy to cops from other countries. I'm hoping that'll happen here, even if I'm no longer a homicide officer."

"Your incompetence is beyond belief, Artemis!" Zeus thundered. "Absolutely unforgivable!"

Artemis held the receiver slightly away from her ear. She had never heard Zeus so furious. She smiled to herself. Speak of the wrath of the gods!

After a little time had passed, she spoke into the receiver, "Zeus, are you calm enough to listen now? You know I have never been as intimidated by you as some of the others. Even Ares, as evil as he is, is frightened silly of you. But not I. I always close my eyes and remember what we once were to each other. How can I be terribly frightened of a man who has gone to sleep in my arms so many times?"

"That is all in the past!" Zeus roared. "You will do well to remember who I am!"

"Oh, I never forget who you are, Zeus, and I always do your bidding, at least I try to the best of my ability. And that's what I did last night."

"But it wasn't good enough, was it? First Ares, my best one, failed twice. And now this. It is too much!" His voice began to climb again.

"You told me to improvise, to do what I could, without adequate planning and supervision. You told me to do it even if I placed myself in danger. Well, I placed myself in great danger to carry out your bidding. I failed by a fluke. I had watched Cassandra rehearse the play a number of times wearing that silly hat. How could I know that that other stupid woman would be wearing it? It was pitch dark in the theater. Even wearing the infrared glasses I couldn't see that well. Besides, I had to do it quickly. I didn't know how much time I had before the lights came back on. As it was, I just had time enough to make good my escape."

Artemis thought it best not to mention that she had dropped the infrared glasses somewhere in her haste. Thinking back over every step of her way out of the theater and down the passageway, she could not for the life of her remember where she had lost them.

"Why did you take the time to stuff the body in that box seat? That was not necessary."

"Yes, it was, it gave me time to escape unnoticed. If the body had been discovered the instant the lights came back on, I would never have gotten away."

Zeus' heavy sigh came over the distance between them, and his tone was calmer as he said, "Well, it's done now."

"Shall I make another attempt?"

"No! Not right after your fiasco. The ship will be in Genoa shortly. We will have to wait. I have already dispatched Apollo to join the ship at Genoa. It will be in his hands now."

"Shall I stay on? I was only booked to Genoa, but I can probably remain on board without difficulty."

Zeus was silent for a few moments. "Yes, Artemis, I think it best that you remain, to keep watch on Apollo. He will not be in a penthouse suite. It was a mistake to allow you and Ares to book penthouse suites in the first place. There are too few of them. I have booked Apollo into a regular stateroom."

"Among the peasants?" Artemis' tone was mocking. "I don't know how he'll take to such a hardship."

"He will do as he is ordered," Zeus said in a snarling voice. "If the girl finds her father, we are all in for a much worse hardship than forgoing a luxury suite."

When the *Star* came into the harbor at Genoa, two Italian policemen were on board the pilot boat that met them. By the time the ship had docked, the two officers had interrogated most of the Mystery Cruise speakers and passengers, as well as Cassandra. In her case the questioning was mercifully brief, especially after she had told them that she wasn't going ashore in Genoa. With a new load of passengers coming on board, she would be far too busy.

The officer in charge was Marcus Bruno, a middle-aged, soft-spoken man, who knew English very well. He was very courteous, Cassandra thought, under the circumstances.

"Since you will be on board your ship, *Signorina* Kanaris," Bruno said, "we will know how and where to find you, in the event that becomes necessary. The others, the ones disembarking in Genoa, will soon be on their way back to their own country. It would be difficult, if not impossible, to get in touch with them later, so we must interrogate them at once."

Cassandra didn't see Jake until shortly before he went ashore. She told him what Bruno had said.

He nodded. "Yes, he told me much the same thing. He

seems like a nice guy. I offered to help him as much as I could, and he let me sit in on some of the interrogations."

"Did anything said throw any light on Claire's death?"

Jake shook his head. "Nope, we're still in the dark. No one knows anything about Claire Thomas, or if they do, they're not telling. She came along on the cruise by herself, so she was only known casually by the members of the Mystery Cruise, and not a soul has any idea of why anyone would want to kill her."

"I wonder how she learned about the Mystery Cruise?"

"She's from Chicago, and she's a member of the Mystery Writers of America. There was a notice in their monthly newsletter about the Mystery Cruise. It seems that Claire had sold a couple of mystery short stories." Jake took Cassandra's hand. "I probably won't be back until late, Cass. I'm going to spend as much time with Bruno today as he will allow. I'll call you some time today. Now you be damned careful. Stay out of dark corners, well away from the railing, and in the company of others as much as possible, you hear?"

Jake had a long, tiring day after he went ashore. He sat in on the interrogations of the rest of the passengers and also dictated a statement of his own, carefully omitting all knowledge of Cassandra's involvement. He had some uneasy moments over that, wondering if, by keeping quiet about what had happened to her, he wasn't putting her in more danger, but it was the way she wanted it, so he kept quiet.

Nothing new was revealed by any of the interrogations, and Bruno was clearly discouragd by the end of the day, when he sat with Jake in his tiny office, smoking a twisted, black cigar that fouled the air.

"Well, Jake," he said with a sigh, "it appears we have reached what I believe you Americans call a 'dead end.'"

Jake nodded slowly. "That's as good a word as any." He

liked Marcus Bruno. The man, he had learned, had been a *poliziotto* for twenty years, but he was still relatively free of cynicism and had retained his faith in justice and the system. Which is a hell of a lot more than I have, Jake reflected sourly.

Bruno said, "At first I was excited by this case. It seemed to offer something more than our usual murder cases, with all the sordid, foolish people involved. Here was a luxurious cruise ship, with all the glamourous, rich people, some of what I think you call the jet set, I believe."

Jake peered at him narrowly. "The jet set? Why do you call them that? To take a cruise like this, you have to be fairly well off perhaps, but I doubt that many jet setters take cruises. They like to mix and mingle only with their own. They fly; that's where they got the name. If they do go by water, they use their own yachts."

"But the people in the penthouse suites? They are very rich, I understand."

Jake leaned forward alertly, remembering that the man who had tried to kill them in Barcelona had been in a penthouse suite. "Did you interrogate them?"

"Indeed, yes." Bruno nodded. "Let's say I tried. The questioning was brief, of course. One of the first lessons I learned was to walk gingerly around the very wealthy. They all denied any knowledge of such a common thing as murder, naturally." Bruno spread his hands.

Jake asked casually, "Did you have any reason to suspect them?"

"No, no." Bruno grinned engagingly. "But they are people of the glamour, and I always enjoy giving them the bad time. We have many of that sort here, along the Italian Riviera outside of Genoa." He gave a fatalistic shrug. "They always brush me aside like an annoying insect. We Italians have a saying, '*Se il sedere avesse soldi si chiamerebbe Don Sedere.*'"

"And that means?"

Bruno grinned sourly. "If one's rear end had money, it would be called Sir Rear End."

Jake erupted with laughter. Sobering, he said, "The penthouse passengers, did they all leave the ship here?"

"Three are left, I believe. A woman named Lisa van Horne and a man by the name of Eric Johanson. The third is also a woman."

"Then they aren't on your list of suspects?"

"What list of suspects, Jake? That is what is so discouraging. I have no list of suspects. I am sure it is the same in your United States. To have a suspect you must find someone with motive and opportunity. On your ship there were almost six hundred people with opportunity, but not a single one with a motive, that we can uncover . . ."

Bruno was interrupted by a knock on the door. He called out in Italian, and the door opened to admit a man in a technician's smock, who had a folder under his arm. They exchanged a few words, and the technician left.

Bruno opened the folder. "The results of the autopsy. I asked them to expedite it." He read quickly, sucking furiously on the cigar. Finally, he leaned back with a sigh, batting smoke away from his face with one hand. "It is as you surmised, my friend. The woman was killed by a massive injection of curare. Death was instantaneous, it is clear. Her vocal chords were certainly paralyzed within a second or so, so she could not cry out. She likely did not even put up a struggle."

"Well, Bruno, I suppose that's it." Jake glanced at his watch; it was after six o'clock. "I have a couple of things to do yet before I return to the ship." He got to his feet. "You can always contact me on the ship over the next two weeks. I would very much appreciate it if you would pass along anything you might learn."

"The chances of that seem very remote." Bruno peered at Jake shrewdly. "On one thing I am curious, amico. What is your interest in this murder? You are not directly involved, the victim was not your client."

Jake hesitated. This man was very clever, and Jake knew he had to tread carefully. He finally gave what he hoped was a disarming grin. "Just call it academic interest. Once a homicide cop, always a homicide cop. In my country they have a saying, 'An old war-horse is always ready to charge into action.' I suppose that's me, an old war-horse."

It was dark when Jake finally left the police station. A block away he found a sidewalk cafe with a pay telephone. He sat down wearily. When the waiter came, Jake managed to convey his needs—a large scotch and coins for the telephone. When the drink came, he took a hearty pull, scooped up a handful of change, and called the Interpol office in Paris. It was a call he had wanted to make all day, but he'd never found the opportunity.

It was so late in the day, he wasn't sure his contact would still be in. His luck held; he was put through immediately.

"Jake Randle! How are you, Jake?"

"I'm fine, Rene, considering."

"I was quite surprised to get your cable."

"Too surprised to answer, evidently," Jake growled.

Rene laughed. "You do me a grave injustice, Jake. I was about to get a report off to you, by courier. That is the reason I am here, in the office, this late. The information you wanted wasn't easy to find."

"You can go ahead and send the report to the ship, but why don't you give me the gist of it now?"

"Well . . ." Rene cleared his throat. "Unfortunately, Jake, I found nothing at all on the passenger, Ian Macomber. It has to be an assumed name."

"I'm not surprised. I had figured that already."

"No way to get fingerprints, I suppose?"

"It's too late for that. He left the ship in Barcelona, and

the suite has been thoroughly cleaned by now, I'm sure. I can get a picture of him, though. It's on the ship."

"Then why don't you slip it in the mail to me, and I'll see if I can run him down. As for the other man, Jason Kanaris. There *is* a Jason Kanaris, or was, at any rate."

"Was? He's dead then?"

"Well, yes and no. The man was supposed to have drowned, oh, some twenty years ago, in the sea off Rhodes. But rumors have cropped up now and again that he's still alive somewhere. Whether there's any substance to the rumors, I don't know. Kanaris always was a mystery man, something of a recluse. At the time of his supposed death he was a very wealthy man. As the son of Aristides Kanaris, the shipping tycoon, Jason inherited millions, somewhere around fifty million, I understand."

"But if he died that long ago, wouldn't he have been declared legally dead by now?"

"In ordinary circumstances this would be true. But there are no heirs to claim his estate, he was the last of the line. There is no one to move to have him declared legally dead."

"How about the Greek government? I assume Kanaris was Greek?"

"Oh, yes. There's a rather strange thing there. It seems that Kanaris liquidated all his assets, including the shipping line, and deposited the funds in various banks in the Cayman Islands. The best I can find out, the money's still there. The bankers there are as closemouthed as the Swiss, so there's really no way of finding out for sure if it's been touched over the years."

If her father *is* dead, Jake thought, the estate is Cassandra's, and she would be very wealthy indeed. He said thoughtfully, "It would almost seem that Kanaris was expecting to die, or intended to disappear off the face of the earth."

"That's a fair assumption, I'd say."

"Did your research uncover any evidence of Kanaris

getting married shortly before he was supposed to have died?"

"No, not a word about that. In fact, to the best of my knowledge, Kanaris was never married." Rene's voice quickened with interest. "Do you know anything different?"

"Well, perhaps, but I'd rather not go into that right now, Rene," Jake said slowly. "Is that everything?"

"The report that I'm about to send you was more extensive, Jake, but I've given you the highlights."

"All right, Rene, I wish to thank you, and I'll send you a print of the picture of Macomber before we leave Genoa."

"That's all I'm going to get from you?" Rene said in disappointment.

"It's a rather involved story, Rene. I'm a long way myself from sorting it all out yet. You just keep feeding me information, and I promise to fill you in sooner or later. I have to go now. Thanks again for your help."

Jake hung up slowly and returned to his table, deep in thought. He finished the scotch, had another, then paid his bill and left. He wasn't too far from the docks and he decided to walk it. He had a lot of thinking to do.

By the time he reached the dock area, everything was closed up for the night. The *Star* was the only cruise ship in port. He could see her superstructure, brilliantly lighted, against the dark sky. His step quickened, as he remembered that he had promised to call Cassandra. She would probably be wondering what had happened to him.

There had been some traffic on the boulevard, but the dock area appeared deserted. He was almost at the ship when he heard a car pull up slowly behind him; he turned to see the venicle, its lights out, come alongside him. Before he could react, they were upon him—two faceless men in dark clothing.

Caught completely by surprise, he didn't have a chance. One big man wrapped powerful arms around him, pinning

Jake's arms to his sides. Belatedly, he tried to struggle.
Then he smelled the sickeningly sweet odor of ether, and a
rag was clamped over his mouth and nose. He tried to hold
his breath and fight free, but he was at too great a
disadvantage.

Finally, he had to take a breath, and the night closed
around him like a thick blanket and unconsciousness took
him.

Ten

Cassandra had had an exhausting day; it was the usual
hassle that occurred when most of the ship's passengers
disembarked and another group was due to board. She had
little time to give any thought to Jake, but she did wonder
why he hadn't called as he'd promised.

At least there were no lounge shows scheduled for that
evening, so she had a little free time after dinner. She
checked Jake's cabin and found it empty. She went up on
deck and leaned on the railing, watching the entryway of
the port terminal. A few passengers came and went, but no
Jake. She alternated between worry and anger. What *could*
have happened to him?

She finally made a decision. She left the ship and
searched for a telephone in the terminal building. It was
almost nine o'clock, and she was afraid that Marcus Bruno

would be gone for the day. But finally, after much difficulty with various people who spoke only Italian, her call was routed through to Bruno's office.

"Ah, *Signorina* Kanaris!" He sounded pleased to hear her voice.

"Is Jake . . . Is Mr. Randle there with you, *Signore* Bruno?"

Bruno hesitated, then said slowly, "No, *Signorina*, he is not. He was with me much of the day, that is true, but he left at least two hours ago."

"Well, he hasn't returned to the *Star*, and I was wondering . . ."

"He did say that he had a number of matters to attend to. I am sure that he will return to your ship before departure time. You're leaving in the morning, I believe?"

"Yes, at nine-thirty. Have you made any progress with your investigation?"

"I am afraid not, no substantial progress, at any rate," he said with a sigh. Then he gave an admiring chuckle. "But your *Signore* Randle is an astute man. He was correct in his estimation of the poison agent used by your murderer. It was curare, as he surmised. Beyond that . . ." He sighed again. "We know very little more. The interrogations were a waste of time and effort. Perhaps we shall get what you Americans call a break. You may be sure that I shall keep your captain and Jake informed if we learn anything of importance. *Arrivederci, Signorina.*"

Cassandra hung up slowly, deep in thought. She hoped that Bruno was right about Jake. But why hadn't he called her? Well, there was nothing she could do but wait. Genoa was a large city, and trying to find him would be like searching for that well-known needle in the haystack.

She returned to the ship and her cabin. Despite her uneasiness, she slept well until her bedside alarm woke her at six. She got dressed quickly and went to Jake's cabin before going on duty. She knocked several times, but there was still no answer.

She finally walked away, her head down. The thought that had been trying to force its way into her mind last evening now reached full bloom. What if he wasn't coming back at all? What if he had decided he had had enough of her and her problems, and had simply walked away?

Wasn't that unlikely, though, in view of the fact that he had paid for the rest of the trip in advance? Surely, he wouldn't forfeit several thousand dollars just to escape her. There were other, and cheaper, ways to end a romance! The other alternative was that something had happened to him on the way back to the ship; after all, he was involved in her affairs now. Whoever had tried to kill her, had tried to kill Jake, also. Or, he could have been involved in a totally unrelated accident. She debated calling Marcus Bruno again. But there was no time.

She went about her duties, determined not to think of Jake, but as she stood greeting the new passengers, she found herself constantly looking along the gangplank, hoping to catch a glimpse of his face, that crooked grin.

He did not appear. The last passengers filed aboard, the gangplank was taken away, but when the *Star* began to move away from the dock, Cassandra still stood at the railing, scanning the faces on the pier.

With only a faint hope, she went to his cabin and again knocked on his door. There was still no answer. Her mind made up, she went back to her own deck, in search of Greta, her cabin attendant. She simply *had* to know. She had thought of asking the purser if Jake Randle had checked out but had discarded the notion. If he had, without telling her, it would be too humiliating to expose herself to the purser.

She found the attendant making up a cabin. Cassandra went straight to the point. "Greta, I need a favor. I'm embarrassed to ask it of you, but . . ."

Greta looked at her interestedly, pushing a strand of blond hair out of her eyes. "What is it, Cassandra?"

"Well, there's a man . . ." She had learned that Greta was an incurable romantic, an avid reader of romance novels and the victim of several disastrous shipboard affairs. "You may have seen him, Jake Randle. He was a Mystery Cruise speaker."

Greta smiled shyly. "Yah, I saw you come out of your cabin together one morning. You are in love, yah?"

Cassandra nodded. "I guess you could say that. But the thing is, he was supposed to be with us for two more weeks, but he didn't come back last night or this morning. Apparently, he missed the ship."

"He's left you in the lurch!" Greta bobbed her head. "Men, they will do that. Yah."

"Well, that's the thing, I'm not sure. It's possible something happened to him, or he was delayed. I need to look in his cabin, to see if his things are still there, or if he did pack up and leave, but I don't want the whole ship to know. That's why I have come to you. Now, I know you don't have a passkey to the cabins on Jake's deck, but could you get one for me? I'd be eternally grateful."

Greta didn't hesitate, which made Cassandra feel a little guilty. "Yah, I will try. Wait in your cabin for me, Cassandra."

Cassandra waited in her cabin, pacing nervously. She still felt guilty about involving the trusting Greta. If it were ever learned that she had appropriated a passkey other than her own, no matter for what purpose, Greta would likely be sacked.

A soft knock sounded on the door, and Cassandra opened it. Greta slipped in, looking worried, and Cassandra had to wonder if she'd had second thoughts.

"Cassandra . . ." Greta took a deep breath. "No one will know about this?"

"No one, Greta. I swear," Cassandra said promptly. "I know you're risking your job . . ."

"Yah. But it is in a good cause," Greta said, smiling broadly now. "Here is the key."

"I'll never be able to thank you enough." Cassandra took the key. "I'll have it back in fifteen minutes, at the most."

Jake's cabin was on the deck above hers. For the past two weeks he had shared the cabin with the man who wrote espionage novels, but Cassandra knew that the cabin was to be Jake's alone for the rest of the voyage. Once on his deck she was relieved to discover that the attendant and her cleaning cart were down at the other end of the passageway.

Cassandra unlocked the door and let herself in quickly. Something crackled under her foot, and she bent to pick up a manila envelope that had been slipped under the door. At first glance the cabin looked empty, everything was neat and the beds were made. Her heart plummeted. But the beds would be made up, she realized, since the attendant would have made them yesterday.

She looked at the envelope in her hand. It was addressed to Jake, with a note attached from the purser's office; it had been delivered by courier and signed for by the assistant purser.

Cassandra dropped it onto one of the beds and quickly opened the clothes closet along one wall of the cabin. Jake's clothes were still there, hung neatly, with three pairs of shoes on the racks. The drawers were filled with ties, socks, and underwear. She looked under the beds and found Jake's suitcases.

She stood still, a finger at the corner of her mouth, deep in troubled thought. It was clear now that Jake hadn't just taken off, not without his clothes. But what *had* happened to him? If for some reason he had been delayed and missed the boat, he would most certainly have radioed the *Star*, and her, by this time.

Cold with dread, she started to turn away, and her glance lit on the envelope. She hesitated for a moment, then snatched it up, tucked it under her arm, and quickly left the cabin. On her own deck she found Greta again, returned the key, and thanked her for a second time. She dropped off the envelope in her own cabin.

At the radio room, she dictated a cable to Marcus Bruno: "Jake Randle missed ship departure. Fear something has happened to him. Please advise any information you discover concerning him. Cassandra Kanaris."

As she emerged from the elevator on her deck Cassandra found Eric Johanson waiting, an unlit cigar in his mouth.

He got a smile of pleasure when he recognized her. "Ah, Miss Kanaris. I am delighted to see you." He doffed his yachting cap.

"Mr. Johanson, how are you?"

"I'm excellent, my dear, excellent." His eyes regarded her closely. "And you? You appear worried. I hope you haven't encountered another accident on deck?"

"No, I've taken your advice and avoided the decks at night." She smiled weakly, and for just a moment toyed with the thought of telling him about the accident in Barcelona.

"But you *do* look worried. Is anything the matter?"

On impulse she said, "Do you know Jake Randle?"

"Not personally, no, but I am familiar with the gentleman in question. A lecturer for your Mystery Cruise, I believe? Why do you ask?"

"You haven't by any chance seen him? I mean yesterday, in Genoa?"

He shook his head. "I'm afraid not. But then I remained on board during our stay in Genoa. A fine city, to be sure, but I had visited there a number of times in the past. Has something happened to Mr. Randle?"

"That's just it, I don't know." She sighed. "He was supposed to continue on with us, but he missed the ship for some reason. I am afraid that something may have happened to him."

"A policeman, is he not?"

She nodded.

"Then I am sure that he is quite capable of handling himself in most situations." He raised and lowered his broad shoulders. "Of course, the world we live in today is wicked, and Genoa has its share of the criminal element. Have you notified the Genoa authorities?"

She nodded again. "Yes, I just radioed the detective who is investigating Claire Thomas's death."

"Ah, yes. A tragic affair, that." He made a clucking sound, then said in a kind voice, "You esteem this man, this Mr. Randle?"

"Yes, I do," she said in a choked voice. To her dismay tears suddenly stung her eyes. "Very much, Mr. Johanson."

He took her hand and patted it. "I'm sure he will be fine, my dear. After all, people have missed ships before. It happens in almost every port, I understand, for various reasons. There could be any number of simple explanations."

"You're right, of course. Thank you, Mr. Johanson. I have to run now."

She hurried toward her cabin, blinking back the hot tears.

The man called Johanson stepped into the elevator, wearing a troubled frown. He didn't light the cigar until the elevator let him off on the Solar deck. He knocked at the penthouse suite adjoining his own and waited for the door to open, then strode in, blowing smoke. "I just received some bad news, Aphrodite."

The woman closed the door. "What is it, Poseidon? Nothing has happened to Cassandra, I hope?"

"No, not Cassandra. But Jake Randle did not return to the ship. He is not on board."

Aphrodite's eyes widened. "Ares?"

"We have no way of knowing, naturally. We do know Ares left the ship in Barcelona, probably on orders from Zeus after the attempt on Cassandra and Jake Randle failed."

"Would Zeus order something done to Randle? I thought that Cassandra was the target."

"She is, of course she is. If Ares did something to Randle in Genoa, I would hazard a guess that it was strictly on his own. He is entirely capable of that, you know. He does not take failure lightly, as we both know."

"But why? For what reason?"

"For vengeance, if nothing else. Ares is a vengeful man. On second thought, there is the possibility that Zeus ordered it, to eliminate any protection Randle might provide Cassandra. Damnation!" Poseidon gestured angrily with the smouldering cigar. "I should have gone ashore in Genoa!"

"You had no way of knowing. After all, Cassandra remained on board, and she is our main concern. If Randle has come to harm, I'm sorry, of course, but then we can only do so much. God knows," she added bitterly, "what we've done so far is little enough. True, you saved her when Ares tried to push her overboard. But look what happened in the theater. But for mere happenchance, Artemis would have killed Cassandra instead of that other poor woman." She laughed suddenly. "I would wager that Zeus is foaming at the mouth by now. Two of his best, and both have failed!"

"But it is far from over yet," Poseidon said grimly. "I have not had an opportunity to tell you yet: Apollo came aboard in Genoa. So you can be sure that Zeus hasn't given up."

In her cabin Cassandra stared long and hard at the manila envelope with Jake's name on it. Finally, with a groan, she picked it up, unsealed it, and spilled the contents out onto the table. She sat down to read. On top was a short note:

"Jake: Here is the material, what there is of it. I gave the meat of it to you over the phone. Don't keep me in the dark forever, my friend. Rene."

She read the note again. This had to be the man in Interpol that Jake had contacted. Jake must have talked to him some time yesterday from Genoa!

With dread she picked up the top sheet, which had a single paragraph: "I can find nothing on Ian Macomber. I can only conclude that, whoever he may be, he has a false identity. I will pursue it further. Rene."

There were three sheets in the other report, and Cassandra gave a start as she saw the name at the top of the page: Jason Kanaris. Jake had asked for a report on her father.

She read quickly, phrases jumping out at her: " . . . man of mystery . . . very wealthy . . . millions in banks in Cayman Islands . . . Never married . . . supposed to have drowned off Lindos on Rhodes . . ."

She sat, mind and body numb, after she had finished. Wealthy? Never married?

She read the material again, more slowly this time. If her mother had married Jason Kanaris, wouldn't there be a record of it somewhere? Cassandra had often wondered if her mother had really been married. It seemed very probable now that she hadn't been, which would make her, Cassandra, a bastard. But whose bastard? Had her mother gotten pregnant by another man, who abandoned her, and then fashioned a fantasy around Jason Kanaris, around a wealthy man of mystery? For the first time Cassandra had grave doubts about her quest. If Jason Kanaris wasn't her father, why continue?

Yet, if that was so, why the notes?

She ran a hand distractedly through her hair. The only thing she had learned from the material was that Jason Kanaris existed. Or had existed.

Why had Jake asked for information about Jason Kanaris without telling her? She supposed it was the natural thing to do, yet why had he kept her in the dark? To spare her feelings in case the man was definitely dead? Another thought came to her. Since Jake had evidently received all this information yesterday by telephone, could he have gone on ahead to Rhodes, to look for Jason Kanaris? But again, why without telling her? Questions, questions. So many questions and no answers. Her head began to hurt.

She returned the material to the envelope and put it away in a drawer in her clothes closet, buried underneath a stack of lingerie. She had to return to her duties; she had already wasted too much time this morning. Leland Dawes was looking more favorably on her work now, so she had to remain in his good graces or risk his displeasure.

She still hadn't decided how she would play it once the ship got to Rhodes, whether or not she would continue with the *Star* after that. It would depend on what, if anything, she learned there. She realized full well that if she quit the ship and remained behind on Rhodes, she would probably never work for the Nordic Lines again.

On the phone Zeus said, "Have you any news for me, Apollo?"

"About the girl, nothing new. But the detective, Randle, missed the ship in Genoa."

Zeus said harshly, "What happened to him?"

"I have no idea, Zeus," Apollo said. "He went ashore in Genoa, of course. The girl did not. From what little information I have gathered, the detective was working with the Genoa police on the investigation of the murder of the Thomas woman."

"Does Artemis know anything?"

"Nothing concrete. She is here in the cabin with me . . ."

Artemis interrupted, "Ask him if he knows the where-abouts of Ares."

"She wants me to ask if you know where Ares is."

There was a lengthy pause. Then, in a hard voice, Zeus said, "No, I do not know of Ares. My last communication with him was when I ordered him off the ship. I had assumed that he was sulking somewhere. If he *has* acted on his own . . ." He bit the words off, then continued, "At least one factor is in our favor. If this detective is no longer allied with the girl, time may not be so pressing. Un-less . . ." His voice hardened again. "Unless he is inves-tigating on his own. I shall look into it, you may be sure. Meanwhile, I want you to proceed slowly. Nothing is likely to occur until the ship reaches Rhodes. If you can make friends with her, gain her confidence, it will be of help to us."

"I had already thought of that." Apollo's gaze went to the mirror across the room, where his stunningly handsome features were reflected. He turned his head back and forth, admiring his profile. "I plan to make contact with her as quickly as possible."

"Proceed with circumspection, Apollo. I do not wish her to be on her guard any more than she already is. Now, put Artemis on."

As Apollo motioned her to the phone Artemis grimaced and crossed over to take the instrument. "First Ares, the psycho, and now you, the pretty boy. You should have taken the name Narcissus, instead of Apollo," she whispered. Into the phone she said, "Yes, Zeus?"

"Artemis, I want you to monitor Apollo closely. Do not let him act hastily. I have ordered him to make friends with the girl."

"Oh, he'll like that. He is always willing to make the conquest of a beautiful girl. And I'm glad you have decided to delay things, it makes the game more interesting."

"Artemis . . ." Zeus sighed softly. "I have said this before. It is no longer a game. If this girl is not stopped, she could bring disaster down on our heads. Do not forget that!"

Eleven

Jake didn't know how long he had been unconscious. He had a vague recollection of awakening once, his mouth and throat parched, his head throbbing. Pinpoints of light had burned before his blurred vision. Then he had felt, as if at a great distance, a prick of pain in his arm, and he went under again.

The next time, he bolted fully awake, trying to sit upright, and restraints, like iron bands, tightened around his arms and legs, and he fell back, stunned. He lay still, probing his surroundings with his five senses.

Wherever he was, it was dark, and seemed damp and cold. In fact, as he strained his ears, he was sure he could hear the plop, plop of falling drops of water. With his fingertips he tested the texture of whatever he was lying on—stone, from the feel of it. There was a little give in the bonds around his wrists. He explored cautiously, twisting his fingers, and soon decided that he was buckled at his wrists and ankles to a stone bench, or bed, with wide straps of leather.

Now that his eyes had been open for a few minutes he realized that a faint light spilled into the room. He craned his neck back painfully and saw a narrow oblong of light behind him.

Jake let his head fall back, wincing at the hard stone against the back of his skull. He cast his thoughts back to last night . . . last night? It could have been several nights ago, he had no way of telling. The last thing he remembered was the car and the two men overpowering him, and then the sickly-sweet stench of ether.

He thought back over every minute of his day in Genoa, trying to recall if there had been any indications that he was being followed. Of course, he had been with Bruno most of the day. If someone had been tailing him, they could have picked him up easily when he left the police station. It certainly had been a planned abduction. There would be no sense to a random snatch—to a random mugging, yes, but not a kidnapping. The target was definitely Jake Randle.

The question was who had done it? And why? It was not unusual these days for Americans to be snatched off the streets in foreign cities; but the targets were always dignitaries, important executives, and the like, certainly not a nobody, a private detective from Miami. He gave a bark of laughter. He could think of no one, not a single soul, who would pay a dime in ransom for him.

No, it had to be the same people who had twice tried to kill Cassandra . . . Cassandra! Christ, she would be worried sick about him.

At least he was still alive, and clearly the intent was to keep him alive, for the time being at any rate, which had to mean that the motive for snatching him was information. Someone wanted to know what he knew about Cassandra. He laughed again. What he knew could be stuffed into a thimble.

He was interrupted by sounds across the room. Raising

his head, he saw a yellow light spilling through iron bars. He was in some kind of a cell!

Metal clanked against metal, and then the barred door swung inward, and the light came toward him. It was a lantern carried waist-high by a tall man. Jake raised his gaze to a shadowed face. As the man came closer he recognized the face—the man in the photo Cassandra had taken in Barcelona.

"I know you, you're Ian Macomber," Jake said, and realized the moment the words were out that he had probably erred. Whatever chance he had had of living was likely gone now, now that he had admitted recognition.

The face was narrow and cold as an axe blade, the eyes black and depthless. Macomber smiled mirthlessly. "That name will suffice, Mr. Randle." He placed the lantern on the edge of the wide, stone bench, the shadows flickering across his face, giving him a satanic look.

"Where am I?" Jake murmured, pretending to more confusion than he actually felt.

"Oh, come now," Macomber said with a mocking laugh. "I would have expected better of you than that ancient cliché."

"Sometimes a cliché applies. I'll ask another . . . Never mind where I am, what am I doing here? What do you want of me?"

"Information, Mr. Randle," Macomber said crisply. "I want to know what you know about the girl, Cassandra Kanaris."

"You won't get much from me, I know very little. You probably know more than I do. You've tried to kill her twice, so you must know her well enough to have a reason to do that."

"Do not take me for a fool," Macomber said icily. "You two are lovers. She has confided in you, one may be sure. What is it you Americans call it, pillow talk?" His grin was a lewd smirk. "It is a well-known fact that after being well screwed a woman confides all her secrets."

Jake felt a rush of anger. "Watch your filthy tongue, you bastard!" He strained against the leather straps.

"What will you do if I don't, beat me senseless? I hardly think you're in a position to do that." Almost casually, Macomber struck Randle across the cheek with his fist.

The blow knocked Jake's head against the stone, hard. The copper taste of blood filled his mouth, and his head rang. He said tauntingly, "Speaking of clichés, Macomber, you don't show much originality. An old dungeon, leather straps. What's next, torture? The rack?"

"I think the setting is rather effective," Macomber said, looking around the cell proudly. "It's ancient, I agree. Long abandoned, it was once used to house political prisoners. It serves my purpose, keeping you immobile." His glance came back to Jake. "As for torture, it won't be necessary, in the usual sense. You'll talk, believe me."

"Even if I knew anything, I wouldn't tell you," Jake said harshly.

"You will, when you get hungry and thirsty enough. How do you feel about rats, Mr. Randle?" Macomber's grin was unpleasant. "This old dungeon is alive with them. They come out at night. I'm surprised you haven't already been visited by them, and have you heard of the Chinese water torture? It's very effective, I understand."

He cocked his head, listening, and Jake, having forgotten the drip, drip of water, heard it again, in the silence. It seemed louder, now that his attention had been drawn to it.

"This isn't exactly the same thing, but it should do the trick. I understand that the dripping doesn't have much effect at first, but after hearing nothing else for hours . . . That combined with hunger, thirst, and the rats nibbling at your ears. Oh, within a day or two, you'll be pleading for a chance to talk."

"And if I do, what happens to me then?"

The man was slow in answering. "Why, if you tell me what I want to know, you'll be free to go on your way."

"Sure, I will!" Jake laughed harshly. "Now who's taking who for a fool?"

Macomber shrugged. "Oh, you're not a fool, Randle, I'll give you that. But consider this, tell me what you know and you'll have a quick and painless demise. Don't, and you'll die horribly, and slowly. It's your choice."

He picked up the lantern and turned away. At the door he paused. "A word of advice, Randle . . . The walls are thick, the building is well isolated. If you shout for help, you'll only make yourself hoarse, you'll only make matters worse for yourself."

In a deliberate gesture of defiance Jake opened his mouth and yelled as loudly as he could, a primal shout expressing his anger. Macomber winced, shrugged, and went out, locking the door with an old-fashioned iron key. Jake continued to shout long after the light had receded down the corridor and disappeared.

Finally, he stopped and fell back, exhausted, his throat raw. In the sudden silence that followed, the dripping sound of the water seemed to grow louder, until it made him want to cover his ears, and he knew that it would be impossible to ignore.

All of a sudden, he heard another sound, the scrabbling sound of tiny feet on stone. Rats! He held his breath, listening. He had never suffered from a fear of rats, but in his present helpless state, he would be easy prey for their sharp teeth. He shuddered.

"Zeus? This is Ares."

There was a brief silence on the other end of the telephone. Ares held his breath, waiting for the explosion.

Then it came. "Are you deliberately trying to provoke me, Ares? It has been nearly a week since you left the ship in Barcelona. Where have you been and where are you now?"

"In Genoa, to answer both questions," Ares said calmly.

Again a short silence. "I have been told that Jake Randle missed the ship in Genoa. Are you responsible for that?"

Ares laughed softly. "You might say that."

"You have defied me! By the gods, you will pay the penalty for that!"

"I didn't disobey you, Zeus. You merely told me to leave the ship in Barcelona. You gave me no orders beyond that. Now, please listen while I explain. I'm confident that you will be pleased."

"I am listening," Zeus said in a voice of iron.

"I came directly to Genoa, thinking that I might be of some value here. And I was right. Randle came ashore, by himself. The girl stayed on board. He was with the Genoa police most of the day, until early evening. I followed him, with a local thug I hired. It was after dark when Randle started back for his ship. We followed him to the dock area, snatched him, and put an ether-soaked rag over his mouth. Right now, I have him hidden away, helpless, and I'm going to question him until I learn all that he knows about Cassandra Kanaris."

"This man you hired, what happened to him?"

"I paid him off. He's only muscle, Zeus, between the ears as well as elsewhere. He knows only what I told him, that I had been hired to prevent Randle from catching the ship. He doesn't know who I am, he doesn't know where I have Randle. There is nothing to worry about there."

"Has Randle told you anything worthwhile?" Much of the anger had faded out of Zeus' voice.

"It's much too early for that. He's being gallant and stubborn." Ares laughed coldly. "But I shall get out of him all he knows, you can be sure. I have handled matters of this nature before, and you know I haven't failed yet."

"I grant you that, Ares, but I am not pleased that you did not consult with me first."

"There are times when I must seize the initiative, to be effective. It isn't always possible to contact you."

"That is true. But Randle now knows you, your face at least. He will be a risk to you, to us, if he goes free."

"He won't go free, never fear. When he gives me what I want, I shall take the greatest pleasure in killing him."

"Very well. Perhaps you did the right thing, after all," Zeus said grudgingly. "But I want you to keep in close touch hereafter. I will keep myself available twenty-four hours a day until this matter is fully resolved."

Cassandra was working the four o'clock bingo game, passing through the crowd in the main lounge, selling bingo cards for two dollars apiece. Leland Dawes and Ben Lomax were at the table with the drum, ready to call a game when all the players had cards. Cassandra usually found this a boring chore, but today she didn't mind too much. It was something she could do mechanically, leaving her mind free.

This was the second day out of Genoa, and there still had been no word of Jake. There was no longer any doubt in her mind: something had happened to him. She had the time free between bingo and dinnertime, and she had made up her mind to call Marcus Bruno and, as Jake would put it, light a fire under his tail . . .

"Cassandra?" A hand tugged gently at her sleeve.

She came to with a start, realizing with dismay that she had been standing still, lost in thought, for several moments.

"Yes, sir?" she said brightly, staring down into the handsomest face she had ever seen. Probably in his late thirties, he was deeply tanned, with bright blue eyes, flashing white teeth, and an impossible dimple in his chin. His face had the charm of a Cary Grant, plus the virile good looks of a Paul Newman. Cassandra seldom thought of a man in movie-star terms, but this man definitely *should* be a movie star, and she had to wonder if he wasn't. During bingo most passengers dressed casually, but he was wearing gray slacks with a knife-edge crease, a blue blazer with an ascot, and smoking a cigarette in an ivory holder. There was an old-world elegance about him that spoke of wealth and privilege.

"I would like two cards, please," he said, holding out four dollar bills. His voice was warm and deep, and he spoke English without a trace of an accent.

Cassandra gave him two bingo cards, collected his money, and had started to turn away when he said, "Aren't you going to wish me luck?"

She returned his smile. "I can't do that. We have to remain impartial. I wish all the players equal good luck."

From the front table Leland Dawes was speaking into the microphone, "Last call for cards!"

Someone two tables away waved a hand holding dollar bills, and Cassandra moved off to serve them. A part of her mind noted that the handsome stranger was all alone at his table, which, of course, didn't mean that he didn't have a wife somewhere on board the *Star*.

Along with the other girls distributing the cards, Cassandra stood at the table while Ben Lomax spun the drum, taking out a numbered ball after each spin, while Dawes called out the number.

Somehow Cassandra wasn't at all surprised to discover, when a voice from the audience shouted, "Bingo!" that the winner was the good-looking man.

She made her way through the tables to check his card with the master card Dawes had filled out. The card checked, and Dawes trumpeted, "We have a winner! One hundred and eight dollars!"

Cassandra returned to the front table, collected the prize money, and went back to pay the winner.

The man accepted the money. "Thank you, Cassandra. Perhaps you *did* wish me luck, secretly?"

She laughed. "I never accept credit where it isn't due."

"Ah, well. The question now is, how do I spend my winnings?"

"That should be no trouble at all, sir."

"My name is Marshall Paris."

A movie-star name to go with the looks, she thought. "Congratulations, Mr. Paris."

"Marshall, please. I can think of a pleasurable way to spend at least a portion of the money. Would you join me for a cocktail before dinner?"

"I'm afraid not, Marshall. I'm going to be busy."

"Ah, well. Perhaps another time." He sighed theatrically. "As they say, lucky at cards, unlucky at love."

"Yes, perhaps another time," she said with a smile.

"I must warn you that I am a persistent fellow. I consider that a promise and shall hold you to it."

At a quarter to six Cassandra was in the radio room, on a ship-to-shore hookup with Marcus Bruno.

"Ah, *Signorina* Kanaris, it is you again."

"Yes. Have you any word of Jake Randle?"

"I'm afraid not. And you?"

"No, and I must admit that I'm quite worried. His things are still in his cabin on the ship, and he didn't check out. Something must have happened to make him miss the ship."

"What do you suggest might have happened?"

"Well, I . . ." She caught herself just in time, about to tell him of the attempt on their lives in Barcelona and Ian Macomber's abrupt departure. Instead, she said lamely, "How do I know? A mugging, something like that."

"Genoa has its random crime, to be sure, but Jake strikes me as an extremely capable man, able to handle himself in most situations. After all, he was once a policeman."

"Policemen are killed all the time."

"You need not remind me of that fact, *Signorina*," he said wryly. "And it does warrant investigation, I must agree. I shall look into it at once, you have my assurances on that. After all, he is a colleague and we look after our own."

"The investigation into Claire's death," Cassandra said hesitantly. "Is there anything new on that?"

"I fear not, *Signorina*," he said with a sigh. "It is beginning to look as if we may have reached a dead end."

"A dead end? You mean you're no longer investigating?"

"Ah, no, not at all. We are not, as you say, closing the book on it. We never do that with murder."

"I see," she said slowly. She had to wonder if he was being wholly truthful, suspecting that the Genoa police would not be pushing too hard. After all, the murder had taken place on board a cruise ship, and the murder victim wasn't one of their own. "You will keep me informed if you learn anything about Jake?"

"You may depend on it, *Signorina* Kanaris. I like Jake Randle, and I share your concern for him. I will set things in motion the instant we conclude this conversation."

"Thank you, *Signor* Bruno."

They said their good-byes, and Cassandra hung up. She thought of trying to call the Interpol man in Paris, but in the end she decided to postpone that until she had a further report from Bruno. Apparently, Jake hadn't told the man from Interpol that Jason Kanaris's daughter was the cause of his inquiry, and if she identified herself, the Interpol man would quite naturally be curious.

As she started down to her own deck Cassandra now wished that she had accepted Marshall Paris's invitation to cocktails. Paris intrigued her; cocktails and a little pleasant conversation would be welcome right now. She even thought of making a tour of the various lounges to see if she could encounter him, making it appear nothing more than a casual, accidental meeting, but then she dismissed the idea.

Missing Jake terribly and worried to death about him, she slowly returned to her cabin. Almost unconsciously, her glance immediately went to the bed.

And there it was—a lavender envelope.

Her heart pounding erratically, she picked the envelope up gingerly. She weighed it in her hand for a long moment before finally opening it. She quickly read the single line: "Cassandra: Please beware of new acquaintances. A friend."

Twelve

The hunger was bad, but the thirst was terrible. Jake felt consumed by thirst; his tongue was so swollen that he could hardly swallow, and his lips were chapped and bleeding. What made his condition even more maddening was the steady drip, drip of water. What he wouldn't give to be able to put his head beneath that drip and open his mouth! Added to the hunger and the thirst was the physical and psychological discomfort of lying helpless in the stench of his own body wastes.

The rats hadn't posed much of a problem, not yet, anyway. He could hear the scrabble of their feet, and now and then during the hours of darkness he felt one run across him. Just after dawn on the second day he turned his head and was eye-to-eye with a whiskered face, but he opened his mouth and shouted, and the creature scampered away. Jake suspected that they were waiting until he was dead, or at least helpless, before feasting upon him.

He slept only in snatches. When he wasn't thinking about food and water, his mind was busy trying to devise some means of escape.

It had been two days since Macomber's visit, and Jake's situation seemed hopeless. Although the dungeon was old, the leather straps were new, buckled securely into iron rings embedded in the stone. He'd had ample time to study his situation. The bench he was strapped to was about four feet wide. He had freedom of movement with his hands, enough so that he could scratch an itch on his nose by turning his head. He could even touch the buckles on the rings with his fingers, but one of his first, the most discouraging, discoveries was the fact that each buckle was padlocked to the ring.

The rings themselves looked old and corroded, and at first Jake had been hopeful that he could tear one free from its moorings; but he had strained and tugged until his wrists were raw, all to no avail—not once had he felt the slightest give. And as time passed and his strength began to go, he decided to husband what little energy he had left, in case Macomber became careless and gave him an opportunity. Jake had decided that was the only chance he had.

That is, if Macomber ever came back. Maybe something had happened to the man, or maybe Macomber had simply decided to let him die there.

Then, on the second day, late in the afternoon, Jake heard footsteps in the corridor outside. Raising his head, he saw Macomber at the barred door. Metal rang against metal, and the door creaked open. Macomber came in, carrying a folding table and chair, and a picnic hamper.

He stood over Jake, smiling coldly. "Well, Randle? Did

you miss me? Have you decided to tell me what I wish to know?"

"I prefer the company of the rats to yours," Jake said huskily. His voice felt rusty, unused. "And I haven't changed my mind."

Macomber shrugged, and went about setting up the chair and the table. From the hamper he took out a snowy cloth, spread it over the table, then started putting items on the table—a bottle of wine in an ice bucket, a tall tumbler filled with water and ice cubes, a cold chicken, a dish of tomatoes and cucumbers, and a thick loaf of bread. The wine bottle was beaded with moisture, and the ice cubes rattled in the pitcher as Macomber poured a glass of water. He set the table elaborately, taking his time, all without once looking at Jake.

Jake swallowed, trying to work saliva into his mouth. He could almost feel the cold water sliding down his throat, and his stomach contracted violently from the smell of food.

Finished, Macomber sat down. For the first time since he came in he looked over at Jake, as he picked up the glass of ice water and drank, then smacked his lips. "Good, good and cold. And wet."

Jake closed his eyes, but within moments he couldn't resist opening his eyes and staring, as Macomber began to cut the chicken. He took a bite, washing it down with wine.

He glanced over at Jake again, his cruel smile in place. "You know it's really too bad. I have much more here than I can eat and drink. I would be most happy to share it with you, Randle."

"You can go to hell," Jake croaked.

Macomber grimaced. "How unoriginal. I would have expected better of you."

As the man began to eat with obvious enjoyment, Jake started to close his eyes, then stopped himself. He'd be damned if he would give the bastard the satisfaction! He kept his head turned toward the table, never once taking his gaze from Macomber.

After several more minutes Macomber glanced at him again, shaking his head. "You must be a masochist, Randle. Do you enjoy suffering?"

Jake refused to rise to the bait again.

Macomber ate almost half of the chicken, then stopped, pouring himself another glass of wine. Drinking it, he contemplated Jake thoughtfully. "You're a stubborn fellow, Randle, more so than I estimated."

"More stubborn than you, Macomber."

"Oh, I very much doubt that. Besides, I have time on my side. I have nothing else to do, while you're slowly dying. In the end you'll tell me what I want to know."

"I don't *know* anything," Jake said wearily. "How many times do I have to tell you that before it penetrates?"

"I think I'll leave you now." Macomber started to gather up the leftover food and dishes. Then he stopped, looking over at Jake, his smile fiendish. "No, I think I'll leave all this so you can see everything and contemplate what a fool you're being. And you can watch your furry friends devouring what could easily have been yours. Good-bye, Randle. I will see you tomorrow, or the next day, whenever I decide that you may be more amenable."

Jake stared after Macomber until the barred door closed and the man's footsteps died away. Then his gaze swung back to the half-consumed chicken, the beaded wine bottle, and the glass of ice water, still almost full, and he felt a welling of hopelessness such as he had never experienced before.

It was ten in the morning, and Cassandra was sitting outside the aft bar on the Promenade deck, charts spread out on the table before her. On the charts were the names of the participants in the daily walkathon. Each time a walker made a full circle of the Promenade deck, he, or she, stopped at her table and Cassandra checked off the name. At the end of the cruise the person who had walked the most miles won a prize.

It was a pleasant day, the sun warm and the sea like glass. Cassandra was having trouble staying awake. She had slept badly last night, her troubled thoughts on Jake.

A deep voice said, "Good morning, Cassandra."

She glanced up into the bright blue eyes of Marshall Paris. This morning he was clad only in blue swimming trunks; droplets of water glistened on his tanned body. He had a magnificent physique—broad shoulders and chest, and strongly muscled legs.

Cassandra felt her heart pick up its beat. "Good morning, Marshall. Are you thinking of joining our marathon?"

He shook his head. "I don't believe so. I don't suppose you'd care to join me in a fast game of Ping-Pong?"

"I'm sorry, but I'm busy, as you can see." She gestured to the table before her. Just then they were interrupted as a walker stopped at the table to have Cassandra check off his name.

After the walker had passed on, Marshall said, "You know, I may join your marathon, after all. At least that way I would get to see you on occasion."

As a woman stopped to be checked off Cassandra used the moment to think. Marshall Paris was an attractive man, and she couldn't spend all her time worrying about Jake. Maybe she was wrong, after all; maybe he *had* just taken off for reasons of his own.

When the walker went on her way, Cassandra looked at Marshall with a smile. "Do you like to dance?"

"I love to dance, Cassandra." He smiled hopefully. "What did you have in mind?"

"I'm free tonight after the main lounge show. Dancing starts in the Astral Lounge tonight at eleven. Would you like to meet me there?"

"I would indeed." He took her hand and raised it to his

lips. It was an old-fashioned gesture, yet it seemed natural to him. "At eleven then?"

As he released her hand and turned away Cassandra stared after him. Her fingers still tingled where his lips had touched, and she felt warm all over.

"Handsome devil, isn't he?"

She glanced around with a start. Lisa van Horne stood beside the table, also gazing after Marshall.

Flustered, Cassandra said, "Yes, he is."

"Almost too handsome, wouldn't you say?"

"Oh, I don't know," Cassandra said, smiling now. "How can you fault a person for their looks, good or bad?"

The woman's eyes, penetrating and wise, fastened on Cassandra. "I've found that both men and women with stunning good looks have a tendency to fall in love with themselves. And that reminds me, have you received any word of Mr. Randle? I understand that he missed the ship in Genoa."

Cassandra tightened up inside. "He did, yes, and I'm quite concerned about him. To answer your question there is no news."

"He seemed like a nice young man, quite attached to you. I do hope nothing has happened to him."

"So do I," Cassandra said. Although she was drawn to this woman, she was a touch annoyed. It seemed to her that Miss van Horne was always trying to meddle in her life. Cassandra knew that a great many wealthy, elderly people, bored and lonely, husband or wife gone, close acquaintances dead, had a tendency to interfere in the lives of others; usually with the best of intentions, she admitted, but still . . .

Those shrewd old eyes began to twinkle, as the woman seemed to read her thoughts. "Interfering old biddy, aren't I?" She tapped Cassandra on the shoulder. "But just remember, Cassandra, handsome is as handsome does."

Now just what did that mean? Cassandra wondered, as

she watched Lisa van Horne stride away, head high, walking with the haughty carriage of a queen.

Twelve hours later Miss van Horne's remark returned to Cassandra as she stood in the same spot, leaning on the railing, gazing back at the *Star*'s churning wake, the foaming of the sea silvery in the spill of moonlight.

The object of the woman's remark stood at Cassandra's side, resplendent in a dinner jacket, smoking a cigarette in the long, ivory holder.

At least Cassandra assumed that Miss van Horne had had Marshall Paris in mind when she issued her rather cryptic statement, but exactly what her remark meant, Cassandra still wasn't sure. Surely she didn't mean that Marshall posed a threat to her; it was too much for Cassandra to believe that a whole parade of people were coming onto the *Star*, all bent on doing her harm.

Then a startling thought came to her. Could Lisa van Horne be the author of the lavender notes? But that seemed equally incredible. That would mean that she would have had to have been in Los Angeles. No, Cassandra decided, Miss van Horne was simply motherly, warning her about Marshall in a romantic sense.

She looked sidelong at Marshall and caught his glance. He smiled. "You're awfully quiet, Cassandra. Is something troubling you?"

She shook her head. "Not really. Just enjoying a few moments of peace. There aren't that many when you work a cruise ship. Also . . ." She laughed. "It's a chance to catch my breath. You're a . . . well, shall I say, active dancer?" They had been dancing for the past two hours.

He laughed. "I could have danced the night away."

"I know, you told me," she said ruefully. "*You* can do that; you're on the cruise for pleasure; while I'm a working girl."

He gave her a musing look. "Perhaps it's time you thought of taking a pleasure cruise for yourself, Cassandra."

"Oh, sure. That would be fine, if I could afford it," she said in a dry voice.

"Oh, I don't mean on a cruise ship; I mean on a private yacht."

"I don't happen to know any multimillionaires, Marshall."

"You do now."

It took a moment for his meaning to penetrate. "You?"

"Yes." He nodded, smiling. "I am a millionaire, several times over. Oh, I take no credit for it. My father made the money, originally in the meat-packing business, then in oil, real estate, probably a lot of things not at all legitimate. But he made the money, then died a few years ago, and I'm spending it. One of the ways I'm spending it is a hundred-and-thirty-foot yacht anchored at Rhodes."

"A yacht . . . Wait a minute. If that's true, then why are you on the *Star*?"

He shrugged. "I had to be in Genoa on business. I finished my business sooner than I anticipated, and I've never been too crazy about flying, so I decided to indulge myself with a short cruise." His gaze was direct. "Now I'm glad I did. I've met you."

"If you're all that rich, I'm surprised you didn't take one of the new penthouse suites."

He looked somewhat taken aback. "Oh . . . Well, I wanted to keep a low profile. To have taken a suite would have been like setting myself up as fair game for every husband hunter on board." The statement was made without conceit, as if his wealth and good looks had made him the target for husband hunters before. Cassandra didn't doubt that this was true.

Marshall continued, "I have never been married and have no thoughts of it in the future."

Cassandra said slowly, "You're proposing that I join you on your yacht?"

"I am. Don't worry about propriety. The *Olympus* has a

staff of ten on board the year round. You will not be compromised, Cassandra." He laughed lightly. "Unless you wish to be compromised, of course."

"I quit my job, just like that?"

He shrugged slightly, as though dismissing the job as unimportant, and she supposed it was, to him.

She said tartly, "I know a job means nothing to you, but I have to earn a living, you know."

"You're young, beautiful, and quite capable. Getting another job should be no problem for you."

Cassandra stared back at the wake of the ship, her thoughts chaotic. His offer might be a solution. Everything she had learned, so far, seemed to point to Rhodes as the best place to look for her father. The *Star* would only be in Rhodes a night and a part of one day, before it steamed on to the other Greek Islands—hardly time enough for her to look for Jason Kanaris.

She said, "Where would we go, on your yacht?"

"Wherever you wish to go. The choice would be yours." His shrug was eloquent. "The island of Rhodes is well worth exploring. There is much to see, the medieval Old Town, Lindos, and the Acropolis. And if you become bored with Rhodes, we can always go to the other islands." He hesitated, face clouded with thought. "If you are really concerned about propriety, I can always invite along some other guests. I know many fascinating people in and around Rhodes. My yacht will accommodate ten guests easily."

She laughed. "You make it sound very tempting, Marshall."

"It is my intention to make it as tempting as possible," he said with a charming smile. "It will be a voyage you'll never forget, that I promise you. Look at it this way. Life is to be enjoyed, Cassandra, and there is no better place to enjoy life than the Greek Isles. I have traveled the world over and have found nothing to compare. That is why I always return here. A cruise ship is no way to see this part of the world, a few hours here, a few hours there. Compare it to a gourmet meal. What true gourmet would be content to sample a few tidbits and not enjoy the full meal?"

His deep voice showed an unexpected passion, and she said uneasily, "Why are you trying so hard to convince me?"

"Don't you know?" He took her hand and looked deep into her eyes. "That should be obvious. You're the first woman to arouse my interest in a long while."

"Well . . ." As unobstrusively as possible she disengaged her hand from his. "I'll have to think about it. This is all so sudden. We still have some time before we dock at Rhodes."

"I suppose I'll have to be content with that, but I must warn you . . . I intend to press my case at every opportunity."

Ares started to whistle a merry tune as he strode along the stone corridor, hoping it would irritate Randle. Randle should be begging to talk by now, in exchange for food and water. Tired of toying with the detective, Ares had waited a full twenty-four hours before coming back.

He stopped at the bars to peer through. In the dim light he could see Randle lying still on the stone bench. Ares grinned with delight as his glance moved to the folding table and saw that the chicken he had left was nothing but a scattering of bones; the rats had been at it. Randle should have enjoyed watching them consume the chicken!

He rattled the key against the bars. "Wake up, Randle! You have company. I'm looking forward to an interesting chat today."

Randle didn't stir. Ares shrugged and keyed the rusty door open. Striding toward the tethered man, he said, "Come on, Randle, I know you're faking. It will accomplish you nothing."

Still, Randle did not move. A tiny note of doubt pinged in Ares' mind. Could he possibly have expired? It couldn't be! As tough a man as Randle should survive another day or two. If he *was* dead, Zeus would not be happy.

Ares stood over the man. "Randle, stop this now."

He clamped a hand on Randle's thigh and shook him roughly. There was no response. He slapped him across the face. Randle's head snapped back and forth, but his eyes remained closed, and there was an odd sort of limpness about him. Ares squinted in the gloom, trying to detect any rise and fall of his chest, but it was too dim to be sure. Finally, he placed his hand on the man's chest; there was no movement.

Truly alarmed now, he bent to place his ear over Randle's heart—and he felt his shirtfront seized in a powerful grip.

He was jerked off his feet and thrown forward. A hard object smashed into his face, and then again. He felt the cartilage in his nostrils crush, and teeth rattled around in his mouth. Pain burst in his skull, and he lost consciousness.

Dazed, Jake almost lost his grip on the shirt. If Macomber fell to the floor, he would never be able to reach him, and it would all be for nothing. As the man started to slide off the bench Jake tried to pull him up again and felt the shirt rip loose in his grasp. Desperately, he snatched at Macomber's arm and got a grip just in time. It was difficult with only his right arm to work with, but exerting the last of his fading strength, he managed to keep Macomber on the bench. He was lucky that the bench was wide enough to accommodate two bodies side by side.

His breath was coming in heaving gasps and he remained still for a few moments. The top of his head throbbed abominably where he had smashed it into Macomber's face. He recalled how many times he had been told that he had a hard head, and he laughed weakly. For once a hard head had been an advantage. In planning this move, he had known it was his one and only chance, and he had had no way of knowing in advance whether or not he would knock himself out as well.

Macomber was still unconscious, yet he could come to at any moment. Awkwardly, hampered by the strap, Jake began going through the man's pockets. It was very difficult, his movements were so restricted. The pocket closest to him disclosed nothing that would help him. It took him agonizing minutes to heave Macomber over so that he could reach the other pocket. He had to be very careful that the man didn't roll off the bench.

He had been hoping to find the key to the buckle padlocks. No such luck. Finally, in the other pants pocket, he found something that might be of use—a combination nail file, clipper, and knife. The knife blade was small, but at least it was very sharp.

Letting go of Macomber, Jake bent his wrist back as far as it would go, and began to saw on the strap. It was slow, agonizing work, and his wrist soon tired from the awkward position. Doggedly, he kept at it. Even when he sliced his thumb open, he kept at it. Sweat broke out on his face, and his strength was waning. It had been so damned long since he'd had food and water.

Once Macomber groaned, stirring, and Jake froze, fearful he was coming to, but the man soon quieted. Jake redoubled his efforts, and finally the leather strap snapped and his right hand was free. He desperately wanted to rest for a few minutes, yet he knew that he didn't dare. Half-turning, he began on the left wrist. It was easier now, since his right hand was no longer bound. He sawed through the strap on his left wrist, then sat up and worked on his legs.

A few minutes later he was finally free. He edged around Macomber, moved him farther onto the bench, and stood up. He swayed, almost falling. He held onto the bench for support, afraid that he was going to pass out. After a minute he had regained enough strength to stand free of the bench. He staggered over to the folding table.

The rats had eaten all the leftover food, but the tumbler was almost full of water, and there was a half-bottle of wine left. He took short sips of the water. He had difficulty swallowing, but the moisture in his mouth felt wonderful, the most marvelous sensation he had ever experienced. Then his throat opened, and the water flowed down. He took the bottle from the wicker basket and upended it over the tumbler, filling it half-full again. Finally, the water was all gone. He eyed the wine bottle askance. Dare he drink wine on a stomach that had gone without food for days?

"Ah, to hell with it!" he said aloud, grinning savagely. "So I get smashed, I deserve it."

He tilted the bottle up and drank. At least it had some nutritional value; he knew that winos could live on the stuff for days, without eating. The wine was going sour, but he drank it anyway. It made him light-headed, and he stood grinning foolishly at nothing.

Then a sound from Macomber brought his head around. The man, half-raised up, was gazing around the cell. His nose was smashed flat, his mouth and chin were smeared with blood. As Jake watched, Macomber opened his mouth and spat out a tooth, which hit the stone floor and clattered toward Jake.

Without really thinking about it, and without the slightest compunction, Jake lurched forward, and brought the wine bottle crashing down on Macomber's head. His eyes rolled back, and he fell back without a sound.

Jake stood staring down at him, trying to get his thoughts in order. Should he leave Macomber here, or should he call Marcus Bruno and tell him what had taken place? If he did that, of course, Jake knew that he would have to tell Bruno about Cassandra and the attacks on her. The Italian wouldn't be too pleased with him about their keeping that information to themselves, but Jake didn't see that he had a whole hell of a lot of choice.

Something occurred to him. In looking for the knife, he

hadn't gone through all of Macomber's pockets. Now he did, frisking him thoroughly. It was as he had feared. Whatever the man had done with Jake's passport, money, and other papers, they weren't on him.

He definitely had to tell Bruno now. Without money and papers, he couldn't get very far. He would certainly need Bruno's help in getting his passport replaced. He did find the key to the cell and a wad of lire notes in Macomber's pants pocket, which he transferred to his own pocket without the least pang of guilt. As he did so, he became aware of the state he was in. His trousers were soiled and stained with his own body wastes, and he was filthy and unshaven.

Well, he couldn't do much about the beard, but he could wash up a bit, using the water from that infernal drip, and Macomber's clothes, while not a perfect fit, would at least be better than his own fouled clothing.

Jake took great pleasure in stripping Macomber of his fine suit, and when he had removed his own clothing, he flung them atop the other man, grinning. From what little he had observed of Macomber, Jake surmised that he was a fastidious man, and having to wear Jake's castoffs wouldn't sit well with him.

Using the key he had taken from Macomber, Jake left the cell, locking the door after him. It was late afternoon when he emerged from the building housing the cell where he had spent an eternity. He wasn't too surprised to discover that the building was located in the dock area, not too far distant from where the *Star* had been moored. After taking a moment to get his bearings Jake walked toward the boulevard he knew to be a few blocks away. Turning onto it, he started past an open cafe and was assailed by the scents of highly spiced Italian food.

Saliva began to flow, and it was borne home to him just how ravenous he was. He was literally weak from hunger. Bruno could wait a little longer. Jake turned into the cafe and took a table near the front. When the waiter came he ordered enough for two men—and ate every bite of it. Afterward, he threw it all up in the men's room.

An hour later Marcus Bruno pulled up before the restaurant in a police car. He was riding in front, a uniformed policeman driving. Jake was waiting for him. Bruno gestured for him to get in, and Jake got into the backseat.

Bruno half-turned, looking back at him. "To say I was surprised to get your call, Jake, is a masterly understatement. We have been looking for you for several days, ever since *Signorina* Kanaris called to inform me that you had missed the ship."

Jake said quickly, "Is Cassandra all right?"

Bruno shrugged slightly. "To the best of my knowledge, she is fine. But you, my friend . . ." He peered closely at Jake. "You do not look so well."

Jake scrubbed a hand across his face, itchy now with the several days' growth of beard. Macomber's clothing hung loosely on him, and despite the attempt to clean himself in the cell, he was still rank. Now he said to Bruno, "I have reason. I've been tied up without food and water since the day the *Star* left. Whenever that was. I've lost all track of time."

Bruno's eyebrows arched. "Tied up? That sounds rather melodramatic, my friend."

"Melodramatic or not, it happens to be the truth," Jake said grimly. "But before I tell you the whole sad story, there's something I want you to do first. I managed to escape, and I have the bastard who was behind all this locked up." He gave directions to the building where he'd been retained.

As the police car pulled up before the building, Bruno grunted. "I know this place. It was once a political prison, but it has been abandoned for a very long time. It has an unsavory history, and people avoid it like the plague, claiming it is haunted by the ghosts of the many prisoners who died here."

Jake gave a bark of harsh laughter. "It almost collected a new ghost. Mine!"

They got out, and Jake led the way into the building and to the cell where he had left Macomber. As they neared the cell Jake, remembering Macomber's taunt earlier that afternoon, called out in a jeering voice, "Macomber! You've got company!"

Triumph gave way to shock as he saw that the door was agape. He covered the last few steps to it in a run and then hurried over to the stone bench. Macomber was gone, along with Jake's own clothes.

Behind him Bruno said, "Well?"

Jake turned, flinging his hands out wide. "He was here, Marcus, I swear. I left him naked and unconscious, and I locked the door. Here!" He dug into his pocket. "See, here's the key!"

Bruno gestured dismissively. "These cells have been unattended for so long, a child could open these locks. Probably a good kick would spring it open."

"But *these* aren't old, see?" Jake fingered one of the straps. "They're brand-new, and they're what's been holding me prisoner, until I escaped today. Look, the blood." He pointed. "That's Macomber's blood, and there's a tooth somewhere on the floor . . ." He looked along the floor without seeing the tooth. "The table and the picnic hamper, he brought those, and the wine and the food. He spread it all out and ate right there in front of me!"

"I believe you, Jake, it's evident that someone was here," Bruno said, nodding. "But it is equally evident that he has, as you Americans say, flown the coop."

"But he can't have gotten very far. He's pretty badly banged up and easily spotted in his condition," Jake said urgently. "You should send out an all-points on him!"

Bruno was shaking his head. "Not until I know what this is all about. Now, suppose we sit down and you tell me about it." He sat down on the stone bench and patted the spot beside him. He turned his gaze to the uniformed policeman. "Antonio, while we talk, suppose you call in for the technicians and get them over, to see what, if anything, they can find here."

Thirteen

During the lull before the dinner hour, Cassandra made her way to the Orion deck and Leland Dawes's office. She hesitated before the closed door, composing herself for what she knew was going to be an unpleasant scene.

Finally, she knocked firmly, and as he called out she opened the door and went in.

"Mr. Dawes, could I have a word with you?"

He leaned back from his perusal of some papers on his desk and smiled genially. "Of course, Cassandra. Is anything wrong?"

"Well . . . Yes."

"I hope it's nothing serious. Sit." He gestured to the chair before his desk. "I've been meaning to have a word with you. I must confess that I was wrong about you; you're doing a fine job. You've convinced me that a woman can handle the position."

Now what, kiddo? she thought with dread. She clenched her hands together in her lap. "Then you're not going to be pleased with what I'm about to say."

He grew still, the smile leaving his face. "Yes?"

"I'm going to . . ." She took a deep breath. "I'm leaving the ship at Rhodes."

"What!" He leaned forward, his face going hard.

"I'm sorry, Mr. Dawes, but I have to." She did her best to keep her voice steady under his baleful glare.

"You can't just march in here, the day before we reach Rhodes, and tell me that you're leaving!"

"I'm afraid I must."

"I suppose your reason for this is just as frivolous as your reason for joining us on such short notice," he said with a sneer. "Are there some mystery writers on Rhodes that you simply *must* meet?"

"My reasons are personal, but I assure you that they *are* urgent."

"Urgent!" He slapped the desk with the flat of his hand. "Look here, Kanaris, this is simply not done. How am I supposed to replace you on such short notice?"

"I'm sure that you can call the head office for a replacement. There's time to fly someone in before the ship leaves Rhodes. Surely, others, far more important, more indispensable than myself, have had to request emergency leave."

"Are you requesting an emergency leave, Kanaris?" he asked, his voice dangerously soft.

She hesitated, then said slowly, "I must be honest with you, Mr. Dawes, I have no idea how long it will take me to do what I have to do."

"I'll tell you what it is, Kanaris . . ." His face had darkened. "It's rank, willful disregard of your responsibilities!"

"I was afraid you would feel that way. Again, I'm sorry."

"Sorry? You're leaving me without due notice and all you can say is you're sorry?" His voice rose. "I was right all along. A woman cannot be trusted with responsibility!"

"That's unfair, Mr. Dawes!" she said in dismay. "You can hardly blame all women because of me."

"I will resign my position before I ever accept another woman as my assistant."

"I suppose you'll do whatever you feel you have to do." She got to her feet. "Good-bye, Mr. Dawes." She started out of his office.

"Just a minute, Kanaris, I'm not through with you."

She stopped with her hand on the door latch and looked back over her shoulder at him.

"If you go through with this, I'll see to it that you never work for the Nordic Lines again."

She shrugged slightly. "I expected as much."

"Or for any other cruise line. Word gets around when a person is as undependable as you're showing yourself to be."

"You'll see that word gets around, I'm sure," she said tiredly. "Well, like I said, you do whatever you feel you have to do, Mr. Dawes."

"Cassandra is leaving the ship at Rhodes."

"Well, that's pretty much what we'd hoped for, isn't it?"

"You don't understand," Poseidon said. "She's going aboard Apollo's yacht."

Aphrodite gave an exclamation of dismay. "Are you sure about that?"

Poseidon nodded. "According to the information I've gathered, that is correct."

"Then she must be stopped. If she gets on his yacht, you know we'll never see her again!"

"But what can we do?" Poseidon spread his hands. "She has been warned to be wary of Apollo, but clearly she is going to ignore the warning. Short of restraining her by force, I don't know what we can do."

"And we can't do that," Aphrodite said thoughtfully. "Could we reveal ourselves to her and tell her what it's all about?"

Poseidon was shaking his head. "It's too early for that. Anyway, that had occurred to me, and I called Hera before I came to your suite. She especially forbade us to do anything that overt."

"I suppose Artemis will also join Apollo on his yacht?"

"I would imagine that she will. There would certainly be no reason for her to remain on the *Star* if Cassandra is gone." He looked at her curiously. "Why wonder about Artemis?"

"Well, she isn't quite as vicious as Ares or Apollo, or any of the others, for that matter. Maybe if we asked her to look after Cassandra?"

"No, that would never do. Artemis is more compassionate, true, but she hasn't the courage to defy Zeus. Don't forget, she tried to kill Cassandra once, and only by a freak of fate killed someone else instead."

Aphrodite sighed. "You're right, of course. But what *can* we do?"

"I will try and talk to Cassandra, warn her as best I can. She trusts me. I did save her life once."

In his stateroom on the Promenade deck, Apollo was on the ship-to-shore to Zeus. "The girl is joining me on my yacht. She just gave her consent an hour ago."

"Excellent!" Zeus said with satisfaction. "We will have her under surveillance at all times, and if we decide to eliminate her, it will not be difficult. I am pleased with you. Inform Artemis that I wish her to join you on the yacht."

"Will you be joining us, also? I told her that my yacht would accommodate a number of people and that I would probably be inviting guests."

There was a moment of silence before Zeus said slowly, "In all probability I will do so. At the moment I am concerned about Ares."

"What has happened?"

"I don't know. That is what is annoying. As I informed you during our last conversation, Ares captured this man Randle and was in the process of interrogating him. But I have not heard from Ares for forty-eight hours. The hotel in Genoa where he is staying informs me that he has not checked out, but neither has he been in his room for two days."

"And Randle, have you any word of him? Perhaps he has escaped."

"My sources have no word of him. If he has somehow managed to escape, Ares is no doubt in a great rage, and he is totally unpredictable when thwarted. He is apt to do something rash and put us at great risk."

"Is there anything I can do?"

"No, your primary concern is the girl. I will continue to pursue the matter. As soon as it is resolved, I will quite likely join you on the *Olympus*. Become intimate with the girl, Apollo; you are my best man at that. Find out how much she knows."

"I'm looking forward to it. You may depend on me."

It was after six o'clock, and the Promenade deck was deserted. The *Star* had encountered a squall. Rain slashed across the deck, and the wind whistled around the shield on the afterdeck, where Cassandra huddled, a raincoat clutched around her.

The weather suited her mood, dreary, unpleasant. She was having second thoughts about her decision to join Marshall Paris on his yacht. In many ways, she knew, she was being foolhardy, staying on board a strange man's yacht, a man she'd known only for a few days. She also realized that many people would question her morals; however, other people's opinion didn't matter that much, and she was confident of her ability to take care of herself.

No, the only opinion that concerned her, was Jake's. What would he think if he suddenly reappeared and learned that she had left the *Star* for the yacht of a man she scarcely knew?

But it was the best means to search for her father. At Rhodes she could use the yacht as a base of operations, and if she discovered that it was necessary to go to other islands, transportation would be available and she wouldn't be rushed. She wasn't worried about Marshall Paris; he was one of the idle rich, with much time on his hands, and would quite likely embrace her search as a means of relieving his boredom. In time she would have to tell him what she was up to, but she wanted to wait until she knew him better.

Cassandra was aware that much of her depression was the result of her concern about Jake's continued absence, her fear that something had happened to him. She determined that she would call Bruno when she got to Rhodes to see if the detective had news of Jake and to let him know where she'd be if he needed to get in touch with her . . .

"There you are, my dear," said a deep voice from behind her.

She turned to face Eric Johanson. "Mr. Johanson! How are you?" She took note of the fact that he was without a raincoat. "Should you be out here without a coat? You're going to get soaked."

"The more important question is, why are *you* out here, alone in the rain?"

"I had some thinking to do."

"But you promised to steer clear of the decks when alone," he said reprovingly. "Just now, you didn't hear me until I spoke to you."

She shrugged. "It's still daylight, and I doubt anyone

would try to harm me in the daytime. Besides, the man who tried to push me overboard left the ship in Barcelona."

His gaze sharpened. "Then you did learn who was responsible?"

"I believe so. I have no proof of it, but I'm sure enough in my own mind."

"But the poor woman who was killed instead of you, that happened *after* Barcelona."

Now it was her turn to look at him suspiciously. "Where did you get that idea, Mr. Johanson? To my knowledge, only Jake and I arrived at that conclusion."

Johanson looked momentarily disconcerted. Then he frowned, gesturing vaguely. "I'm sure that I heard it somewhere. Perhaps it's just a rumor going around the ship."

Cassandra was far from satisfied with his answer, but before she could probe further, he spoke again.

"I understand you're leaving the ship in Rhodes?"

"The news has gotten around, has it?" she said ruefully. "Yes, it's true, I am leaving. I have some . . . some business on Rhodes, and Marshall Paris, one of our new passengers, has been kind enough to extend an invitation to stay on board his yacht while I'm there."

"It's none of my business, of course, but do you think that's wise, Cassandra?"

Her temper stirred. "You're absolutely right, Mr. Johanson, it *is* none of your business!"

He persisted. "But to stay on board the yacht of a man you hardly know? I'm assuming, of course, that you've just met this man."

"You're right, I just met him. He got on board in Genoa," she said tightly. "But I believe Mr. Paris is trustworthy. A wealthy businessman—what harm could he do to me? It's not as if he were kidnapping me, or as if I were sneaking on board. After all, you know about it," she pointed out. "And I'm sure others do. If it's my virtue you're concerned about, that's old-fashioned thinking, isn't it? I'm quite capable of defending my virtue, thank you very much."

Johanson appeared uncomfortable. "It's not that so much, my dear . . ."

"Then what *are* you worried about?"

"There have been attempts on your life. How do you know that Paris isn't one of your . . . uh, enemies?"

"Marshall Paris, try to kill me? Whatever for?" she said incredulously.

"Things are not always what they seem, dear Cassandra," he said sententiously.

"Please, no more cryptic sayings." She looked at him closely. "You seem to know a lot about my affairs, Mr. Johanson. Why is that?"

"I like you, Cassandra. I would hate to see you harmed in any way."

She peered at him closely. "You wouldn't have anything to do with the lavender notes I've been getting, would you?"

Something flickered deep in his eyes, then was gone instantly. He said blandly, "What notes?"

She motioned impatiently, weary of the exchange. "Never mind. Good-bye, Mr. Johanson. Thank you again for saving my life. And I don't wish to sound ungracious, but please remember that it *is* my life."

Cassandra turned away, entered the darkened lounge, and started toward the elevators. Despite her dismissal of his warning, a seed of doubt had been planted in her mind. Could it be possible that Marshall Paris posed a threat to her? No, it couldn't be! He was just what he seemed, a member of the jet set, a rich playboy. It was too easy to become paranoid, to see danger in every face.

Even if Johanson was right about Marshall, she was still determined to go ahead. At least she might be able to learn something about what or who was behind what was happening to her. The mystery of the whole thing was infuriating.

Opening the door to her cabin, her glance went immediately to the bed. She drew a breath of relief. There was no lavender envelope.

Jake was feeling much better after a good night's rest in a hotel. He'd had a good dinner last night and a hearty breakfast this morning. He had cashed a check at American Express, bought a complete new outfit of clothes, and now had a reservation on the next flight to Rhodes.

By the time Bruno had finished grilling him last night, it had been too late to call Cassandra. He had intended to call the *Star* the first thing this morning, but, completely exhausted, he had overslept. By the time he awoke, the ship had already docked, if it had kept to its schedule, and he knew there was no direct communication with the ship while it was at the dock. Well, he would be in Rhodes in plenty of time to catch the ship before it left, and he decided it would be better to see her in person. Bruno had told him of Cassandra's two calls and her concern, so it would appear that nothing had happened to her in his absence.

As he sat over a last cup of coffee in the hotel restaurant Jake thought back to last night. Bruno had been nice enough about the whole thing, yet he had been decidedly displeased when he learned about all that he had not been told originally.

Bruno had said coldly, "You lied to me, Jake."

"Not really, Marcus. There were some things I didn't tell you, true, but Cassandra is my client, and most of what I knew was confidential . . ."

"Not if that withheld information interferes with an investigation, Jake. Then your client privilege does not hold. That is true in your country, and it is true in Italy."

"Yes, I know all that, Marcus. But I wasn't sure that the

death of Claire Thomas tied in with Cassandra. In fact, I'm still not all that sure."

"I am not an idiot, Jake. The connection is obvious, and your withholding that information has impeded my investigation. I would have taken a totally different avenue of approach in my questioning of the passengers." Bruno added bitterly, "Now they are all gone, spread to the four corners of the earth."

"I'm sorry, Marcus. But I truly didn't know, not until this Macomber started asking questions about Cassandra. My main concern all along was to protect her."

"And my concern is with solving a murder. Tell me everything again, Jake, word-for-word."

"Must I? I've told you all I know, so why go through it a second time?"

"You know why; you were once a homicide officer. Something is always left out. You will tell it as many times as I want, until I'm convinced I have it all. Don't forget, my friend"—Bruno smiled with relish—"you have no passport, and you will find it difficult to get a replacement without my intervening on your behalf. Certainly you won't get it right away. Also, I could place you under arrest for withholding information pertinent to an investigation, for obstructing justice, even as a possible murder suspect, if I want to get really nasty."

And so Jake told his story again, and yet a third time. He left out only the information that Rene had given him about Cassandra's father. Some instinct told him to keep that to himself for the time being.

Finally, Bruno took pity on him. "I believe you have told me everything, Jake." He sighed, lighting up another evil-smelling cigar. "And now that I know what you know, I'm not much better off."

"I told you I didn't know that much," Jake said wearily.

"This case is . . . It's bizarre, that is the only word I can think of that fits."

"You might say that, yes."

"Why would someone want to kill your Cassandra? Two weeks ago she didn't even know she was going to work this particular cruise, and you claim that no one else knew, except her superiors, until she arrived in Florida. Yet, there have been three attempts on her life! And this Macomber fellow then abducts *you,* with the express purpose of asking you questions about *Signorina* Kanaris. No logic, Jake, no pattern."

"I know, I know. Speaking of Macomber, is there any word of him?"

"*Niente.* Nothing," Bruno said absently. "He has clearly found a . . . What is your expression? . . . a bolt-hole? We will continue looking, but I would not wager much on our success." He blew smoke. "My friend, someone, or several someones, do not want the *signorina* to find her father. That is the conclusion I have reached."

"I'd reached that conclusion some time ago," Jake said dryly. "But who? And, more important, why? Why should someone *not* want Cassandra reunited with her father. We can reasonably assume, I think, that this Macomber tried to kill her twice, but he was gone from the ship when Claire Thomas was killed, which means there are more than one. And the notes, who's writing the notes?"

"Questions, always questions." Bruno smiled. "But that is our business, is it not, Jake? Finding answers."

"We're not having much success," Jake said glumly.

"Ah, well, there's always another day." Bruno seemed to have cheered up a bit, Jake thought.

The Italian leaned toward him. "And this day is finished, it is nearing midnight. You'd better get some rest, Jake."

Bruno had promised to take him to the airport at Milan. Outside the hotel Jake paced, waiting for the Italian.

His head was clearer this morning, and he had been considering a possibility that hadn't occurred to him before.

Suppose the man behind all this was Jason Kanaris himself? After all, if he was still alive, he must have faked his death all those years ago, and for what other reason than to escape Cassandra's mother and avoid acknowledging a bastard daughter? *If* Cassandra's surmise was right, and her parents were never married. Kanaris was a very wealthy man; maybe he didn't want an heir to pop up in his life. It wasn't a pleasant concept, a man plotting the demise of his own daughter, yet it would not be the first time such a thing had happened.

Jake was debating whether or not he should lay this theory out for Cassandra when the beep-beep of an automobile horn broke into his reverie. He raised his glance and saw Marcus Bruno pulling up to the curb before the hotel.

Jake went around and got into the car.

"You look a little better this morning, my friend."

"At least I caught up on my sleep."

Bruno pulled the car out into traffic and started the long drive to the Milan airport. There was little conversation between them until they were out of town and the traffic had thinned out considerably.

Finally, Bruno said, "Did you arrive at answers to any of our questions?"

"I'm afraid not, Marcus. And you?"

"No. My poor brain is whirling." Bruno took a cigar from his coat pocket and put it into his mouth without lighting it. "I didn't tell you last night, but I had hopes of joining you on your flight to Rhodes, to continue my investigation in person. But my superiors would not authorize such an expenditure. They seem of the opinion that we have enough unsolved murders in Genoa to work on, without my going far afield on one that did not even take place in Italy." He sighed, shooting a quick glance at Jake. "So, I must depend on you, *amico*, to keep me informed of any progress."

"I'll keep you up-to-date, Marcus," he said. "*If* I ever learn anything."

"It's not so much a thirst for justice, you must understand. If our murderer is ever unearthed, it will likely be your doing, Jake, and out of Italy, out of our jurisdiction. But I have this curiosity about this crime, and I will never be content until it is satisfied."

"I feel much the same way."

The drive to the airport in Milan was a long one, and there was only a fifteen-minute wait before Jake's plane left.

Bruno didn't bother to get out of the car. "*Arrivederci*, my good friend. I will leave you here. Good hunting, as they say."

Jake shook Bruno's hand. "Good-bye, Marcus. It has been my pleasure, knowing you. I'll keep in touch, you can be sure of that."

"Give my regards to the *signorina*, Jake."

"I'll certainly do that."

It wasn't a particularly long flight to Rhodes, but in spite of his troubled thoughts and his having slept ten hours the night before, Jake slept most of the way. He thought that if he ever had trouble sleeping again all he would have to do would be to recall those sleepless hours in the cell, and he would sleep in simple gratitude for his eleventh-hour salvation.

From the Rhodes airport, after clearing Immigration, he took a taxi directly to the *Star*.

On board, he went down to Cassandra's cabin, hoping that she would be there. To his astonishment the door was opened by Betsy Clark, the other female member of the cruise director's staff.

Her eyes widened as she recognized him. "Mr. Randle! You're all right! Everyone's been worried about you, especially Cassandra."

"Where is she?"

Betsy caught her breath. "Oh." Her glance slid away.

Jake caught her hand. "Where is Cassandra? Has something happened to her?"

"No, no." Betsy shook her head violently. "She's fine. In fact . . ." She began to smile. "I wouldn't mind being in her shoes right now. She's left the ship, Mr. Randle."

"Left? You mean she quit her job?"

Betsy nodded. "I'm afraid so. Oh, Leland was absolutely furious."

"Where *is* she?"

"There was a guy boarded the ship in Genoa. Marshall Paris. A gorgeous hunk. He's rich as sin and has a private yacht. Cassandra is staying on his yacht for a couple of weeks."

Jake's breath left him in a rush. "She's on some guy's yacht? I find that hard to believe."

Betsy blinked at him. "So do we all. But then you never know, do you? I certainly don't blame her, though. Like I said, I wish I was with her."

"Betsy!" He had to exercise his self-control to keep from shaking her roughly. "Where *is* she? Where is this yacht?"

"Oh. I'm sorry. It's the *Olympus*, docked up near the yacht club, so I understand."

"Thanks." He swung away, and Betsy called after him, "They're still holding your cabin for you, Mr. Randle. Don't you at least want your things?"

"Later, I'll be back later," he called back over his shoulder.

His thoughts were bleak on the ride out to the yacht basin. How could Cassandra be so foolish as to go kiting off alone? And to stay on the yacht of a man she'd just met!

He put aside personal considerations for the moment, although he had to choke back a rise of jealousy. What concerned him the most was the risk she was taking. Three times these people, whoever they were, had tried to kill her. How did she know that this Marshall Paris wasn't one of them? Jake had the bone-deep feeling that she was in grave danger.

At the yacht club basin he strode along the beach searching for a yacht named the *Olympus*. There were a great many yachts of all sizes and shapes at anchor, but he couldn't spot the one he was looking for.

Jake could not speak Greek, and although there were a great many men working along the docks, they all shook their heads when he asked about the *Olympus*.

Finally he approached an aged, weathered man fishing off the pier. "Sir, do you speak English?"

The fisherman beamed a broad smile at him. "*Málista* . . . A little."

"A yacht named the *Olympus* . . . A big, fancy boat. Have you seen her?"

The man bobbed his head, his smile widening even more. "*Málista* . . . Big, big boat." With his fishing pole he pointed out into the basin.

"But where is she?" Jake asked urgently. "I can't see her anywhere."

"Gone, big boat gone. Sailed." He pointed out to sea. "Morning tide."

Despair filled Jake. Without hope he asked, "Where? Do you know where she sailed?"

The fisherman's smile died. Slowly, he shook his head. "No, *Kirie*. I not know."

Fourteen

In the morning Cassandra awoke to motion and thought at first that she was on the *Star* and they were leaving Rhodes. Not yet, not yet! She had learned nothing about her father. She couldn't leave Rhodes yet . . .

She sat up, a cry dying in her throat, and then realized that she wasn't on the *Star*, but on Marshall's luxurious yacht, the *Olympus*. And it *was* luxurious, beyond her wildest imaginings.

But wait! Why were they moving?

She scrambled out of the big bed and hurried to the porthole. The yacht was in motion, gliding slowly out of the basin; she could hear the throb of the great engines now.

Marshall had said nothing about leaving this morning. Cassandra took two steps toward the door, then stopped, belatedly realizing that she was wearing nothing but a sheer nightgown. She could hardly go charging out on deck dressed like this.

Anyway, what could she do beside protest? If she created much of a fuss, it would set Marshall to wondering. Insofar as he knew, she had agreed to come with him for the simple pleasure of the trip.

And it could be very, very pleasurable, she thought, remembering her introduction to the *Olympus* and the life of a wealthy yachtsman. She plumped up the pillows against the headboard and settled back, her thoughts going back to last night.

Marshall had given a party in her honor and to introduce her to his guests. There were four altogether, and Marshall had told her that another man would be joining them in a couple of days, perhaps sooner. Cassandra could tell that the guests were all wealthy. Although they were dressed casually, their clothes were obviously terribly expensive, and their manner was one she had become familiar with among wealthy passengers on cruise ships.

It had been a warm evening, and the party had been held on the spacious aft deck. There was a four-piece orchestra, and white-jacketed waiters moved among the guests carrying drinks and trays of hors d'oeuvres.

Cassandra had been properly dazzled and somewhat intimidated, not so much by her surroundings, as by the interest the guests seemed to have in her. Almost every time she turned around, she found herself the target of pointed questions.

Once, during a moment alone with Marshall, she casually remarked on this. "All of your guests seem to be strangely curious. They keep asking me all sorts of questions, about my life on cruise ships, which I can understand, but also questions about my life before I started on the ships, about my parents. Some of the questions are a little embarrassing, Marshall."

He threw his head back and laughed full-throatedly. "Sorry about that, love. They're long-time friends and a little overly protective, I imagine. I've never been married, you see, and any time I have a good-looking lady around, they check her out to see if she's suitable."

"Well, you can put their minds at ease," Cassandra said tartly. "I have no designs on you, marriage-wise."

He sobered, looking at her intently. "They'll be glad to hear that, I'm sure. But I'm not sure I am." He took her hand in both of his.

A flow of warmth radiated outward from his touch. He

was undeniably physically attractive, dammit! She tried to keep it light. "I thought you weren't the marrying kind?"

"That's true, but any intelligent man reserves the right to change his mind." His voice had become husky, intimate, and his eyes, intent on hers, had an almost hypnotic quality; Cassandra felt herself swaying toward him.

The moment was shattered by the sound of a motor approaching the yacht. Both turned to look toward the shore. A woman stood up in the stern of a water taxi, waving her hands over her head. As the taxi swung alongside the *Olympus* the driver silenced the motor. The woman called out, "Marshall! I made it!"

Marshall leaned over the railing. "Daphne! Darling, I'd about given up on you."

"I had some errands to do first," the woman called up.

"Then hurry on board, my dear. The party is in full swing."

Marshall gave the woman a hand up onto the deck. Still holding her hand, he turned with her to Cassandra. "Cassandra, you must know Daphne Moray. She was a passenger on the *Star*. Daphne, this is my guest of honor, Cassandra Kanaris."

It wasn't until then that Cassandra recognized the newcomer, a large, dark woman of perhaps forty, with pretty features and dark, inscrutable eyes. She had been one of the penthouse suite passengers. Cassandra said, "Why, yes, Miss Moray, I do remember you. You spent most of your time in your suite, however."

The woman's laughter was throaty. "When I take a cruise, it's mostly for rest and recuperation. That's what I like about the Nordic Line's new suites. With the suite's own private deck, one can enjoy the sea and the sun with complete privacy. I'm essentially a private person, you see."

"I've known Daphne a long time, Cassandra. I was quite surprised to learn that she was on board the *Star*. Daphne, come along and I'll introduce you to my other guests. I suppose I should say, renew acquaintances, since I think you already know most of them."

As the couple walked over to the others, Cassandra remained where she was, staring after the big woman. Something in the way she walked, seen from behind, stirred an uneasiness in Cassandra's mind, then was quickly gone . . .

In her cabin Cassandra stretched. Yes, last night had been pleasant, and she had enjoyed feeling like one of the "beautiful people," but she still felt a bit upset by the unscheduled departure.

She'd better get dressed, find Marshall, and talk to him about it.

Daphne Moray smiled coldly when Marshall opened the door to her knock. "I'd like a word with you, Apollo."

He nodded. "I'd like the same word with you. I wasn't expecting you tonight, Artemis, although I had to play it as if I had. What are you doing here?"

"Zeus ordered me to join you. You know very well that he did. You were supposed to pass the word to me."

"I must have forgotten." He shrugged negligently, and said, "Why does he want you along? To carry tales, I suppose?"

"Ours is not to question why," she said with an airy wave of her hand.

"You've talked to him then?"

"Yes, this afternoon." She became serious. "He said he'd be joining us some time before morning."

"I thought he was waiting until he'd talked to Ares?"

"He's made contact with Ares. Poor Ares," she said with mock sorrow. "It seems he blew it with Randle. The detective managed to escape Ares' clutches and damaged him severely in the process—broke his nose and knocked out some teeth. I imagine dear Ares is beside himself."

"You can be a bitch, you know that, Artemis?"

"Perhaps. But then what does that make you, brother dear?" She smiled sweetly. "How are you doing with the girl?"

"It's too early yet, for Christ's sake," he said impatiently. "She hasn't even been on board a whole day!"

"Zeus hasn't the patience of the gods, you know," she said with a brittle laugh. "He passed on some instructions for you. He has word that Randle is flying to Rhodes and the *Star*. Which means he will learn that Cassandra is on your yacht. Zeus wants you to be ready to move it as soon as he comes on board, no later than the morning tide."

In her suite in the Metropolitan Capsis Hotel, Hera was meeting with Poseidon and Aphrodite. She was agitated, striding back and forth, snapping at the two in displeasure. "Why couldn't you have stopped her from boarding Apollo's yacht?"

Aphrodite, feeling her age after the taxi ride to the hotel through the crowded streets of Rhodes Town, was not in the best of moods. "Do you for a moment think we didn't try? I warned her, Poseidon warned her, but she paid little heed. Cassandra has a mind of her own." She smiled suddenly. "What would you have had us do, Hera? Kidnap the girl?"

"Perhaps it might not have been a bad idea. It would have kept her out of their clutches, at least. That's what Ares did to the detective."

"And not very successfully, I've learned," Poseidon said. "Randle came to the *Star* earlier today looking for Cassandra. He probably knows by now that she is on the *Olympus*."

"As is Zeus," Hera said grimly. "He boarded the yacht sometime after midnight last night. Hermes is keeping watch on the *Olympus*."

Aphrodite said, "That is not good. God help Cassandra.

Zeus is liable to do something drastic. He must be furious about the failed attempts on her life."

"That is precisely why I am so concerned . . ." Hera was interrupted by the telephone. She answered the ring, "Hello?"

She was silent for a few moments, listening, a frown gathering on her otherwise smooth brow. "You have no idea of their destination? I see. Let me think for a moment." She covered the mouthpiece with her hand. "It's Hermes. The *Olympus* upped anchor very early this morning and sailed off. He hasn't learned where. Now what do we . . . ?" She broke off, speaking into the phone again. "Hermes? Charter a plane and cruise around Rhodes. They haven't had time to get very far, and I doubt they will move far away from Rhodes, in any event. Let me know the instant you learn anything."

She hung up and gazed at the others. "I have the dreadful feeling that matters are nearing a climax, and we can do nothing until we find out where the yacht is headed."

Poseidon said, "Maybe it's time to contact Jason?"

Hera shook her head. "We can't do that, not yet."

Aphrodite said forcibly, "Perhaps we should break the rules of the game. Cassandra's life is at stake now."

"It was all along; that hasn't changed." Hera shook her head emphatically. "We just have to keep as close a check on Cassandra as possible. Maybe we can figure out some way to get her off that yacht, and then will come the hardest part of all. Getting her together with Jason."

Camera looped around her wrist, Cassandra found Marshall Paris in the wheelhouse, monitoring the man at the controls.

At her entrance Marshall turned around, beginning to smile. "Cassandra! Good morning. How are you?"

"I'm fine, but I'm a little disturbed by something."

"What disturbs you, love?"

"You said nothing about leaving Rhodes. Yet here we are," she motioned, "out in the open sea."

"Oh, that. Not to worry, love." He laughed lightly. "I told you I would show you Rhodes, did I not? Well, Rhodes is more than just the town. You can do the tourist bit anytime. You must see the rest of the island, maybe some of the other Greek Islands. I would have told you, but I just decided to up anchor last night."

She was still dubious. "Well, that's fine, but I saw nothing more of Rhodes than the harbor and the section of town the taxi drove through to get to your yacht."

"Plenty of time for that." He batted a hand airily. "Right now, we're headed downcoast for Lindos. You'll love Lindos, I guarantee it."

Lindos! She fastened onto the name avidly, and all of her reservations vanished. Lindos was where her father was supposed to have drowned! She said casually, "I've heard something of Lindos."

"Everybody has. It's not far, some thirty miles down along the east coast of the island. The Acropolis, perched on a high headland, the land falling away to the sea, should first be seen from the sea. The Acropolis is ancient and impressive. To my mind, it is one of the most priceless of Greek treasures. The Acropolis at Athens is, of course, far better known, but I prefer Lindos. Actually, my favorite of them all is Delphi; although it is mostly in ruins.

"But that is another story." His slow smile struck Cassandra as somehow secretive. "Lindos must be seen to be appreciated." He broke off, staring past her. "Ah, there you are, Alex."

Cassandra turned about to see a tall man entering the wheelhouse. He was dressed impeccably in yachting clothes and walked with an erect, graceful carriage. As he came into shadow out of the bright sun she got a closer look at his face, and she realized that he was older—at least in his mid-fifties—than she had thought from his springy step. He was handsome, with a noble nose, a chiseled profile, and wisps of iron-gray hair escaping from his cap. A most impressive figure of a man.

Then his eyes swung around to meet hers, and she received a shock. His eyes were deep black and burned with a cold intensity that was a little frightening.

Marshall was speaking, "This is the other guest that I told you about, Cassandra. He arrived last night after you retired. Cassandra Kanaris, meet Alexander Chato. Alex, Cassandra."

Alex Chato removed his cap and dipped his head. In a neutral voice he said, "I am delighted to make your acquaintance, Miss Kanaris. I understand this is your first time in this part of the world. I do hope you enjoy yourself."

Cassandra was struck by an odd fact. Now that he was up close, she noticed that his face was totally devoid of expression, and he had yet to smile. There was something . . . well, dead about his face, as though the facial muscles were paralyzed. She had to wonder if he'd had a face-lift that had gone wrong.

She gave a nervous laugh and said, "I fully intend to, if Marshall gives me a chance. Do you know, Mr. Chato, that he practically kidnapped me? I thought he was going to show me Rhodes, and then I woke up this morning to find that we were steaming away!"

Chato aimed a questioning glance at Marshall, who appeared to shake his head almost imperceptibly. "Cassandra is being facetious, Alex," he said with a strained smile. "I was just now explaining to her that she will have all the time in the world to see Rhodes Town, but first she must see Lindos."

"Oh, indeed, Miss Kanaris," said Chato. "Lindos is a must . . ."

Cassandra was staring past him. The yacht was just passing the entrance to the picturesque harbor, which had once been straddled by the awesome bronze statue, the Colossus, and now was bracketed by the pillars bearing statues of roe deer, the symbol of Rhodes.

She exclaimed, "There's the *Star* on her way out to sea. I must have a picture!"

She hurried out of the wheelhouse. At the railing she aimed her camera at the *Star*, which was turning in the other direction. She quickly snapped two pictures, experiencing a feeling of melancholy. A large chunk of her life was sailing away with the *Star*, and she wondered if she would have occasion to regret her impetuous action. She knew that Leland Dawes was right: she would never be able to work for the Nordic Lines again. Maybe this task she had set for herself was foolish in the extreme. If Jason Kanaris was truly her father, why hadn't he tried to contact her over the long years? One answer, of course, was that he had no wish to do so, and if that was true, he certainly wouldn't welcome her with open arms.

She shook her head sharply, trying to dispel her doubts, and turned her back on the *Star*. That part of her life was over, she had to put it behind her.

She saw Marshall and Chato talking in the wheelhouse, their heads together. Without thinking about it, she raised the camera and aimed. They might not show up too clearly shot through the glass of the wheelhouse, but . . .

Just as she started to press the button, Alex Chato looked her way and seemed to freeze, glaring hard at her. Cassandra felt a chill ripple down her spine, but she took the picture anyway.

In the wheelhouse the late-arriving guest said, "That damned girl just snapped our picture!"

Marshall looked out the wheelhouse window. "She did? I'm sure it means nothing, Zeus. The girl's a camera fiend. She'd take pictures of grass growing if there was no other subject available."

"I do not care," Zeus said in a low growl. "I want the film

in that camera before she has a chance to develop it. I want no pictures of myself floating around, especially not in *her* hands."

"I'll see to it, never fear," Marshall said soothingly. "She can't develop any film on the yacht, and I'll see to it that the roll is destroyed before she steps onto land again."

"Very well." Zeus relaxed a little. "Have you gained her confidence yet?"

"I haven't really had the opportunity," Marshall said defensively. "And sailing this morning without warning got her back up. You heard what she said . . ."

Zeus drew himself up. "Are you questioning my orders?"

"Of course not," Marshall said hastily. "But she is suspicious about our having left so suddenly and without telling her. I think I managed to soothe her ruffled feathers just before you came."

"It had to be done. I had word that Jake Randle was flying into Rhodes today. We have to keep them separated. That idiot Ares!" The eyes under the yachting cap blazed. "He had Randle at his mercy and let him escape. I cannot depend on anyone these days."

"You can depend on me, Zeus," Marshall said confidently. "I now have Cassandra where I can operate freely. I will soon have her complete confidence and will be able to manipulate her at will."

Shortly before noon, Cassandra was leaning on the railing as the *Olympus* approached Lindos; Marshall came out of the wheelhouse to stand beside her.

She had her camera in hand, but most of the way down the coast there had been little to photograph—an occasional small village, olive orchards, and fishing boats bobbing at anchor. But now the scenery changed as Lindos gradually took shape at their approach.

The bay itself was beautiful, with its lovely beach. To the left rose the hill on which perched the Acropolis, and running partway up the hill were the white houses, glittering in the brilliant sun, of the village of Lindos.

Cassandra's breath caught. "You're right, Marshall, it *is* spectacular!"

"I thought you'd like it," he said. "Do you know the story behind it?"

She shook her head. "Not really."

"Well, it's quite a story. The whole town, of course, has been designated as an archeological site, which means that it will always be preserved with loving care. It is ancient, attributed to Danaos and his fifty daughters, who came here from Egypt in flight from Aegyptos and his fifty sons. Or so the story goes."

His voice took on a faintly lecturing tone as he pointed. "We're close enough now so that you can begin to make out the columns of the temple of Athena Lindia. Aside from the Acropolis itself, which you must see of course, the view of the surrounding countryside and the sea, from up there, is magnificent. There is one unfortunate factor, the only way up is on foot or by muleback, and there are a great many steep steps."

Cassandra was scarcely listening. She was thinking that her mother had once been here, and her father; she could even have been conceived here. She felt a throb of love and compassion for her mother. It hardly mattered that much of her mother's story might have been a fabrication. Penelope had loved *someone* enough to have conceived a child by him, and then had been deserted or left alone by his tragic death.

Was it remotely possible that someone in Lindos would remember an American woman staying here with a man? Would she find anyone here who remembered the name Jason Kanaris? After more than twenty years it seemed a hopeless cause, and Cassandra felt a wave of discouragement wash over her.

She leaned on the rail, camera in hand, ready to take a picture when they got closer.

Marshall said, "We'll anchor out here in the bay and go ashore in the launch anytime you like."

Cassandra nodded absently.

"I have to return to the wheelhouse to supervise. Why don't you go to your cabin and change?" When she didn't answer immediately, he said, "Cassandra?" and took her by the arm to turn her toward him. In doing so he managed to hit the camera in her hand, knocking it out of her grip and tumbling over the railing.

"Oh, hell!" Marshall exclaimed, and lunged for it.

He was too late. In dismay Cassandra watched it tumble over and over and go into the water with a faint splash. There were several shots of Jake in there, she thought unhappily. Luckily, there were also some pictures of him on the roll she had developed after their day in Barcelona.

"I'm sorry, love," Marshall was saying. "That was unforgivably clumsy of me. I'll buy a new camera to replace it as soon as possible."

She shrugged slightly and looked at him. "It's no great loss, I've had it a long time. But I do feel kind of like I've just lost an old friend . . ."

Her gaze was drawn past him. On the deck a few yards away stood the man called Alex Chato. Those glittering black eyes were fastened on her, and they blazed with unholy triumph.

The two of them stood frozen for a long moment, stares locked. Then Chato turned away abruptly, and Cassandra shivered violently, hugging herself. Marshall had already walked away toward the wheelhouse. She didn't like Alex Chato. There was something malevolent about him, and this caused her to wonder about Marshall. What connection did Marshall have with the man?

* * *

Consequently, she was not overly pleased that afternoon when she discovered that Chato was accompanying them to shore in the motor launch. Aside from the seaman who drove the launch, the only others on board were Chato and Marshall.

"The rest of your friends aren't going in with us?" she asked Marshall.

"They've all seen Lindos many times," he explained. "They spend part of every year on Rhodes, either on my yacht or in villas they own or rent."

Then in a low voice she said, "Your friend, Mr. Chato? Is he rich, like all your other friends?"

Marshall looked toward the rear of the launch, where Chato stood out of hearing, his back to them. "Alex? I would imagine he's wealthier than any of us. He owns one of those Greek shipping lines you've heard so much about."

"He's Greek then?"

Marshall looked faintly startled, then amused. "I'm not sure anyone knows Alex's nationality. I'm not sure he even *has* a nationality. I overheard someone ask him that question once, and Alex replied that he considered himself a citizen of the world."

"But he must have some place of origin. Surely, he's not The Man Without a Country!"

"I'm sure he has, love, but I don't know it. I would imagine that he's a Greek citizen now, since his money is made in Greece." Marshall stared at her. "Why this sudden curiosity about Alex?"

It occurred to Cassandra that it might not be wise to pursue this further. She said casually, "Just a woman's curiosity, I suppose. I'm curious about all of you. I've never really associated with the jet set before."

He laughed. "Is *that* what we are?"

"Well, you all seem to have money, you don't seem to do much work, and you have all kinds of leisure time, spending most if not all of your time flitting about the world. You, for instance, you're certainly not Greek, yet you spend most of your time in the Greek Isles."

"That's true enough," he said with an indulgent smile. "But I'm not too flattered by the 'flitting.' I spend my time here because I prefer it. And no, I'm not Greek. I'm as American as you are. I'm originally from Chicago, where my father made his money in the meat-packing business. What can be more American than that? But I spend only enough time in the States nowadays to keep my American citizenship . . ." He broke off as the launch slowed, maneuvering in alongside a rickety pier. "Here we are, Cassandra."

As the launch bumped the pier Marshall took up a rope from the deck, uncoiled it, and looped it over a piling.

He gave Cassandra a hand up, then stood back as Alex Chato stepped out onto the pier. Marshall extended his arm. "Shall we go, love? It's a fair walk to the village, and the Acropolis even more so, but I'm afraid there's no help for that."

Cassandra took his arm, and the three of them started off, without a word to the man in the launch. Cassandra supposed he knew enough to wait, forever if necessary. It was something that she had gradually grown aware of with Marshall, and his friends as well. They rarely addressed a remark to any member of the crew of the yacht. They almost acted as if the crew didn't exist, as if they were robots programmed to do what was expected of them. She wondered what happened if one of them botched a task— were they dismantled and tossed into the scrap heap, to be replaced by a spanking new, better-programmed model? It was a rather cavalier manner in which to treat hired help, and it didn't say much for the humanity of Marshall and his guests.

Cassandra glanced sidelong at Chato, walking a few feet to her right, looking straight ahead, his profile void of expression, unspeaking. In fact, she realized, he hadn't said a word since they had boarded the launch.

She glanced away from him and turned her gaze to the white crescent of beach. It was here, she thought, that her mother had sunned all those years ago, and here— Cassandra looked left at the waters of the bay—that her father had drowned. Or so her mother had been led to believe.

"Cassandra?" Marshall pressed her hand.

She said, "Yes?"

"You look sad. Is something wrong?"

She shook her head, smiling with an effort. "Not really. I . . ." She hesitated briefly, then took the plunge. "My mother told me that she was here once, before I was born."

"But why should that make you sad?"

"Mother died not too long ago." She was watching his face carefully for some reaction but could detect none. "And being here, where she once was, made me think of her."

"I am sorry, love." He squeezed her hand.

Something compelled Cassandra to look again at Chato, and she caught him staring at her, those hypnotic eyes glittering strangely.

She glanced quickly away, feeling absurdly that Chato had peered into her mind and soul.

They began climbing along a path on a slight incline, through the clutch of houses that was the village of Lindos. They strolled along the narrow, white-walled streets of the town, which were crowded with tourists and lined with cafes and colorful shops displaying clothing and folk art. Here and there a door was open, and Cassandra could see into charming courtyards, bordered with plants and paved with polychrome pebbles.

They continued upward, past the small stable where burros stood lazily, waiting for those visitors whose energies were not equal to the climb to the Acropolis. Soon, the trio left the narrow-walled streets for the even narrower path.

As they navigated one sharp turning they came upon a middle-aged woman, clad in the traditional black, squatting over her display of finely embroidered linens. Cassandra was struck by the strong beauty of her face. She looked as if she were made of the same eternal stuff as the earth and rocks, strong and patient.

The angle of the path grew as they neared the summit and wound around the base of the ancient stone wall that surrounded the Acropolis. The last stage of the climb consisted of a steep rise of stone steps; and Cassandra, despite the fact that she considered herself in good condition, was breathing hard as they finally gained the narrow, arched entranceway to the Acropolis. Once through the dark, tunneled entryway, they came out into bright, hot sunlight, that dazzled the eyes.

Cassandra drew in her breath as she gazed around her. The ruined columns were elegant and clean-lined against the fierce blue of the sky. Small clumps of wild flowers nestled in ancient marble. Bits and pieces of a civilization long vanished, and yet, in some strange way, it was still present in these last reminders of its greatness.

Marshall took her by the hand and led her to where she had a clear view of an ancient rise of stone steps, fronted by a row of ruined columns. "These are Doric," he said softly. "Aren't they lovely?"

She only nodded. It seemed almost a sacrilege to speak here.

Gently he took her arm and turned her, moving her toward the ruins of another building, out on the rocky point, where she could see the azure colors of the sea below.

"And this is the temple of Athena."

She turned to him and smiled. "I'm almost afraid to talk here. I almost feel as if the old gods can hear us."

Marshall's face creased in an odd smile. "Perhaps they can," he said, still smiling. "Perhaps they can."

They remained at the Acropolis for well over an hour, but when Marshall suggested that they return to Lindos, for lunch, Cassandra still did not want to leave.

From the hilltop she could look down on the bay below, and the mixture of sea, sky, and the powerful magic of the ruined Acropolis created a feeling of peace and separation from the ordinary world that Cassandra found most appealing.

But Marshall, pleading near starvation, at last prevailed, and they descended again to Lindos proper, which, Cassandra had to admit, had a beauty and charm of its own.

Midway through their lunch, in an open-air restaurant off a small plaza, Cassandra pushed her plate away, and said, "If you don't mind, Marshall, I'm going to explore a little."

The two men looked across the table at her. To the best of her recollection Chato had yet to speak since they left the yacht.

Marshall arched an eyebrow in surprise. "You haven't walked enough yet? I should think your feet would be worn down to nubs."

She forced a laugh. "I haven't done the shops yet. I want to buy a few things."

He made to rise. "I'll go with you."

"No, no." She waved him back down. "You haven't finished your lunch yet. Besides, men are always bored shopping with women. I won't be long."

Marshall shot a glance at Chato, then looked quickly away, dropping back down into his chair. Cassandra was already walking away. As she crossed the plaza she risked a glance back. Both men were staring after her. She walked faster, soon losing herself in the crowd.

She had to see if she could find anyone who remembered Jason Kanaris, yet she was under a severe handicap: she knew no Greek at all. She wandered in and out of various shops, but most of them were manned by salespeople not much older than she; she had to find someone who would have been here more than twenty years.

Finally, in one small shop selling colorful Greek blouses and skirts, she saw behind the counter a brown, wrinkled woman who had to be in her sixties. Cassandra idled about, fingering blouses and skirts, waiting until the shop was empty. Finally, there came a moment when she was alone in the shop with the saleslady.

Taking a blouse from the rack, she walked up to the counter. With a small prayer, she said, "Do you speak any English?"

The woman looked at her with small brown eyes, smiling slightly. "A little, miss lady."

"How long have you been here? I mean, how long have you lived in Lindos?"

"Thirty years, the shop," the woman said proudly. "My man, he die five years now. I run alone."

"My mother was here, in Lindos, twenty-six years ago, with my father. Jason Kanaris. Does that name mean anything to you?"

The shopkeeper looked blank. "Not know. Is Greek?"

"Yes, yes." Cassandra bobbed her head. "He's supposed to have died here. He drowned, in the sea off Lindos somewhere. Surely you'd remember a man drowning, even that long ago."

Something flickered in the woman's eyes, and Cassandra leaned forward eagerly. "You *do* remember something! Tell me, please!"

But now the dark eyes were blank again, and then Cassandra realized that the woman was staring past her. Cassandra turned slowly, and a chill raced down her spine. Alex Chato stood in the doorway of the tiny shop, less than twenty feet away, and she was sure he'd heard every word. His face was as dead as ever, but those eyes blazed into hers.

Cassandra turned quickly back to the old woman. Voice trembling, she said loudly, "How much?" She held the blouse up. "The blouse, how much?"

"Four thousand drachmas. Good bargain, miss lady."

At the current rate of exchange that sum would be roughly fifty dollars, and Cassandra knew that she was being overcharged, but she said, "I'll take it."

Fumbling in her purse, Cassandra shot a glance back over her shoulder at the doorway. Alex Chato was gone.

Fifteen

Once on board the *Olympus* again, Cassandra found refuge in her cabin and tried to sort out her conflicting thoughts. She was sure that the name Jason Kanaris was known to the woman in the shop, and if that woman knew something about him, there must certainly be others who could supply Cassandra with information.

However, the thing foremost in Cassandra's mind was apprehension—and a mounting fear. Chato was a frightening man, and the conviction was growing in Cassandra that her presence on board the yacht was the reason he was here. She should have listened to Eric Johanson, and not accepted Marshall's invitation. She had the uneasy feeling now that all of the people on board the *Olympus* were her enemies, and that could even include Marshall Paris. And if that meant she was paranoid, so be it. She smiled without humor as she recalled a saying she had heard once: "Even paranoids are right part of the time."

And what made it even worse was that she was, in effect, a prisoner on board the yacht. She sensed that they would never let her go ashore without one or more of them accompanying her. She was a fair swimmer, but anchored where they were, she couldn't swim ashore without being spotted, at least not in the daytime. Perhaps at night, after they'd all retired? It might be a solution, even if she had to leave all her things behind.

Yet, that evening, most of her fears were allayed. It was a warm, splendid evening, with a full, yellow moon, and Marshall gave an impromptu party for his shipboard guests and some friends who were staying in Lindos. The orchestra played again, and this time there was dancing on the aft deck.

All of the guests were either English or American; one couple had come from Los Angeles originally. "In your honor, love," Marshall said with a broad grin.

The couple were in the movie industry, Ernest Hayworth, a well-known movie director, and his wife, Jean, who had played roles in a number of films. Hayworth was in his late fifties, Jean around thirty. She was a former model, with the lean and starved look they all seemed to have, and possessed a wicked tongue.

After they had all gotten sorted out, Cassandra found herself sitting with the Hayworths. She was relaxed now, not nearly so apprehensive, and she supposed it was because Alex Chato had not put in an appearance. It was only with effort that she refrained from asking Marshall if Chato had left. The rest of the yacht's guests seemed to have finally accepted her as one of them; at least they weren't asking so many probing questions.

"Yes, Cassandra," Hayworth was saying. "We got tired of the rat race. We have all the money we need, and directing is no longer a high for me. It's a chore, and frankly most of the movies they're making nowadays are shit. Splatter movies, blood all over the place, or skin flicks, just barely this side of X-rated. So I bought a villa here on Rhodes and here we are."

"And vegetating," Jean drawled. "It's boring, boring. If we didn't have a few friends like Marshall, and get-togethers like this, I'd go out of my gourd."

"Now Jean," her husband said, patting her hand paternally. "It's not really all that bad. It's a peaceful life, no smog, little traffic, no hassle. We'll live longer."

"But who wants to, *here*? And I just may die of utter and complete boredom."

Hayworth said, "This is considered a choice vacation spot. Hell, people pay a great deal of money to spend two weeks a year here."

"But they don't have to *live* here."

Cassandra was listening to the exchange with amusement. She liked the couple. There was no real rancor in their banter and they weren't as phony as many movie people she'd encountered. She said, "I thought very few people ever retired from the movies, especially performers, until they got too old, and that certainly doesn't apply to you, Jean."

"Thank you, Cassandra." Jean preened. "But I didn't retire, hon. God, this man dragged me here, kicking and screaming all the way. I might have been a big star by now."

Hayworth merely smiled. "Don't pay any attention to her, Cassandra. My child bride is a creature of rare beauty and not a bad actress, by and large, but she is one of those unfortunate people who do not come across well on the screen."

"So says my husband, the has-been director."

"Now be honest, angel. You know that the biggest role you ever had was playing Daphne to Marshall's Apollo."

Cassandra sat up alertly. "Marshall made a movie? The

first time I saw him I thought that he looked like a movie star!"

Hayworth laughed. "Well, I wouldn't say that he's exactly a star. He made one movie a number of years ago, *The Olympians*, all about the mythical Greek gods of old. He played Apollo. It was a real turkey, Cassandra, and I can say that, even though I directed it. That's how we met Marshall. He talked me into it, to my regret, and even provided some of the financing."

"And I played Daphne," Jean said. "And I helped make it a turkey, because Ernie is right, I'm a terrible actress. But that Marshall! Isn't he a gorgeous hunk?"

"*The Olympians*? I never even heard of it," Cassandra remarked.

"I'm not surprised. Very few people did," Hayworth said. "It went right down the tubes. So bad, in fact, that television hasn't even picked it up, and that should give you a clue right there. The trouble was, I made the mistake a director should never make, but at the time I needed the bread. Marshall talked all of his rich friends into investing in the film, in exchange for their acting in it. They seemed to come out of the woodwork, all eager for a chance to play Greek gods and goddesses."

Cassandra said casually, "Marshall's friend, Alexander Chato, did he play in it?"

Hayworth looked at her curiously. "Have you met Alex?"

"Why, yes, he's on the yacht."

"I didn't know. But no, Alex didn't play in it. Alex is a very private person, and he would never dream of exposing himself like that. The fact that he's on board and didn't even show for the party should tell you something."

Jean said, "It was during the film that Marshall became so interested in the Greek gods."

Cassandra nodded. "I gathered that he had some interest. He told me that Delphi is his favorite place."

"Oh, yes. He's really turned on by the subject. He even joined a . . ."

"Angel." Hayworth gripped his wife's hand. "That's a no-no. We're not even supposed to . . ."

He broke off as Marshall approached them, a cigarette burning in the ivory holder. He smiled. "This is a cozy little group. You've been chatting it up for some time over here."

Jean laughed gaily. "We've been talking about you, dear."

Marshall's face grew still. "Nothing dire, I hope."

"I just told Cassandra what a hunk you are. Surely, you don't mind that?"

His smile came again, and he seemed, to Cassandra, to strike a pose. "No, not in the least, although I'm not too enamored of the word." To Cassandra he said, "Love, the night's about over. This is to be the last number by the band tonight. May I claim this last dance?"

He held out his hand, and Cassandra took it, getting to her feet. As they moved off, Marshall said, "I told them to play a waltz, instead of disco. A waltz seems more fitting to finish off the evening."

As the band started up and Cassandra moved into his arms, he said, "Did you enjoy yourself this evening?"

"Oh, yes, very much. I especially enjoyed talking to your friends, the Hayworths." She smiled up into his face. "They were telling me about your movie career."

He missed a step. "Oh? What did they tell you?"

"They told me you played Apollo in a movie titled *The Olympians*."

"I'd rather they hadn't told you. Movie people tend to be too gossipy."

"But why shouldn't they tell me?" she asked, still looking up into his face. "I'd be proud to have it known that I played a big part in a movie."

"Not if it was as terrible as *The Olympians*. Of course, it wasn't too well handled, from the producing and directing end, although I suppose Ernie did his best, and it was a bad script to begin with." His voice took on an edge of bitterness. "In addition, it was never picked up by a major distributor. The name of the game in the movie business, you know, is distribution." She felt him shrug slightly. "Ah, well, I wasn't meant to be a movie star, I suppose. It's damned hard work, love. Nobody told me that."

They waltzed across the deck in silence for a few moments, before Cassandra said, "The Hayworths also told me about your interest in the Greek gods."

She felt his hand go tense on her back. "Did they?" His short laugh was brittle. "Jean was serious, wasn't she, when she said they'd been talking about me?"

"Nothing bad, Marshall. I certainly see nothing wrong with an interest in Greek mythology."

"It's just a hobby. Every man must have a hobby." After a moment he continued, "It's just that the gods were larger than life-size. They performed great, heroic deeds." His voice had gathered intensity. Now he gave a strange laugh. "You said mythology, Cassandra. What if they weren't as mythical as all that?"

She craned back to look up at him, puzzled. "What do you mean?"

All at once, he seemed to draw back a little, his glance darting around the deck. "Oh, nothing, really. I suppose when you become as absorbed in the story of the Olympians as I have down through the years, they tend to become real."

The music stopped and they glided to a halt. Marshall said, "Thanks for the dance, love. People will be leaving now, I have to see them off." He strode away without looking at her again.

Cassandra had the strange feeling that he was glad to seize an excuse to end the conversation. She crossed the deck to say good-bye to the Hayworths, who were preparing to leave. Then she stood about uncertainly for a moment before deciding to go to her cabin; she hadn't grown familiar enough with the other guests to feel it necessary to say good-bye.

As she walked to her cabin Cassandra kept looking around for Alex Chato, recalling Hayworth's remark that Chato was a private person. To her relief she didn't see Chato anywhere.

In her cabin she recalled the thought she'd had earlier about the possibility of fleeing the yacht in the night, but somehow the evening had put her fears to rest. It struck her, now, as foolish—diving off the yacht and swimming ashore, leaving all of her things behind.

Besides, what would she do, coming ashore on Rhodes with only the clothes on her back and those soaked? She could take her money with her, but she knew no one on land, and she couldn't speak the language. After all the things that had happened to her, she was just jumpy, that was all. So Alex Chato was a little weird. She would just stay out of his way as much as possible.

She undressed and took a nice, hot bath, which relaxed her even more. Dressed in a robe, she was brushing her hair when a knock on the door startled her. "Who is it?"

"It's Marshall, love."

After a moment's hesitation, she belted her robe tighter around her, unlocked the door, and opened it.

Marshall was carrying a bottle of champagne in an ice bucket and two stemmed glasses. He arched an eyebrow at her. "Why did you lock the door, Cassandra? Surely you don't think someone would bother you on my yacht?"

She shrugged. "Just habit, I guess."

He hefted the ice bucket. "I thought we might have a small nightcap. I know it's late, but I didn't get to see much of you with all the guests here tonight."

A small doubt slid into Cassandra's mind, but she gave a mental shrug and stepped back. "Okay, come in."

He bustled in, uncorked the champagne bottle adroitly,

and poured two glasses. "Did you enjoy your afternoon on Lindos?"

"Very much," she said. "Can we go back again tomorrow?"

"Of course, love. Whatever you want, you shall have." He handed her a glass. "Let's have a toast. What shall we drink to?"

"Oh, how about . . . to Rhodes?" She added impishly, "And to your Greek gods?"

A shadow moved across his face and was quickly gone. "I'll always drink to that."

They clinked glasses and drank. Cassandra sat on the window seat, drawing her robe tightly around her. She was suddenly, acutely, aware that she had absolutely nothing on under the robe.

Marshall refilled their glasses, then sat down on the seat close to her. He looked at her intently, until she began to feel uncomfortable. There was an unaccustomed air of tension about him tonight, as though he was angry with her about something and trying to hide it.

Abruptly, he said, "About those Greek gods . . . Do you think I'm weird for having such an interest in them?"

"No, not at all. You said it was a hobby. I can certainly think of worse." She smiled slightly. "Now if you believed in them, *that* I might find a little strange."

"Some people do, you know."

"Some people believe in hobgoblins and things that go bump in the night. I won't say that I disbelieve in the supernatural, but I'd have to have some kind of proof before I accepted the fact that such things really exist."

Marshall put his glass down on the table and took her hand, leaning toward her. His hand was warm and supple, and a tingle ran up her arm. She wondered if the tension she'd noticed about him was sexual in nature, and she realized that her heartbeat had accelerated and she was breathing shallowly and rapidly. His face loomed closer.

With his other hand he cupped her chin and tilted her face up, then lowered his mouth to hers.

His lips felt hot, and there was a certain demand implicit in the pressure they exerted.

A part of her couldn't help but respond, and instinctively, she found herself kissing him back.

Then she felt his hands beneath her robe, his fingers touching her tender nipples, and although she felt the beginning of arousal, she pulled away. Marshall was very attractive, and she admittedly felt drawn to him, yet when he began touching her, she had immediately started thinking of Jake. Even if it weren't for Jake, she wasn't certain that having an affair with Marshall would be a good idea. She had never been one to leap lightly into bed with just anyone, had never been able to practice the "sex as recreation" philosophy. To her, sex included a certain amount of emotional involvement, and she was already involved with Jake.

Drawing a shaky breath, she disengaged Marshall's hands and pulled her robe closed, trying to think of the right words, words that wouldn't wound his vanity or make him angry.

At her gesture of withdrawal, a puzzled expression crossed his face, and he reached for her again, grasping her shoulder with one hand, and her robe with the other.

Trying to fend him off, she felt awkward and foolish. "No, Marshall. I'm sorry. I really am."

He stared at her in astonishment. "What do you mean, you're sorry?"

She pulled her robe closer about her and moved farther away from him. "I guess I mean that I'm something of a one-man woman, at least one man at a time. I hope you'll understand."

A dark look came over his handsome face, making it, for the moment, look weak and petty. "Understand? I'm afraid I don't. If you're talking about Randle, well, he doesn't seem to be around, does he?" Suddenly, his expression cleared, and he reached for the champagne bottle. "What you need is another drink or two."

Cassandra felt the sexual arousal she had begun to feel fading rapidly. She was very good at reading nuances, and Marshall's expression, and his words, made it perfectly clear to her what he was thinking. What he was thinking had something to do with the old cliché that when a woman says no, she means yes; or that she only says no because of convention, and once lip service is paid to that hoary saw, it is all right to get on with the seduction.

Anger was quickly taking the place of passion, yet Cassandra accepted the glass he handed her, stalling for time. Despite her annoyance, she didn't want to antagonize him too much; she had placed herself in the position of being dependent on him and his yacht.

Marshall had drained his champagne glass and now reached for hers. As he took it from her unwilling fingers with one hand he quickly shoved her back against the couch with the other, following the movement smoothly with his body so that before she could protest, his lips were again insistent upon hers, and his hands once more pushed aside her robe, and were taking liberties with her body.

Really angry now, and not a little frightened, she pushed against his shoulders, to no avail; his mouth smashed down on hers with enough force to keep her head pinned against the couch pillows, and his body was heavy and demanding on hers. At last he broke the kiss and raised his face from hers, but the pressure of his body remained.

Looking directly into her eyes, he smiled smugly, as, with one hand he began to tease her nipples, and slowly rotated the lower part of his body against her so that she could feel the rigidity of his penis.

Again, his expressions and actions said it all. He was so damned sure of himself, she thought, convinced that all he had to do was push the sexual buttons, caress the right erogenous zones, and she would go mad with passion. Well, he didn't know much about women, especially not *this* woman!

Giving in to her anger, she gritted her teeth, and with an effort that took most of her strength, she managed to push him away.

"I said no, dammit! And that's what I meant!"

Marshall, his face blank, stared at her in incomprehension. Taking advantage of his surprise, she got up from the couch and pulled her wrinkled robe closely around her. This time she didn't worry about Marshall's ego or try to spare his feelings. "I think you'd better leave now, Marshall."

His handsome face contorted. "You're telling *me* to leave? Just who do you think you are? Why do you think I invited you along on my yacht? I'm not operating a free travel service here!"

Cassandra gave him a cool smile. "Then you should have told me what the price would be beforehand. Sorry, but it's too much to pay."

His face darkened further, became, for a moment, ugly. "You cold little bitch! You lead me on, and then . . ."

"It seems to me that you took the initiative. You invited yourself into my cabin. *You* made the move! You know something, Marshall? I think I'm really seeing you as you are for the first time, ugly and nasty. Maybe that's the side of you that came across in your movie."

His eyes burned with venom, and his hand flashed out to slap her. Cassandra moved just in time, stopping the hand in midair, both hands locked around his wrist, yet she knew that her strength was no match for his. "You're stronger than I am, Marshall, so I suppose you can beat me into submission, if that's to your liking."

They stood locked that way for a long moment, then the tension went out of his arm, and he said, "Ah-h, hell!"

He turned away toward the door. On the way he passed

the full-length mirror on the closet door and stopped to look at himself. Cassandra saw his features smooth out, the handsome veneer back in place. Without looking at her again, he left the cabin, slamming the door behind him.

Cassandra went limp with relief. Thoughts tumbled over and over in her mind. She had the feeling that she was in imminent danger now. She should have listened to the warnings of Lisa van Horne and Eric Johanson; she knew instinctively that the threat that had hung over her on board the *Star* had followed her to the *Olympus;* somehow, Marshall was in league with the others, whoever they were.

Moving quickly, driven by a sense of urgency, she scavenged through the clothes closet and found a small plastic bag. She gathered up a complete change of clothing, including a pullover sweater and a pair of pants, and stuffed them into the bag, along with a few other necessities, including her purse holding two thousand dollars in travelers checks, all the money she had in the world. She tied the neck of the bag as tightly as she could with a long cord, praying that it would be waterproof.

She changed into a two-piece swim suit, then opened the cabin door slowly, peering out into the corridor. With a sigh of relief she saw that it was empty. The bag over her shoulder, she went hurriedly along the corridor and out onto the deck, which also seemed to be deserted. It was well after midnight, and she hoped that all the guests, as well as the members of the crew, were in bed.

But as she made her way toward the rail, lights came on in the salon, splashing across her, and she could hear the sound of angry voices. Shrinking back against the cabin, she edged down a few feet, out of the light. She looked at the bag. If she went into the water holding the bag, she would have only one hand free. Luckily, the cord was long. She ran the end of the cord through the bottom half of her suit and knotted it securely. It would still hinder her somewhat, but it was the best she could do.

She stepped to the low railing, climbed up, drew a deep breath, and dove off, in the direction of the lights of Lindos in the distance.

In the main salon Zeus wheeled on Marshall Paris. "Are you telling me that you failed, then?"

Trying to control his anger and humiliation, Marshall said, "It's just a temporary setback. I'll be able to get back into her good graces in the morning."

Daphne Moray said mockingly, "The great lover has failed, is that it? I guess Cassandra has more sense than I gave her credit for!"

Zeus scowled at her. "Be quiet, Artemis. We have no time to indulge in such pettiness." He turned his burning gaze on Marshall. "Something must have made her suspicious. You must have said or done something to put her off."

Marshall shook his head stubbornly. "It was nothing I did, I'm sure. You told me that she saw you in that village shop, when you overheard her talking about Jason, asking questions. That must be it."

"That would not have involved you; not that I can see. You must have given yourself away . . ."

He broke off, his head swinging around as they all heard a splashing sound outside. "Damnation! It must be the girl; she's getting away! We cannot afford to have her loose on Rhodes. After her!"

Sixteen

In Rhodes, Jake took a room in an inexpensive hotel, with a view of the Mandraki Harbor, within easy walking distance of Old Town. After learning that the yacht where Cassandra was supposed to be had sailed away, destination unknown, he had tried every way that he could think of to learn the whereabouts of the yacht, without any success. The language barrier was a big obstacle; although people in the hotels, restaurants, and shops spoke some English, it was almost impossible for him to communicate with the rest of the population.

Hs only hope was that Cassandra and the yacht would eventually return, so he got a hotel room and settled in. Each morning, he decided, he would pay a visit to the yacht club, to see if the *Olympus* had moored.

The rest of that day he played the part of tourist. At least Rhodes Town was well worth seeing. He walked endless miles. The tourist season was at its height, and the beaches were crowded with colored umbrellas, arranged in close-ranked rows along the sand.

The most interesting part of Rhodes Town, was Old Town, the medieval city of the Knights Hospitallers. Thick walls encircled the ancient town, which was honeycombed with narrow streets spanned by arches. There were charming, round plazas, with great plane trees shading ancient fountains. In the background, slender minarets rose above the cupolas of mosques and Byzantine churches. Numerous narrow, cobbled alleys splintered off the main streets, all of which were lined with shops selling Greek folk art.

Jake wandered, returning to his hotel several times in hopes of finding a message about Cassandra. He had earlier paid a visit to the police station and informed them that he was looking for Cassandra Kanaris, who had mysteriously disappeared. They evinced little interest but finally produced a man who could speak perfect English, a tall, swarthy man with a cold, formal face.

"I am George Pangalos," he said distantly. "What is your problem, Mr. Randle?"

Briefly, Jake told him about Cassandra.

Pangalos informed him that nothing could be done unless she was officially reported missing; and Jake received a rather dubious look when he said that she *was* officially missing as far as he was concerned. But when Pangalos pressed him for details, Jake had to back off; he didn't feel free to yet make Cassandra the target of an all-out search. So far as he knew she was in no actual danger; it was his bone-deep conviction that she was, yet he had no proof to offer. In the end Pangalos promised to contact Jake at his hotel should they have any word of Cassandra.

Jake finally called Marcus Bruno. When he had told the Italian what little he knew, Bruno said, "You have my sympathy, my friend, but the police there are correct. Tourists are a strange breed, Jake. It is not unusual for them to leave tour groups, sometimes even their companions or relatives, and wander off on their own. The police are accustomed to this and have learned it is best not to take action unless there is some evidence of foul play. Otherwise, it can be embarrassing for all concerned."

"But we do know what this Macomber did to me in Genoa," Jake said.

"True, but that was to you, not to the *signorina*. As for his earlier attempts on both your lives, we have only your word for that. Not that I disbelieve you, my friend, but then I know you."

"I know you're right," Jake said with a sigh. "But it is damned frustrating."

"I am well aware, Jake. I would suggest this . . . If you discover any lead to her whereabouts and need the cooperation of the local police, please call me at once. I, in turn, will contact the police in Rhodes Town and exert what influence and persuasive powers that I may possess in your behalf."

"All right, Marcus. And thanks."

"*Arrivederci*, my friend."

At noon on his second day on Rhodes, Jake returned to his hotel and found the lead he'd been hoping for. The moment he entered his room he spotted the lavender envelope on the bed. He snatched it up and opened it with trembling fingers: "Mr. Randle: You will find Cassandra on board the *Olympus*, anchored in the bay off Lindos. A friend."

The handwriting was the same as that of the other lavender notes Cassandra had received. Jake stood a moment in thought, pinching his lips between thumb and forefinger. Once again, there appeared to be two factions involved in Cassandra's life, one friendly, the other hostile. And both sides apparently had unlimited resources at their command; either that or they were omniscient. One or the other always seemed to know either his or Cassandra's whereabouts.

But his paramount emotion at this moment was optimism. At least Cassandra was still alive! He had never been involved in a case with so many frustrating dead ends. Another day or so of this inactivity and frustration, and they would probably have had to lock him away in a rubber room. Now he could move!

He picked up the phone and waited impatiently while his

connection was made to Genoa. To his disappointment Marcus Bruno wasn't in his office. Jake left a message: "Tell him it's Jake Randle, and that it's urgent that he call me as soon as possible. He has the number of my hotel. I'll wait right here at the phone."

He slammed down the receiver, and said aloud, "Damn the luck!"

He paced the room, considering his options. He could go to the local police with the lavender note, but he doubted very much that they would act on his say-so. He could go to Lindos on his own and try to bull his way onto the yacht, demanding to see Cassandra, but that would be doing it the hard way, and just might result in putting both their heads on the block. The third alternative was to wait for Bruno to call back. That, of course, meant letting time pass, and God only knew what danger Cassandra was in at this very moment.

More than an hour went by before Bruno called back, and Jake was just about at the end of his patience. He quickly read the note to the detective. The Italian was silent for a moment.

"Well?" Jake demanded. "I'd think that would be enough to get the cops here off their asses."

"I suppose you are right, my friend."

"You don't sound too sure. For God's sake, man, it's plain, to me at least, that Cassandra is in danger."

"Yes, that seems clear enough. Yet it is equally clear that this Marshall Paris is a man of both wealth and influence."

"What the hell does that have to do with it?"

"My friend," Bruno said in a chiding voice. "Surely I don't have to tell you. Is it not the same way in your country? As a policeman, did you not have to tread gingerly around people of wealth and influence?"

"That's true, in fact that's exactly what forced me out of the department. But that doesn't change the fact that Cass's life is in danger. If the police won't act, I'll see what I can do on my own."

"No, no, Jake, that would be most foolish. I shall see what I can do with a telephone call to the local police. You remain close to your telephone. I will call you back within the hour."

Bruno was as good as his word; the phone rang forty minutes later. Jake snatched it up on the first ring.

Bruno was brisk now. "I have mostly good news, my friend. Through my pleading your case, an agreement has been reached to board the *Olympus* in a search for the *signorina*."

"Thank God!" Jake breathed. "And thank you, Marcus."

"It was not easy to accomplish. This man Paris is well-known in Rhodes and is well-thought of, mostly because he contributes a great deal of money to the economy there. But I convinced them that he is a possible suspect in my murder investigation. A slight extension of the truth, but it served. That and the fact that Paris is an American by birth. If he had been Greek, I doubt that I would have prevailed. Now." Bruno paused to take a breath. "The police will go by helicopter to Lindos. A car will pick you up at your hotel shortly and take you to the airport to board the helicopter . . ."

Jake interrupted, "At least they agreed that I could go along."

"That may not be all to the good. I was told that if the *signorina* is not on board the yacht, *Signor* Paris will undoubtedly be furious. So you will be, what do you call it? The scapegoat. If this is a fiasco, my friend, you will quite likely be in for a bad time."

"That will be nothing new. I can take it."

Bruno said wistfully, "I desire that I could be there, my friend. It should be most interesting. Ah, well, what is not to be, cannot be. I wish you good luck, Jake, and please keep me informed."

The car arrived within fifteen minutes, but Jake wasn't too happy to see that George Pangalos was one of the three policemen in the car.

When Jake got into the backseat with him, Pangalos frowned in stern disapproval. "If you had informed me that Ms. Kanaris was involved in a murder investigation, I would have given more credence to your story."

"I couldn't do that, not without Bruno's official sanction," Jake said. "Besides, Cassandra is not *involved*, in that sense. She just happened to be on the scene."

"Well, I do hope, for your sake, Mr. Randle, that this isn't a wild goose chase. Marshall Paris is an important man hereabouts, and I can't feature him being involved in the disappearance of an American citizen. If your girlfriend isn't on board his yacht or is there on her own accord, in no danger, we will not be happy."

"Yes, I've already been told that by Bruno," Jake said heavily. "All I know is that Cassandra told people on the *Star* that she was boarding his yacht, and she is in danger, although she may not be aware of it."

"In danger from Marshall Paris?" Pangalos said dubiously. "I can scarcely credit that. Good heavens, for what reason? I have once attended a cocktail party on board the *Olympus* and met Mr. Paris. He is a handsome man and a womanizer of some repute." He sneered. "If *that* is the danger you're referring to, I very much doubt that Ms. Kanaris would seriously object. So, if you're a jealous lover in pursuit of his lady love, I seriously suggest that you call this off before it goes any further, Mr. Randle."

"I love Cassandra; I won't deny that. But my motive is concern for her welfare, not jealousy."

"Very well, Mr. Randle." Pangalos shrugged. "We will proceed. The consequences are on your head. If nothing comes of this, I will not be responsible."

At the airport the helicopter was waiting for them. Jake and the three policemen boarded, and the helicopter lifted off, blades whirring angrily. Pangalos introduced Jake to the other two policemen, none of whom had any command of English; but their attitude was definitely unfriendly.

Jake gazed down at Rhodes Town, sparkling in the bright sunlight. It was a colorful sight, he had to admit, the many spires and minarets like fingers pointing to the heavens, the beaches dotted with umbrellas of almost every possible color, the waters along the coast swarming with boats of every size and description. Sailboats, sails filled with wind, skimmed along the water like low-flying gulls.

The aircraft flew along the coast, and when they were beyond the city limits, Jake could see olive orchards and pastures of grazing sheep. Always off to his left was the azure sea.

The flight didn't take long. Pangalos nudged him, then pointed up ahead. "Lindos," he said.

Jake followed his pointing finger, and he could see the bulk of the hill rising above the town. Squinting against the bright sun, he could see the Doric columns of the ruined Acropolis. And below the town lay the sandy crescent of the beach with the bay spreading out between two spits of land. Jake pressed his forehead against the side of the bubble, trying to spot the *Olympus* amongst the dozens of boats anchored in the bay. He saw one boat that had to be the yacht, dwarfing all the other craft, a brilliant white in color.

He said to Pangalos, "Is that the yacht?"

Pangalos leaned across him to peer out, then nodded. "Yes, that's it, Mr. Randle."

Jake felt an immense relief. At least it was still here; a fear had lurked in him that it would be gone. Now if only Cassandra was there and safe.

The helicopter set down on a landing pad up from the beach, and they all quickly climbed out. They headed for the beach and the small pier, where a couple of motorboats were tied up.

Pangalos led the way out onto the pier, and Jake saw that

one of the boats was a harbor patrol boat. Pangalos said, "I called ahead to have a patrol boat waiting for us."

After they were on board, the man at the controls fired up a noisy engine, and they were underway, plowing through the placid waters of the bay, sending up a fine spray. As they neared the *Olympus*, Jake could see a group of people at the rail. There were at least three women, but strain his eyes as he might, he couldn't see Cassandra.

The boatman maneuvered the craft alongside the yacht and cut the engine. A tall, good-looking man leaned over the rail, and called down, "To what do I owe the honor?"

In a low voice Pangalos said, "That's Marshall Paris." He raised his voice. "Mr. Paris, I'm George Pangalos, of the Rhodes police. Do you remember me?"

Paris nodded. "Yes, I remember you. Am I to understand that this is an official visit?"

"I'm afraid so, Mr. Paris. Do you know one Cassandra Kanaris?"

"Yes, I know Cassandra," Paris said tersely.

"This is Jake Randle." Pangalos propelled Jake forward. "It seems that Ms. Kanaris quit her job on the cruise ship, and it is Mr. Randle's contention that she is on board your yacht. Is this true?"

"It's true as far as it goes. She *was* with us, yes."

Jake spoke up. "Was? What does that mean?"

Paris said, "It means that she suddenly decided to leave us last night."

"Do you know where she went?" Pangalos asked.

"I'm afraid that I haven't the least idea. She just suddenly decided to go off on her own, exploring Rhodes. I tried to persuade her otherwise, but I wasn't successful."

"I don't believe him for a minute," Jake said to Pangalos in a low voice.

Pangalos looked at him dubiously. "You insist on pushing this then?"

"I insist," Jake said stubbornly. "For Christ's sake, man,

we can't just take this guy's word for it. We came here prepared to search his yacht. Let's do it!"

Pangalos sighed and turned back to the man on the yacht. "I'm afraid that Mr. Randle will not be satisfied without a thorough search of your vessel, Mr. Paris."

Paris said harshly, "Well now, I don't know about that. It seems to me that I'm being accused of something here, and I don't know if I like my yacht being subjected to a police search . . ."

Jake saw one of the other men at the railing lay a hand on Paris's shoulder and lead him aside from the others, where they conversed in low tones.

Pangalos said worriedly, "Mr. Randle, I'm not sure about the wisdom of going through with this."

"We're going through with it," Jake said. "If he's telling the truth, what does he have to worry about? If he's lying, which I happen to think he is . . ."

He was interrupted by Paris, who had stepped to the rail again. "All right, come on aboard, and search to your heart's content."

Pangalos spoke a few words in Greek to the other officers, and they started at once up the yacht's ladder, with Jake and Pangalos right behind them.

As Jake stepped on board, Paris said, "I'm not overly delighted about this, Officer Pangalos, and you may be sure that I will lodge a protest with your superiors. Come along." He motioned for them to follow him. "I'll show you the cabin Cassandra was using."

As they followed his lead Jake glanced sidelong at the man who had conferred with Paris and found that the man was staring at him. His face was totally without expression, but his cold gaze was unsettling, and Jake could sense a tide of animosity flowing from him.

In the cabin that Paris said had been Cassandra's, the three policemen quickly and efficiently searched. There was no sign of Cassandra, no indication that she had ever been there.

"There, you see?" Paris said with a self-satisfied smile. "Like I told you, Cassandra packed her things and left last night."

Pangalos looked inquiringly at Jake, who said, "Dammit, man, I didn't expect her to be in this cabin, but we have to search the whole ship to be certain she isn't on board."

As he spoke Jake was staring directly at Paris. The too-handsome features showed extreme displeasure, but Paris sighed and said, "You're free to search every nook and cranny, but I warn you it's a waste of time."

Two hours later, a discouraged and despondent Jake stood at the head of the ladder with the policemen and Marshall Paris. One of the policemen glared at Jake and spat angry words at Pangalos in Greek. Pangalos nodded wearily and motioned for them to board the motorboat. To Paris he said, "You have my apologies for the trouble we've caused, Mr. Paris."

"The trouble I don't mind all that much," Paris said with a show of indignation. "But this search was uncalled for, humiliating in the extreme, and cast suspicions on my good name. I promise you that I shall lodge a strong protest with your superior, sir!"

Jake, watching him closely, had the strong feeling that Paris concealed a gloating triumph; Paris might not have Cassandra on board his yacht—that was apparent, unless there was some secret compartment they had missed in their search—but he knew much more than he was telling.

Pangalos was urging Jake on ahead of him. Then, at the top of the ladder, Pangalos detained him for a moment. "You realize, of course, that all of us are upset as hell with you, causing all this trouble for nothing."

He nodded down at the motorboat, and Jake, noticing the angry glares of the officers now in the boat, knew that

Pangalos was right. From the looks on their faces, they would be happy to dump Jake overboard on the way in.

"You can't say I didn't warn you," Pangalos announced smugly. "And if Paris complains to our superiors, I wouldn't be at all surprised if you're asked to leave Rhodes, Randle."

No longer *Mister* Randle, Jake noted. But he had little time to worry about his own plight; his thoughts were on Cassandra. Where *was* she? Was Paris telling the truth—was she out there somewhere on the island, wandering around in search of her father?

Or was she dead? Had Paris and his cohorts killed her and gotten rid of her body and all her belongings? He thought of his own imprisonment; they were obviously ruthless, whatever their reasons.

The thought chilled him, and he turned around to gaze along the deck. The tall man with the dead face stood alone now, staring at him with venomous eyes.

"Come on, Randle," Pangalos called up from the motorboat. "Get on board, or we may just leave you behind."

Zeus paced the salon angrily. "Incompetence, that's all I find in my people. Utter incompetence."

Paris said, "Who was it thought to get rid of her clothes and such? I did, and if I hadn't, we would have been in trouble should that search party have found them today."

Zeus rounded on him. "But you let her get away, just like Ares let Randle escape his clutches. You should have locked her in her cabin!"

"Zeus . . ." Paris shrugged. "If I had done that, she most certainly would have been suspicious. Besides, I had no idea that she was going to take off like that."

His rage subsiding slightly, Zeus asked, "Have any of the men you sent after her reported back yet?"

"Two have. Nothing. They found no trace of her. The others haven't returned yet." He added hopefully, "Perhaps she drowned in the bay. It's a long swim to the beach."

"That is possible." Zeus nodded. "If such is the case, her body should show up sooner or later."

"Look at it this way, Zeus," Artemis said brightly. "If she hadn't taken off last night, she would have been here when they searched. Then where would we be?"

He scowled at her. "If she had been on board, I wouldn't have advised Apollo to let them search. I very much doubt they would have pushed it if we had refused. They are not anxious to tread the toes of important people."

"Anyway, it's only a minor setback," Paris said. "She knows no one on the island, she doesn't speak the language, and she knows we'll come looking for her. How can she find Jason all by herself?"

"Did it ever occur to you that she might have some help?"

"Help?" Paris stared. "You mean some of Hera's people?"

"Who else? Every since the schism between us, that damned woman has tried to thwart me in every way she can. We know she is the one who involved the girl in this in the first place. But for her, Cassandra would never have known about Jason. And if one of Hera's people finds the girl first, they can lead her directly to Jason."

Paris said agitatedly, "Then we must find her first."

"That may not be so easy, now that she has a head start. I want all of your crew members on the hunt, as well as everyone of us here on the yacht." Zeus looked at Artemis. "You're supposed to be the huntress, Artemis, so suppose you bend all your resources to it. We are now definitely at risk. You failed me once. Do not fail me again!"

Seventeen

By the time Cassandra was halfway to the shore, she was exhausted. Lindos was much farther from the yacht than it had appeared. Her arms and legs were numb, and despite the warm night and the physical effort of swimming, she was chilled through. The cumbersome plastic bag didn't make swimming any easier, of course; she had thought of dumping it and would have except for the fact that it contained her purse. It would be bad enough going ashore—if she made it—in nothing but a swim suit, but without money and papers she would be virtually helpless.

For a time she turned on her back and floated, but she didn't dare rest too long. Turning back on her stomach, she began to swim again. The scattering of lights on the shore seemed no closer.

She fixed her gaze on one light brighter than the others, partway up the hill, and swam toward it. It must be a pole light illuminating the small plaza she had been in yesterday. Yesterday! It seemed an eternity ago. So much had happened in the hours since. If she had followed her instincts when she caught Alex Chato spying on her in the shop and slipped away in town, instead of returning to the yacht . . .

Suddenly a cramp seized her calf. The pain was excruciating and caused her to double up instinctively. She went under, tumbling down. She tried to straighten the leg, which only made the agony worse, and she continued to sink. Caught unawares as she had been, she hadn't taken a breath when she went under, and already her lungs were laboring for oxygen.

Fighting back panic, she reached for the rigid muscle and kneaded it fiercely. Just when she thought her lungs would burst, the muscle relaxed, and she struck out for the surface, exploding out of the water, gulping for air, and almost went under again. She managed to turn onto her back and floated for a few minutes. Gradually, her panic subsided, and she cautiously tensed the muscles of the leg. It appeared to be normal again.

Taking firm hold of her bundle, she started swimming again, raising her gaze to fix it on the bright light. She couldn't find it! Panic threatened her again—there were *no* lights in front of her!

Then the roar of a motor suddenly broke the stillness of the night, and a bright searchlight swept over the water off to her left. She realized, almost too late, that she had become disoriented and was swimming back *toward* the *Olympus*. And a second, more horrible realization struck: they had discovered she was missing and were searching for her!

If she needed any further verification that she was in danger from the people on the yacht, this was it. Now she noticed that the searchlight beam was moving inexorably in her direction. She took two deep breaths and went under, staying under as long as she could before surfacing again. When her head broke water, she was relieved to see that the beam had passed on. She turned and began to swim toward the shore, swimming hard, but trying to make as little noise as possible. Every few strokes she risked a glance back over her shoulder. Fear had sent a charge of adrenaline through her, and she forgot her weariness and accompanying discomforts. Once more the beam of light was coming her way, and once again she went under.

When she surfaced a second time, Cassandra realized

that the roar of the motorboat was lessening, and she saw that the boat was heading toward the shore. She redoubled her efforts, changing her direction so that she was angling away from the boat. She was rapidly tiring now, but she drove herself hard, not daring to rest. All at once, her leg started to cramp again, and despite all her efforts she began to sink. Despair gripped her; she was going to drown!

She floundered, fighting to stay afloat, and then her flailing feet struck bottom. She had made it!

She stood up and hurried toward the beach, staggering as the cramping leg threatened to give way under her with every step. She desperately wanted to lie down and rest for a few minutes; but even as she thought this, she heard loud voices from the direction of the pier. One rose over the others: "Spread out and search every foot of the beach!"

Untying the bag from her suit she ran on, staggering and lurching, toward the line of small trees some yards distant. And then she gave a strangled scream as a figure rose up from the shadow of a beach umbrella and came toward her. Cassandra tried to veer aside, and then the figure was upon her, taking her arm in a firm grip.

"Cassandra! Come with me!"

She struggled weakly in his grasp.

The low voice said, "It's all right, Cassandra. I'm a friend. Come! We haven't much time before they spot us. Here, I'll take that."

He took the plastic bag from her, and supporting her with one arm around her waist, he hurried with her toward the trees. It was difficult to run in the soft sand, but eventually they made it to the comparative safety of the trees. Cassandra sagged and would have fallen, but her rescuer supported her.

He whispered urgently into her ear, "No, we can't stop here. We have to get out of the area."

"Who are you?" she gasped.

"I'm a friend, trust me. If they find us now, they'll kill you."

She nodded, not bothering to speak. There was enough moonlight for her to see his face now. Although he was in rough, dark clothing, his face was boyishly handsome, clean-cut, and open. He was quite young, Cassandra thought, probably not much more than twenty. She had never seen him before.

They hurried on, up the slope toward the village. The voices of the searchers grew fainter behind them. Soon, they crossed the little plaza that Cassandra remembered from yesterday. Even at this hour it wasn't totally deserted, and a *taverna*, facing on the plaza, was open, with the sounds of music and loud laughter pouring out.

The man by her side slowed now, holding them down to a walk. He put his arm around her shoulders, his face close to hers, breath warm on her cheek. "We are lovers, out for a midnight stroll," he muttered.

Walking slowly, they traversed the narrow, shop-lined street. Without warning, her escort turned them into a narrow alleyway between two buildings. It was dark here, and he had to guide them by touching the walls; there was barely enough room between the buildings for them to walk abreast. Cassandra ached with fatigue, but at least the cramp had relaxed, so that she could walk normally.

They came to a covered, outside staircase, wide enough for only one person at a time. He propelled her on ahead. "You go first, Cassandra. And be careful, don't stumble in the dark. I don't want to risk a light, it's too dangerous. It's only one flight."

Cassandra went up the stairs, feeling her way one step at a time. She was sorely puzzled. How did the man know her name? More importantly, how had he known where, and when, she would be coming ashore? It would be more than stretching coincidence to assume that he had been there accidentally, just as she came up out of the sea!

Her groping hands encountered a door, and she halted. Her rescuer spoke behind her, "It's locked, Cassandra."

She stood back as he squeezed past her to insert the key. He stepped inside, holding the door open, then closed and bolted it without turning on a light. "Just stand there for a moment while I draw the blinds."

She stood, beginning to shiver again. The swim suit was cold and clammy against her skin. She could hear the man moving about the room, and the clicking of blinds being closed.

Then a light blossomed. She was in a small apartment. The furnishings were simple, functional, giving no clue as to the apartment's inhabitants. Her glance went at once to the man in dark clothing, who stood smiling at her.

Cassandra tried to make her voice firm through chattering teeth. "Now. I do appreciate your being down there to help me, but you're an utter stranger to me. Who are you and how did you come to be there?"

"All in good time, Cassandra, I promise," he said gently. "But first I think you'd better get out of that wet suit and have a hot shower. There's a bathroom back there." He indicated an open door with a jerk of his head. He held out the plastic bag. "I assume you have a change of clothes in here?"

"Yes, but I want to know . . ." She broke off as a chill seized her, setting her teeth to chattering again.

He took her arm. "First things first. Out of that suit. That's an order, Cassandra." He started her toward the open door.

Without further argument she took the bag and went down the hall. The bathroom was at the end of the short corridor, and as she went down the passage, she noticed a small kitchen on her right, a bedroom on her left. The bathroom had no tub, only a shower stall, but there was ample hot water, she discovered.

She remained under the steaming water for a long time,

until it had driven the chill from her bones. Using a rough towel, she rubbed her skin until it was pink. Fortunately, the plastic bag had kept her clothes dry, and she quickly changed into them.

Dressed in lavender pants and a blouse, she started back to the front room, then stopped just short of the door, as she heard his low voice. Evidently, he was talking on the phone.

She heard only a few words: "All right. I'll do what I can, but don't expect too much," followed by the sound of the receiver being replaced.

She went on into the room. He was sitting by the phone on the end of the long couch, two tumblers of liquid on the coffee table before him. He smiled at her, getting to his feet. "Feel a little better now?"

"Yes, I do feel much better, thank you."

He indicated the end of the couch. "Please sit down." He sat down with her and handed her one of the glasses. "Brandy. I thought you might need it."

She took a sip of the brandy. It warmed her all the way down. She closed her eyes, letting the warmth seep through her; it also relaxed much of her tension. In a moment she opened her eyes and found his gaze on her. He had thick blond hair and gray eyes. His face was grave, and Cassandra realized that he was a bit older than she had first surmised, probably about twenty-five. It was his boyish smile that made him appear younger, she concluded.

"Now," she said, "you promised to tell me who you are and how you came to be on the beach when I . . ."

He smiled quickly. "Like Venus rising out of the sea." Then he sighed. "I did promise, didn't I? Well, my name is Troy Brooke."

"You're British, aren't you? The accent isn't all that pronounced, but it's there."

"I was born in London, yes, but I haven't resided there for some years. I've lived in your United States, Cassandra, among other places. I've been on Rhodes for over a year now. I really consider myself a sort of a citizen of the world."

"I seem to be running into a lot of those lately," she muttered to herself.

"I beg your pardon?"

"Never mind." She gestured. "Now I know your name, Troy, but not the bottom line . . . How did you know *my* name?"

"Cassandra . . ." His glance slid away. "There are some things I'm not free to tell you, not just yet. Let's just say that . . . uh, certain people have been keeping a watch over you."

She stared at him, feeling a measure of anger. "Why? Why have certain people been keeping a watch on me?"

He motioned helplessly. "That's one of the things I'm not at liberty to reveal to you. In time it will all become clear. Believe me, it's best you not know just yet."

She shook her head in bafflement. "At least you can tell me this . . . You, or rather your people, aren't the ones who have been trying to kill me? The ones who are after me now?"

He smiled quickly. "The answer to that should be fairly obvious. I helped you tonight, didn't I?"

"On the surface, it would seem so, but how do I *know*? This could all be just a ruse to keep me off guard. You could be working for *them*, for all I know. After all, I've never met you before tonight."

"I know it's a lot to ask, Cassandra, but you're just going to have to trust me."

"That is asking a lot, but I guess I have no choice," she said slowly. "But after what's been happening to me since I left the States, I don't know if it's smart to trust anybody."

He was nodding. "I fully appreciate that, but I do have my orders."

"Orders from *whom*? I know, I know—you can't tell me."

She turned away from him, taking another sip of brandy while she tried to get her anger under control. She had the feeling that she was trapped in a maddening maze, and now that she had found a door, a door opening to some of the answers, it was, in effect, slammed shut in her face.

She got to her feet and began pacing the small room. She took another sip from the brandy glass and whirled on him. "But why? These others, the ones you claim are not your people, why are they trying to kill me? Why are Marshall Paris and this other man, Alex Chato, after me?"

Again, he looked away, and said miserably, "I can't tell you that, either, Cassandra. Just trust me, please."

"Dammit!" she cried wildly. "How can I trust a total stranger, someone who knows at least some of the answers I want, but won't give them to me?"

"I can't. There are certain rules . . ." He bit the words off abruptly.

"Rules? *Rules!* Is this some kind of a game? If it is, I don't want to play anymore."

He was silent, looking away from her.

"Can you tell me this much, do you know Jason Kanaris?"

He hesitated, finally turning to her again. "I suppose I can tell you that much. I don't know him personally, but I know of him."

She dropped down onto the couch, leaning toward him eagerly. "Is he alive?"

"As far as I know, yes."

"As far as you know? I've been given to understand that he's my father, a father I've never even met, a father I thought was dead before I was born. *Is* he my father? Can you tell me that much?" She took his hand in a painful grip. "Troy, I have to know, can't you see? Is he my father? I'm going crazy not knowing!"

"It is my understanding that Jason is your father, yes."

"But where has he been all these years?"

"That's another question I'm unable to answer right now."

Unheeding, she rushed on, "And why hasn't he been in touch with me?" When he didn't answer, she glared at him. "Does he even know that he has a daughter?"

"That I can't answer because I honestly don't know."

"Is he here on Rhodes?"

He hesitated again. "I believe so, but I can't say for sure."

"You have to take me to see him, Troy." She clutched at his hand again. "I beg of you!"

"That's not my decision to make. I do know that it was our intention to have the two of you reunited, but I don't know if the time is right. I'll have to check that out."

"Don't know if the time is right?" She shook her head to clear it. "What does the time have to do with it?"

He placed his other hand over hers, and said gently, "Like I said, it's not my decision to make. In any case, we don't dare leave this place until the hunt for you has lost some of its momentum. I'll check with . . . I'll check in the morning. Now I think you should rest, you must be exhausted."

"It's why I came here, you see, to find my father," she said intensely.

"Yes, Cassandra, I'm aware of that."

"Do you know what it's like to believe all your life that a father you never knew is dead and then be suddenly given the hope that he may be alive after all?" She freed her hand and stared blindly at the wall. "You're torn by two emotions. First, you long to see him, and then you have moments when you actively hate him. Why has he never made himself known to you?" She gave a bitter laugh. "You say to yourself, 'Maybe he doesn't *want* to make himself known to you, kiddo.'" To her dismay Cassandra felt hot tears flood her eyes.

"Ah, Cassandra, don't! Don't cry."

He took her into his arms and cradled her head on his shoulder. Cassandra stiffened for just a moment, then let herself go, weeping brokenheartedly. The tears gave her a long-needed release. She had not cried from the moment she had read the first lavender note, but now that she had had it confirmed that Jason Kanaris was her father, now that she was so close to him, the tears were a catharsis. She cried for a long time, and Troy stroked her hair and made comforting noises.

Finally, she sat back, dashing the tears from her eyes, flustered at breaking down in the arms of a stranger. "I'm sorry," she said, gulping back a final sob. "I'm not a weeper, not usually, but so much has happened."

"It's all right," he said gently, his eyes warm and caring. "Crying is probably good for you. Both my parents died when I was still quite young. I cried then, and I would probably cry now if I learned that, through some minor miracle, either my father or mother were still alive." He wiped the last tears from her cheeks. "I can promise you this much . . . You'll see Jason soon. But arrangements have to be made first, and I have to know that it's safe to take you to him."

"Arrangements," she echoed dully. "I have no idea what you're talking about, and I'm sure it'll do no good to ask." She saw him now through a daze of weariness, and she slumped back against the couch.

"Cassandra, you must get some rest now. You take the bedroom, I'll sleep here on the couch."

"All right," she said submissively, and as Troy got to his feet, extending a hand down to her, she said, "Tell me one thing, Troy. Did you write those notes to me?"

He smiled down at her. "Not me personally, but one of us did."

"That makes me feel a little better. I felt a certain violation at those notes popping up on my pillow, but I finally came to see that the writer wished me no harm. So I can assume that you don't, either."

She let him help her up, and they went down the hall to the small bedroom. Turning on the light, he said, "If you need anything in the night, I'll be in the front room." Then he left her.

Cassandra got undressed tiredly, depleted emotionally and physically. She got into the nightgown she had thrown into the plastic bag and got under the covers. She switched off the light by the bed and then saw that the door had been left open a few inches, letting light in. She was too weary to make the effort to close it. Just then she heard Troy coming back from the bathroom.

She called out, "Troy?"

"Yes, Cassandra?" He poked his head in the door.

"Tell me something, are you wealthy?"

"That's a rather strange question, but I suppose you could say that I am, yes. My parents left me a great deal of money."

"That figures," she murmured.

"I'm sorry, what did you say?"

But she was already asleep, her face becoming young and vulnerable in slumber. Troy gazed at her pensively for a time, then sighed and turned away, closing the door.

"No, Hermes, I cannot permit it, not yet . . . I feel compassion for the girl, too, but it cannot be until things are ready," Hera said into the phone. "Do whatever you have to do, but keep her in that apartment until I tell you it is time to move."

Hera hung up the phone and faced the man and woman in the hotel suite with her.

Aphrodite said, "I gather that Cassandra has fled Apollo's yacht?"

"Yes, she jumped into the water and swam for the beach," Hera said with a smile. "She has spunk, I must say."

"Foolish, headstrong girl," Aphrodite said in exasperation. "Poseidon and I warned her, but she wouldn't listen."

"No more headstrong than you were at that age, my dear." Seated beside her, Poseidon patted her hand fondly.

He directed his gaze at Hera. "But she is all right, I gather?"

"She is safe for the moment. Hermes was there when she came out of the water, and he has her hidden in an apartment over the shop in Lindos he owns. He said that Zeus' minions are in full cry after her. I told him not to expose Cassandra until Zeus decides that she is no longer in Lindos and moves the hunt to somewhere else."

Aphrodite said shrewdly, "I gather from your end of the conversation that she is demanding to see Jason?"

"Yes, but it is not yet time."

"It has to happen sooner or later, Hera. After all, that's the reason we got her over here."

Hera was nodding. "That's true, but it's too much of a risk at the moment, with Zeus trying so hard to stop her. I must say that I never conceived he would go to such lengths. We know now that he will kill to stop her; he will kill Cassandra or anyone who helps her. If that happens, all our efforts will be for nothing."

"The poor girl must be beside herself, not knowing what is behind all this," Aphrodite said. "I feel sorry for her."

Hera said tartly, "But you'd feel even sorrier should she be killed."

"Yes, of course I would."

Poseidon said, "How about Jake Randle? We told him that Cassandra was on the yacht. Do we tell him where she is now?"

"I've been thinking about that, but I'm afraid we can't risk it."

"He must be frantic, thinking that she must be dead."

"He will have to endure. You can be sure that Zeus will be keeping a close watch on Randle, now that he brought in the police to search the *Olympus*. If we tell Randle where Cassandra is, he will immediately rush to her side, thereby leading Zeus right to her. No, we have no choice but to leave him in the dark for the time being. This may all be academic anyway. It's quite possible that Mr. Randle may be forced to leave Rhodes. The police aren't at all happy with the trouble he caused them, especially when they found no evidence that Cassandra had come to any harm."

Aphrodite said, "Can't we help him in some way?"

Hera shook her head. "No, he is on his own. We have enough to do protecting Cassandra. Mr. Randle did not figure in our plans originally, and he is more of a distraction than anything else."

"But he saved Cassandra's life," Aphrodite said stubbornly, "and they are in love."

"Aphrodite, matchmaking is not what concerns us here. Leave Mr. Randle to his own devices."

Jake was still on Rhodes, but he was there on sufferance. Pangalos had told him: "You cause any more trouble, Randle, and you're gone."

"I'm an American citizen and I've broken no laws."

"That's the reason you weren't on the first plane out. But you've made a nuisance of yourself, as far as the police are concerned. You're an ex-policeman, you know how easy it is to find some law you've broken, any excuse will do. Cause us any more trouble, and we'll find something to charge you with."

"Goddamnit!" Jake exploded. "Why can't I make anybody understand that there is a woman in danger? She may already be dead."

"Now you're accusing Marshall Paris of murder?" Pangalos said incredulously. "Now that's exactly the kind of thinking that's going to get you ejected from Greece."

"But she's missing, you can't deny that."

"She's missing two days. Tourists come here all the time and backpack across the island, even sleep on the beach, in good weather, for a week, two weeks, even more, and nobody thinks they've been murdered."

"There have been other attempts on her life."

"So *you* say."

"Ask the Italian detective, Bruno."

"I have, and all he knows for sure is what you've told him. *You*, Randle, no one else. Not even Ms. Kanaris told him that her life was ever threatened."

"There is a reason for that . . ."

Pangalos cut him off with a gesture. "I don't want to hear about it. As far as I'm concerned, you're a lovesick guy who's burned up because his girl took off with another man."

Jake's anger had threatened to get out of control at that remark, and he had stalked out of Pangalos's presence before he took a poke at him.

At the hotel he put in a call to Bruno, who wasn't a great deal of help. "I share your concern for *Signorina* Kanaris, Jake, but I do think that Pangalos is correct. This Paris and his friends would scarcely dare kill her on such a conspicuous place as a yacht."

Jake said, "I'm not all that sure. The thing that has struck me all along is the arrogance of these people. They act as if laws do not apply to them. And if Cassandra is still alive, where is she?"

"Well, she admittedly came to Rhodes in search of her father, so perhaps that is what she is about now."

"Then why did she leave Paris's boat, when she intended to stay on it for some time?"

"There is one thing that occurs to me," Bruno said with a chuckle. "What if this Paris tried to get amorous, and she was not interested. Wouldn't that be sufficient reason for her to leave his yacht?"

Jake felt a flare of hope. He said slowly, "You know, I never thought of that. You could be right, and if you are, I should be able to find her. Rhodes isn't all that big."

"I wish you luck, my friend. Keep me informed."

Jake made another telephone call, this time to his friend,

Rene, in Paris. He gave him the name of Marshall Paris and asked for a rundown on him.

Rene said, "For someone supposedly on a vacation, Jake, you're certainly busy."

"Yes, I got myself involved in some deep shit, Rene," Jake said ruefully. Briefly, he sketched in something of what had taken place.

At the end of it Rene gave a low whistle. "You are in deep *merde*, Jake. I'll see what I can find out about this Paris for you. I did some more checking on the other two names. I still came up with a blank on Ian Macomber, but I did run across a rumor that Jason Kanaris is alive and living on Rhodes."

Jake was instantly alert. "Any smell of an address?"

"Not a whiff; I'm sorry. He's still very much the man of mystery, I'm afraid, and I must caution you that it is only a rumor."

"Well, keep at it, Rene, and I want you to know that I do appreciate your help very much."

Jake rented a car and spent the rest of the day driving along the streets of Rhodes Town, acquainting himself with the city and constantly scanning the people for some sight of Cassandra. He had not fully realized before just how many women thronged the streets, in all stages of dress and undress, and more than once he received a blatant come-on when the object of his attention noticed that he was staring. There were a good many more women than men on the streets, in the shops, and along the beaches, which of course made his task only that much harder.

Somehow though, he had the feeling that Cassandra wasn't in the city. If she had left the yacht in Lindos, it was doubtful that she would return to Rhodes Town, at least not right away. So, Jake bought a detailed map of the island and studied it that evening over dinner, in a restaurant up the block from his hotel.

Frantic with worry over Cassandra, he had been paying

little attention to what he ate, content with whatever he could pick up at fast-food places, but tonight, about to embark on what could turn out to be an arduous motor trip across the island, he had decided to have a good meal in a Greek restaurant.

Before dinner he had an *ouzo*, that particularly potent drink favored by the Greeks. Following the instructions in his guidebook, Jake added water to the liquor, which caused it to turn cloudy. It had the taste of aniseed; Jake didn't care for it and wished he had stayed with scotch. But gamely, he ordered and drank a second. Then, again following the advice given in his guidebook, Jake went into the kitchen, looking in pots and pans and at the restaurant's offerings of meat courses for the evening, before deciding on his choices. The guidebook stated that this was the custom in Greece, especially for those people not familiar with the language. Jake reflected amusedly that such a request in the United States would likely result in the patron being unceremoniously tossed out. However, here no one seemed to mind, and he was allowed to browse to his heart's content.

He finally decided on prawns, rice pilaf served with a tomato sauce, and a dish of glazed tomatoes; and he had a half bottle of white wine, *retsina*, a wine mixed with resin. It was a favorite with Greeks and, according to the guidebook, was an acquired taste, which Jake, on sampling, decided he would never acquire. Still, he was determined this one night to partake of the food and drink of the country, so he doggedly finished most of the wine.

Aside from the wine, it wasn't a bad meal. It wasn't on a par with a New York steak, but what the hell, he told himself, a man can't have everything. And when in Rome . . .

The next morning, early, he checked out of the hotel, and left in the rented car. He took the road along the coast leading south toward Lindos. The traffic wasn't heavy, a few farm trucks, a sparse flow of cars, and an occasional tour bus.

To Jake's surprise, there were a number of young people walking along the highway in both directions, carrying packs, and he remembered Pangalos's remark about tourists backpacking across the island. Each time he spotted a woman walking in his direction, Jake slowed until he could be sure it wasn't Cassandra.

About halfway to Lindos he became aware that he was being followed.

He'd noticed that a black Renault had been hanging back behind him for most of the way, but he didn't really think anything of it until he stopped a boy and a girl hiking toward Rhodes Town. They were golden blond, healthy, quite young.

Smiling at them, Jake said, "You're both American, right?"

The boy chose to be spokesman, looking at him with truculent suspicion. "You got that right, man. So what's the problem?"

Jake's eyes were on the rearview mirror. The black Renault had stopped also, pulling off the road about fifty yards back. Whoever he is, Jake thought, he isn't trying to keep it a secret that he's following me. Jake wondered if the tail was from the Rhodes police, and then decided that it must be. Well, hell, he thought; let them follow me. Then if I find Cassandra, I'll have a witness that I'm not crazy.

In answer to the boy's question, he said, "No problem, son. I'm looking for a woman, Cassandra Kanaris." He gave a quick description of Cassandra. "Have either of you seen a woman answering to that description?"

The pair exchanged glances, and then the boy's blue eyes regarded Jake with some contempt. "Your old lady, man? She take off on you?"

Jake concealed his annoyance. "I suppose you could say that, yeah."

"Well, sorry, man, we ain't seen her," he replied, then added, "You know my advice to you? Any time a lady leaves, let her. It's not worth the hassle, especially not when there's always another right down the road." He threw a careless arm around the girl's shoulders and hugged her to him. Then he flipped a hand at Jake. "Stay cool, man." And the pair passed on.

Jake sat, his glance going to the mirror again. The Renault was still waiting. Jake could see the outline of one person behind the wheel, but the distance was too far to make out any details. He toyed with the idea of getting out and confronting whoever it was, then decided against it. He was confident that he could lose a tail anytime he wished to do so.

He started the rental car and drove on toward Lindos.

Eighteen

Cassandra awoke to the odor of bacon frying. Bright sunlight poured in through the small window, and she could hear voices on the street below. It wasn't until she heard the clatter of burro hooves on the cobblestones that she realized where she was.

She got out of bed and hurried down the hall to the

bathroom and quickly performed her morning ablutions, then got dressed and made her way into the tiny kitchen.

From the stove Troy greeted her with a smile. "Good morning, Cassandra. How do you like your eggs?"

"Scrambled, if that's not too much trouble."

"No trouble at all," he said cheerfully, and got four eggs out of the carton. "Why don't you sit down? Breakfast will be ready in short order."

She sat down in the breakfast nook. "You like to cook?"

"Not only do I like to cook, but I'm bloody good at it." He flashed a smile back over his shoulder without missing a stroke with the egg whisk.

"You told me you had money, but you don't have any hired help here?"

"For this place? Hardly." He shrugged. "I bought this building, which includes a shop on the ground floor, so that I'd have this apartment to use when I happen to be in Lindos. It's easier than using a hotel, especially since Lindos isn't exactly overflowing with hotels."

He arranged bacon strips on two plates, dished up the scrambled eggs, and set the plates on the table. Then he fetched a plate of toasted English muffins and a jar of marmalade.

"There now! Eat up, Cassandra." He took a seat across from her. "I neglected to ask you last night if you were hungry."

"Not really, there was a party on board the yacht, and I ate from the buffet." She attacked the food hungrily, and they ate in companionable silence for a little. Taking a sip of coffee, she looked at him over her cup. "I've been thinking over the things you told me last night . . ."

He met her eyes. "Yes, Cassandra?"

"You say there are certain things you're not at liberty to tell me yet?"

"That is unfortunately true."

"You did admit last night that 'one of us' wrote the

lavender notes. I got the first one in Los Angeles, as you probably know."

He smiled slightly. "Oh, yes, I know. I didn't write it, but I did deliver it."

"You did?" She sat back, nettled. "Why did you do it?"

He shrugged. "I am sometimes called the messenger."

"You mean, you're like an errand boy, fetch and carry?" she said cruelly, hoping to sting him into an incautious retort.

He merely smiled, unruffled. "You may put it that way, if you like."

"Evidently, the purpose of the notes was to alert me that my father was alive, leading me to him by stages."

"That is my understanding."

"But why a little at a time? Why not all at once, instead of by stages, like some kind of a game?" She leaned forward. "Is that what you meant by 'rules'? Is this some kind of a game, with me an unwitting player?"

He looked startled, and she could sense his withdrawal. She said hastily, "I'm sorry, that's forbidden territory, right? Tell me this then . . . This 'one of us,' is it Eric Johanson or Lisa van Horne? Or more likely, Lisa van Horne, since the writer is a woman?"

"You're very quick, Cassandra," he said with an admiring nod. "I suppose there's no harm in telling you that much, not now. Yes, Lisa wrote the notes."

"But both are, quote, on your side?"

He gave another quick nod, looking down to pick up his coffee cup.

"Both tried to warn me about Marshall," she said thoughtfully. "But I wouldn't listen, and they were right; I did put myself in danger. But why didn't they come right out and say what they meant, instead of throwing broad hints at me?"

"That was as far as they could go at the time."

"The others, Marshall and Alex Chato, they're on the other side? They mean me harm?"

"I should think that would be blatantly obvious by now," he said in a dry voice.

"Nothing's obvious about this whole crazy business. Except . . ." She shivered suddenly. "Marshall's friend, Alexander Chato, he's creepy. I had the feeling that nothing is beneath him, when something stands in the way of what he wants."

Troy nodded soberly. "In that, you're most certainly right, Cassandra. Alex is the very essence of evil, if I may be forgiven the cliché."

She stared at him. "Then, if he's that kind of a person, and people know it, why isn't he in prison, instead of running around loose?"

"Zeus is . . ." Troy broke off, motioning. "Alex Chato is a very rich, very powerful man. In many respects he is above the law."

"I can't believe that." She made an unladylike sound. "I refuse to believe that anyone is above the law, no matter how rich and powerful they are."

He looked at her sadly. "You have a lot to learn then, Cassandra. You're in for a great deal of disillusionment."

"You said something, or started to say something, about . . . What? Zeus, did you say? What does that mean?"

He avoided her glance. "Nothing, just a sort of joke among people who are familiar with Alex." He got to his feet abruptly. "I have to leave you for a bit, Cassandra. I have something to do. Now whatever you do, don't leave this apartment until I get back." He gripped her shoulder. "Don't even open the door to anyone but me. Do you understand?"

She squirmed under his hand; his fingers were digging in cruelly. "Yes, I understand—Troy, you're hurting me!"

"Oh, I'm sorry." He loosened his grip at once. "It's just

that I don't want anything to happen to you now that I've rescued you. I don't think they know that I own this building, but anything is possible. I won't be gone long, Cassandra."

He let himself out the door, and she heard the lock click after him. She sipped at the coffee and found it cold. She emptied her cup, then refilled it with fresh from the pot. Despite her promise to Troy, she was sorely tempted to wait until he was safely gone, and then just leave. She was tired of being manipulated by people. Even if he had come to her rescue, Troy was still manipulating her. Perhaps on orders from someone else, but still . . .

What finally decided her to wait until he returned was his vague promise to take her to Jason Kanaris. Even if Troy was lying about that, he still had told her more about her father than anyone else had.

She picked up the phone and put through a call to Genoa and Marcus Bruno. There should be some word about Jake by now. To her disappointment she was unable to connect with him. When she finally got someone who spoke enough English to understand what she wanted, Cassandra learned that Bruno was off-duty that day and had taken his family out of the city. The man she talked to either knew nothing about Jake or he was lying. When he asked if she wanted to leave a message for Bruno, Cassandra hesitated, then finally said, "No, I'll call back." She dared not leave Troy's number for Bruno to call back.

Next, she tried to put through a call to the *Star*. To her further dismay, she failed again. The ship was passing through a severe storm, and even if she could get through, the reception would be terrible.

She hung up, drumming her fingers on the receiver. Should she call the local police and report what had happened to her? She decided against it; she doubted that anybody would believe her; it was all too incredible.

Even as she was debating this, there were the sounds of

footsteps on the stairs, and she tensed, remembering Troy's warning. Then she relaxed as a key rattled in the lock—it was Troy.

He came in smiling. "She's gone, Cassandra. The *Olympus* is gone!"

"Is that where you went, to check on her? Marshall didn't wait around long, did he?"

"I'm surprised, too, surprised that they'd give up that easily. They must have decided that you didn't linger long in Lindos. After all, as far as they know there's no reason you should. We can leave Lindos now, I would think, at least as soon as we can get ready."

"You don't think it might be a ruse, to lure us into thinking they've given up?"

His face went still in thought, then he shook his head. "No, I don't think they're all that subtle. Oh, they may have left somebody behind just in case, but I'm sure they know that Jason isn't in Lindos, so why should you stay here?"

"Then you *do* know where he is!"

He wagged a finger playfully at her. "Now, I didn't say that, Cassandra. But I do know that he isn't in Lindos."

"Don't make fun of me, Troy!" she said angrily. "This may not be serious to you, but it is to me."

He sobered. "My apologies. I know very well how serious it is to you. But the thing is, you *are* persistent. Now wait." He held up both hands. "Before you say anything else, I have to make a phone call."

She backed off, sitting down across the room from him while he dialed a number. His back to her, he spoke in a low voice, but she could catch a word here and there: ". . . has left the bay . . . wants to see . . . Demands to see him . . . All right, Hera."

Troy hung up and faced around. "Arrangements are underway, but it may take a day or so, or even more, for connections to be made. Are you an outdoors person, Cassandra?"

She stared. "Not really. My idea of an outdoor excursion is a beach picnic, and that's usually spoiled by all the sand. Why do you ask?"

"We're going backpacking, you and I, across the island . . ."

She interrupted him. "Are you out of your mind? Why should I agree to something like that?"

"Because you want to see your father, don't you?"

"Of course I do; but I fail to see the connection."

"I can't take you to Jason for a few days yet, and I think we'd both go crazy cooped up in here for that length of time, not to mention the risk of being discovered."

"How about being discovered walking across the island, bold as brass?"

Troy shook his head. "They would never think you would do something like that. And besides, this time of the year, Rhodes throngs with people backpacking. This is the best way. It's too risky in an automobile; they'll be looking for you to take a car."

"But I have no clothes for camping out."

"That's no problem. We won't be leaving until tomorrow sometime. You give me your sizes, and I'll buy everything you need."

"You, a man, buying my clothes?"

"What's wrong with that?" He was unperturbed. "Buying clothes for women is a part of my business. In addition to the shop downstairs, I own a number of others, scattered across the other islands and the Greek mainland."

"I don't believe it," she muttered. "I finally came across one of you who does something useful, besides count your money."

"What did you say?" He looked at her narrowly. "What does that mean?"

"Everybody I've run into since I left Fort Lauderdale"—she flung out one hand—"on whichever side, seems to have all the money in the world. But so far, you're the first one I've met who seems to *do* anything to earn it."

"I had the money to begin with, Cassandra. I inherited it . . ."

"Just like the others."

". . . but I like to keep busy. Otherwise, I get bored." He lowered his voice. "Maybe if the others . . ."

"If the others what?" she demanded. "They wouldn't get bored and indulge themselves in this mysterious game? Is that what you started to say?"

He gave a rueful sigh. "You don't give up easily, do you? I have no comment. I have promised that your questions will eventually be answered and they will, Cassandra. You have to exercise a little patience."

"Patience isn't one of my virtues."

She remembered, all of a sudden, telling Jake to be patient, not to rush her into committing herself to him, and she felt an ache of longing so intense that it brought tears to her eyes. Jake, where are you, she thought; I want you, I need you!

She shook her head, pushing all thoughts of Jake out of her mind. "If we're going hiking, I'll pick out my own clothes, thank you."

"But I told you, I'd rather you stayed here, out of sight."

"Troy, I'm going crazy, cooped up in here. Besides, if someone is watching, they'll see us when we leave tomorrow, anyway. So why not find out now?" She linked her arm in his. "Come on, let's go shopping!"

They didn't get a particularly early start the next day, but when they did leave, Cassandra felt a little ridiculous. She was wearing heavy hiking boots, pants, and a man's loose shirt, bulky enough to conceal any femininity, and she wore her hair tucked up, her face shaded by a floppy straw hat. "The sun here on Rhodes is fierce, Cassandra," Troy had told her. "You can get burned easily if you're not careful."

Strapped to her back was a pack containing a nylon sleeping bag, a few other camping essentials, and several changes of undergarments.

One thing to the good, she thought, it was very doubtful that anyone would recognize her in the getup.

Troy was attired pretty much the same way; he also had a pack on his back, a bit heavier than hers.

Yet, even disguised as she was, Cassandra felt exposed and naked before the world; she was positive that anyone searching hard enough would spot her. The narrow street was elbow to elbow with people, but they proceeded along it, unchallenged. In a few minutes they were out of the crush, Troy gave her his arm, and they took the road out of town.

Jake, inching along in bumper-to-bumper traffic on the main road into Lindos, was busy looking for a place to park the rented car and was only peripherally aware of the pair in hiking clothes and wearing backpacks. Just as he drew abreast of them he saw a sign indicating parking off to the right, and he turned off the road without sparing a second glance at the pair.

The small lot was crowded, but he finally found a parking place. As he walked out of the lot he paused before turning toward the center of town and glanced back the way he had come. The black Renault was there, pulled off to the side of the road, too far back for Jake to see behind the sun glint off the windshield. He wondered where his tail would park his vehicle, then shrugged the question aside and walked on.

The first thing he did when he entered the plaza was to walk to the guardrail on the bay side and look out over the water. The *Olympus* was gone! Did that mean they had given up on Cassandra? Or did it mean they had upped anchor and left because she was dead?

Since he had no ready answer, he put it out of his mind and turned away, joining the foot traffic on the street, searching the face of every woman he met. Of course, it was an impossible task, and undoubtedly a waste of time; she could be miles away from here. If she was still alive . . . .

He shook his head sharply, angry at himself. He had to stop thinking such thoughts. As for a waste of time, he had nothing else to do with his time.

After a bit he found himself standing before the stable where the burros were kept between trips up the hill to the Acropolis. Should he make the climb? No, Cassandra wouldn't be there. He suddenly remembered something— a trip he had taken to the Grand Canyon. It was on his honeymoon; in fact, the last trip he'd taken before the cruise. Beverly had talked him into taking a mule ride down to the floor of the canyon, a matter of some four hours. Neither one of them had ever been on a mule before, and they learned something. A mule was considered the safest animal on dangerous trails, much safer than a horse, but a mule ride was also about the most grueling possible.

Jake had wondered why people always gathered at the mule pens on the canyon rim about the time the mule train was due; that afternoon he found out. He slid off the mule, and fell to his knees, his legs giving out on him. Fortunately, one of the mule handlers, knowing what to expect, had given Beverly a hand. Both were sore and stiff for days, the insides of their thighs chafed raw and there had been no lovemaking that night.

He laughed aloud. No, he would pass up the burro ride, and he didn't feel like making the steep climb on foot.

A hand tugged at his sleeve. He glanced down, down into the dirty, upturned face of a barefoot, raggedy urchin of about ten. Without speaking, the boy thrust an envelope into Jake's hand and spun away.

Jake took a step after him. "Hey! Wait a minute, dammit!"

The boy was already gone, swallowed up in the crowd.

Jake looked down at the envelope in his hand, unsurprised to see that it was lavender. He stepped to one side, his glance raking the immediate area. Was someone watching him? His tail, for instance? He somehow doubted that the tail had sent the envelope via the boy, but on the other hand, how could anyone else know he was here?

He opened the envelope, took out the fold of lavender paper, and read the single line: "Mr. Randle: Try the apartment over the Helen of Troy Ladies Shoppe. A friend."

Keeping his face as expressionless as possible, just in case he *was* being watched, Jake returned the note to the envelope and put it into his inside coat pocket.

It took him awhile to find this one particular shop among the many, since he didn't want to ask directions, but he eventually located it. He hesitated before going into the shop, and then was glad he did. A small alley went toward the back, between Helen of Troy and the next building.

Jake slipped between the buildings and soon came to the bottom of an enclosed staircase. Casually, he looked behind him, saw no one, and mounted the stairs. At the top he knocked loudly on the door.

"Cassandra! Babe, it's me, Jake."

He heard nothing from inside. He knocked once again and waited, then put an ear to the door panel. There was no sound from inside. He tried the door and found it locked. He looked back down the dim stairwell, took out his card case, removed a credit card, and went to work on the lock, which, luckily, was not a dead bolt. It took him only a minute to open the lock and slip inside. It only took him a few more minutes to go through the small apartment, and his disappointment was bitter when he discovered it was empty; there wasn't even any indication that Cassandra had been there.

Not satisfied, he went through the place again, combing it as carefully as he would have combed a crime scene, and this time he found something that raised his spirits. Under the bed in the one bedroom, he found a lavender scarf. Several times Cassandra had worn scarves of that shade, he recalled; and while there was no guarantee that this one belonged to her, he was reasonably confident it did. It could easily have fallen to the floor and been inadvertently kicked underneath the bed.

He rubbed the scarf back and forth between his fingers. If his surmise was correct, and this was Cassandra's, she was probably still alive!

Stuffing the scarf into his pocket along with the lavender note, Jake went down the short hall and back to the living room, ruminating on his next move. Although he had no basis for such a theory, he had the feeling that even if Cassandra had been here, she wasn't coming back . . .

In the living room he skidded to a stop. Just inside the room, leaning against the closed front door, was Ian Macomber. He had a .38 pointed at Jake's heart. Bruises were black underneath his eyes, and his nose was heavily bandaged.

"Where is she? Where is the girl?"

As the man's lips drew back over his teeth, Jake was pleased to see several missing, and he began to grin.

"Well, Macomber," he said in a taunting voice, "you're not quite so pretty anymore." He took a couple of casual steps toward him.

"You're going to pay for that before we're through," Macomber said through gritted teeth. "But first I want to know where the girl is."

"What girl?" Jake asked innocently. "I don't know who you're talking about." He took another step, wondering just how knowledgeable the man was about guns.

"Don't play stupid with me, Randle! Cassandra Kanaris. I know she's here. I followed you all the way from Rhodes Town."

"There's nobody here. You can see for yourself." Jake

swept a hand around, taking another step. There was now about eight feet separating them. "Search to your heart's content." He grinned lazily. "If Cassandra were here, you'd frighten her to death, looking like that. You'd better have a plastic surgeon work on you."

"Stop right there!" Macomber jabbed the gun out.

Jake stopped, tightening up inside. The man was working himself up into a fine rage, but there was still too much distance between them for Jake to make a move.

Macomber snarled, "It'll go easier for you if you tell me where she is."

"How can that be?" Jake drawled. "You're going to kill me, any way it goes."

"But first I want to see who else is here."

Jake let his eyes flicker evasively. "There's nobody here but us chickens. Would I lie to you?"

"You're in no position to be flip, Randle. Turn around." Macomber motioned with the gun.

Jake turned slowly, holding his breath. Then he felt what he'd been hoping for—the prod of the gun barrel in the small of his back.

Macomber said, "Now together, we're going to search this place."

"It won't take long; it's not that big."

"Just shut up and move!" Macomber prodded him viciously with the gun.

Jake took a half-step and pivoted to his right, at the same time swinging his right arm around and back. He struck the gun barrel an instant before it discharged, the bullet whining harmlessly across the room. Jake grabbed Macomber's gun hand, quickly brought his knee up, and cracked Macomber's wrist across it. Macomber yelped, and the gun flew out of his hand.

Swiftly Jake whipped a left and a right into the man's face, the right connecting with the recently reset nose. Macomber screamed shrilly, and Jake almost felt sorry for him. He hit him again, a hard, fast right and left, and Macomber went down, sprawling across the couch.

Jake stood over him, rubbing the stinging knuckles of his right hand. Macomber didn't move; he was out cold.

"The next time, friend," Jake said to the unconscious man, "you'd better take a few lessons. When you've got a gun on a man, especially with an ex-cop, never stick it in his back. You're just begging to have it taken away from you."

He crossed the room and picked up the gun. He saw that it was a .38 Police Special; it felt like an old friend in his hand. As a private cop, he hardly ever carried a weapon, but he had been wishing for one the last few days. He checked the chamber; just that one bullet had been fired. Sticking the pistol in his belt, he eyed the unconscious man. What should he do with him?

He doubted that a call to the police would do any good. Bruno would certainly like to get his hands on Macomber, but getting the Italian to exert pressure on the local police would eat up valuable time, time better spent looking for Cassandra.

There was an old saying—Never leave a poisonous snake alive to bite another day. Macomber was certainly poisonous enough, but Jake had never shot a man in cold blood, and he couldn't bring himself to do it now. There was no doubt in his mind that Macomber would come after him again and would keep coming after him until it was all over.

"What the hell!" Jake said aloud.

He gave a shrug, turned on his heel, and left the apartment.

Nineteen

Once she got into the rhythm of it, Cassandra found that she enjoyed hiking. She realized that their excursion was mainly a ruse to divert her from insisting on seeing her father right away, but evidently they—whoever "they" were—would get around to it in their own good time. At least she had a link to him, however tenuous, so long as she stayed close to Troy.

They didn't follow the coastline but struck out across country, staying away from the main thoroughfares, using seldom-traveled roads. Before too long they began to climb slightly to a higher elevation. The countryside wasn't wild, yet was not thickly settled. Farther inland, there were few signs of agriculture. The land, dry and rocky, was devoted to the raising of sheep and goats, with an olive orchard or a vineyard here and there.

"I notice there's very little cultivation of crops, Troy. Why is that?"

He gave a shrug. "You must realize that the land here, Cassandra, is very, very old. It is worn out from hundreds of years of use. About all it is good for nowadays is running sheep and goats, and not too good even for that."

"Should I expect to find my father's a sheepherder then? Or a goatherd?"

He laughed. "Jason Kanaris? Hardly, Cassandra."

"Yet here I am, traipsing across the countryside with you, supposedly on the way to seeing my father."

He gave her a look of concern. "Is it all too much for you?"

"Not at all. In fact, I'm rather enjoying it. I went through a lot of trouble to get to Rhodes to find my father—people all along have tried to prevent me from finding him—and here I am enjoying an outing." She faced him directly. "Tell me the truth, Troy. Are we to meet him out here somewhere?"

"No, Cassandra. I have no idea where Jason is at the moment, but I doubt that it's out here." He sighed. "Until arrangements can be made, we thought you'd be much safer out here than in town somewhere."

"Arrangements again. How will you know *when*?"

"Oh, I'll be calling in every day. As a matter of fact, there's a taverna along this road, with a telephone. We'll arrive there near the end of the day. I'll call in from there." He took her hand. "Believe me, Cassandra, a meeting with Jason will be arranged, and soon. Meanwhile, you're safe here, with me. Why don't you just relax and enjoy yourself?"

"That's a little difficult to do, what with all that's happened," she muttered.

They resumed walking. True to his promise, a small village came into view late in the day; a cluster of perhaps a dozen buildings. As they stopped before one with a wooden sign over the front taverna, Troy said, "It's growing late. I'll make my call here, and we'll have dinner, if that's all right with you."

What the hey, kiddo, Cassandra said to herself. Like the man says, relax and enjoy. The way matters stood, she didn't seem to have much choice in the matter. "That sounds good to me, Troy."

He gave her a searching look. "That doesn't sound like you."

She laughed. "I've decided to go with the flow, at least for the time being." All of a sudden, she had a warm feeling toward him, she was beginning to like Troy Brooke.

He returned her smile, took her arm, and they went into the tavern. It was dim inside, redolent of wine and beer and tobacco smoke. There were a half-dozen tables and a short counter. The only people in the place were two old men at a table, smoking pipes, with glasses of wine before them, and a heavy-set man behind the counter-bar, head bald as an egg but with a thick, curling moustache.

In a low voice Troy said, "We've come at a bad time for food. People here eat late lunches, sometimes as late as three o'clock, and dinners aren't customarily served until eight or nine. But maybe I can jolly the fellow behind the bar into serving us something in the way of food."

He ushered Cassandra to a table and she took a seat, while he went over to the bar and engaged the moustachioed man in animated conversation. They talked for quite a little while, with much gesticulating by both men. Finally, Troy nodded, slapped the bar, and came over to the table. He shucked his backpack and put it on the floor beside Cassandra's.

"He's agreed to serve us something. He has a pot of ragout simmering on the stove and *imám bayildí*."

She stared. "What in heaven's name is that?"

Grinning, he said, "Do you like eggplant?"

"I can take it or leave it."

"Well, that's what it is, eggplant stuffed with tomatoes and onions. They're great on tomatoes here, if you hadn't already noticed. I told him to go easy on the tomatoes."

"I thought olive oil was the big thing in Greece."

He nodded. "It is, and I told him to go easy on that as well. You know what *imám bayildí* means?"

"Not exactly."

"Actually, it's a Turkish phrase, and it means 'the priest fainted.'"

"Oh, great! That sounds delightful."

"You'll find a great many Turkish words sprinkled in the Greek language. The Turks were one of the many people to overrun Greece down through the ages . . ."

He was interrupted by the arrival of the proprietor carrying a tray with glasses, a wine bottle, and several dishes. He placed everything before them—a loaf of bread, a dish of tomatoes and another of olives, and a wedge of cheese.

As the man went away, Cassandra pointed at the olives. "I see what you mean."

"You may not like the cheese; some people don't. It's goat cheese." He began pouring the wine. "He had a bottle of Moscháto, a wine from Samos. In my opinion, one of the best of the Greek wines. As the poet Byron once wrote, 'Fill high the bowl with Samian wine.'"

She looked at him in surprise. "You're full of surprises. Poetry yet!"

His glance slid away, and he seemed embarrassed. He mumbled, "I'll make my telephone call now," and quickly left.

Bemused, Cassandra followed him across the room with her gaze. She saw him confer briefly with the proprietor, then the two men disappeared into the back.

Discovering that she was hungry, Cassandra broke off a chunk of the bread and bit into it, washing it down with wine. The bread was surprisingly good; the wine was a little sweet for her taste yet not bad. She nibbled at the cheese and decided that she was one of those people that didn't care for it.

The food came before Troy returned, an earthenware bowl of pungent, steaming ragout, and a platter of eggplant. The eggplant was all right, but hardly delicious enough to cause her to faint; the ragout, however, was very good, with several vegetables and more than one kind of meat.

She heaped her plate full and began to eat without waiting for Troy.

When he did come back, he looked unusually somber. He sat down heavily and leaned toward her. "It's a good thing we left the apartment when we did, Cassandra. Somebody broke in not too long after we left."

She drew in her breath. "Who was it?"

"That, we don't know. Probably one of Marshall's people."

"Then they didn't leave Lindos!"

"Well, not all of them, in any event."

"How do you know that someone broke in?"

He shifted uncomfortably. "Someone was watching the place."

"But they don't know who it was?"

"The person who was watching is not really one of us and doesn't know any of . . . uh, Marshall's cronies. We just wanted someone to keep an eye on the place, to see if anyone did check it out. In fact, there's even more of a mystery. Perhaps I shouldn't tell you this, but a gunshot was heard."

She stopped eating, feeling a dart of fear. "A gunshot? Was anyone killed?"

"Apparently not. The apartment was checked out later, and there were no bodies, no blood. There were two people involved, two men, that much we know."

"That *is* very strange," she mused. She resumed eating, but more slowly.

Troy also began on his food. After a moment he looked over at her. "So you see, it's a good thing I got you out of there."

"I suppose, but how can I tell?" she said in frustration. "Since I have little idea of what's going on."

Troy didn't respond, but bent to his food. After her hunger was appeased, Cassandra took a look around. It was dusk, and the taverna was slowly filling up, but she noticed that the patrons were predominantly male; there were only two women present.

Troy said, "How did you like the food?"

"Everything was fine, as you should be able to tell from the way I ate."

"How about a dessert?"

She hesitated. "What do they have to offer?"

"They have cheeses, of course, and usually you can find Turkish cakes, but they're pretty heavy. This time of the year, there's still plenty of fresh fruit. I would especially recommend the yellow peaches, they're delicious. And coffee, of course. What was once called Turkish coffee." He smiled slowly. "Nowadays, it's called Greek coffee."

"I'll settle for the peaches and coffee."

Troy nodded. "I'll get it. The owner's pretty busy now, and apparently he doesn't have any help."

He went around the bar, and returned a few minutes later with tiny cups of coffee and several peaches.

As Cassandra started to peel a juicy peach, she heard the sounds of an accordian playing a rollicking tune. Glancing toward the bar, she saw a wizened little man energetically pumping an accordian.

"Are we to expect the breaking of plates soon?" she said with a laugh. "And then Zorba the Greek, played by Anthony Quinn, dancing about?"

Troy smiled. "Not bloody likely. If you'll notice, most of the people in here are a little ancient to be so energetic."

"I've noticed there are no young people. Why is that?"

Troy shrugged. "Most of them leave for the towns and cities when they get old enough. There's little opportunity for them in the country. Oh, if this was Friday or Saturday, you might find a few young couples in here."

Troy's recommendation was accurate—the peaches were very tasty. The coffee was a bit strong, and after one cup Cassandra declined a refill.

Troy seemed to be growing restive, glancing at the entrance every time a new customer arrived.

Cassandra said, "Troy, are you expecting someone?"

He smiled self-consciously. "Not really. But there's no way of knowing for sure."

"You mean, there's a chance someone knows where we are?"

"They shouldn't know, but there's no absolute certainty."

"That's encouraging," she said dryly.

"If you're through, I'd like to push on."

"I'm finished, but you're making me nervous, Troy."

"I'm sorry, Cassandra. I'm sure there's nothing to worry about, but on the other hand, maybe it's not a bad thing if you're on your guard. We could probably find accommodations in the village for the night, but I'd feel better if we didn't stay here."

Cassandra suddenly felt mulish and was tempted to balk him, but she shrugged resignedly. "You're calling the shots."

Troy simply nodded, dropped several drachmas onto the table to pay their bill, helped Cassandra to shoulder her pack, then strapped on his own.

It was full dark outside. As they left the few lights of the village behind, Cassandra said nervously, "I'm not too happy about bumbling around in the dark. I keep wondering about snakes and such things."

He chuckled. "No snakes on Rhodes, Cassandra. Haven't been for hundreds of years. As soon as we're out of sight of the village, I'll switch on my torch. We'll unroll our sleeping bags before too long, anyway."

In a short time Troy turned on his battery-powered torch, which at least saved them from stumbling along in the dark.

Cassandra said, "One thing you haven't mentioned about this safari . . . If we don't stop at inns overnight, what do we do about washing up, especially in the mornings? That's one thing I've never particularly cared for in this camping out."

"We stop at a farmhouse. Strangers are always welcome. Greeks are known for their hospitality. In fact, as a symbol of their hospitality, a stranger is immediately offered a spoonful of preserved fruit and a glass of cold water. I've always thought that was a rather touching gesture. Here . . ." He shined his light to the side of the road into a grove of trees, a sort of dell. Cassandra could hear the tinkle of running water. "This looks like a good place to spend the night."

Troy spread their sleeping bags out on the grass, close together, close enough that Cassandra could reach out to him during the night, if she wished. She was touched by his concern. She removed her boots and her outer garments, and crawled gratefully into the bag. The day of unaccustomed walking had been fatiguing, and she was pleasantly tired.

"Good night, Cassandra," Troy murmured from his bag. "Have a good night's sleep."

Contrarily, Cassandra didn't fall asleep immediately, as she had expected to. She wasn't used to sleeping out-of-doors; it was a strange environment to her. She lay awake listening to the rustle of small animals in the underbrush. An owl suddenly hooted, causing her to jump. She lay wide awake, staring up at the brilliance of the stars. A full moon appeared, dimming the stars.

Her thoughts swung to her father and all the things that had been happening to her. That, too, was not conducive to sleep. Thoughts chased each other around in her mind. The mystery was deeper than ever. She wanted to shout out her frustration.

She thought of Jake. If he was all right, she was certain that he would be looking for her. If he had caught up with the *Star*, he would know that she had left for Marshall's yacht; but should he have gone there looking for her, she was confident that Marshall would have told him nothing. On the other hand, if Jake was dead . . .

She sighed, a sound louder than she thought, for Troy stirred. He said softly, "Cassandra, can't you sleep?"

"Too much on my mind, and I'm not used to things that go woo-woo in the night." She laughed shakily.

"There's nothing out here to harm you. Take my word for it."

His hand groped out for hers across the small space separating them and he squeezed it reassuringly. And then she felt him turn on his side and take her hand in both of his. He raised it, and she felt the soft, shy touch of his lips.

Her first impulse was to pull away, then she sighed again and murmured, "Troy . . ."

"Cassandra, I've been watching you at a distance since the *Star* berthed at Mandraki Harbor, and I was already half in love with you before I ever saw you face to face." His voice throbbed.

"Oh, come on now, Troy!" She laughed lightly. "Love at a distance. That's too much."

"It's true." He was close now, so close that she could feel his breath warm on her cheek. "Remember the movie, *Laura?* The detective in that fell in love with the Laura in the painting, before he ever saw her in the flesh. Why can't I also worship from afar?"

"*Worship?* Troy . . ."

"And when I finally did meet you, I knew it was true. That first night in my apartment back in Lindos, I didn't sleep a wink. All I could think of was you, just down the hall from me, all warm and soft."

"Then you'd better go to sleep now, you must be dead on your feet," she said with a nervous laugh.

He rushed on. "I know about Jake Randle, but he's left you, hasn't he? I would never leave you, Cassandra," he said passionately. "Never!"

She drew back. "Jake? What do you know about Jake?"

"Only that the two of you were in love, and he deserted you."

"How can you know that for sure?"

"Well, he's not here and I am," he said in a reasonable voice.

She was silent, thinking hard. Now he sounded young again, proclaiming the extravagant passion of the very young; still, it was flattering, and certainly more acceptable then Marshall's calculated seduction-by-the-numbers.

Suddenly, he was pressed against her, kissing her gently. There was a comfort and a sweetness in his kiss that made her reluctant to pull away, and she found herself grateful for this caring human contact. During their long walk today she had been all too conscious of just how precarious her position was. Troy was, at the moment, her only connection with security.

Just as gently she kissed him back. There was a feeling of goodness about Troy, an innocence. However, there was nothing innocent about the stroking hands now slipping into her sleeping bag onto her body. Cassandra shivered as his hands touched her bared nipples.

She thought of stopping him, but thought again—why? Under the circumstances it seemed foolish to resist something that would bring both pleasure and comfort. She might never see Jake again. If Alex Chato and his minions found her, she might never see anyone again. Relaxing, she let Troy's hands have their way.

Mouth still fastened on hers, Troy began to pull the bag down, in much the same way as he would remove a garment. Cassandra raised herself up to accommodate him, and very soon she was on top of the sleeping bag, not in it. His fingers now caressed the insides of her thighs and then touched her mound, and Cassandra drew in her breath. She reached out to him and was surprised to find that he was completely naked.

His lips released hers and fastened around an erect

nipple, his hands busy, expertly exploring her body. Cassandra was amused at herself. Innocent, was he?

She twined her fingers into his hair, forcing his mouth closer. She was fully aroused now and forgot everything in the sweet abandon of the moment. Whimpering deep in her throat, she urged him to her with plucking hands.

He moved, adjusting his position, and as he went into her in one long thrust Cassandra murmured, "Yes, oh, yes!"

He lay still for a moment without moving, his weight partly supported on his hands on both sides of her. One of her breasts was touching his left side, and she could feel his heart pounding like a drum. His excitement thrilled and moved her, and her own desire mounted.

Then he began to move, driving into her with all the young strength of him. Her arms around his shoulders, she felt his skin, almost as smooth as her own. It was a sweet loving that culminated in a shuddering release for both of them. When it was over, he lay atop her for several minutes. She found his weight and warmth pleasant, and caressed the back of his moist head, as she might a child.

When at last he rolled off of her, he lay beside her, with his head cradled on her breasts. His breath was hot on her skin as he said something, but the thrumming of her own blood in her ears was too loud for her to hear.

"What did you say, Troy?"

"I said that I love you, Cassandra."

"You don't have to say that."

"But I do love you; I swear I do," he said vehemently, raising his head.

"All right, all right. Sh-h, quiet now." She stroked his head, pushing it down onto her breasts again.

All of a sudden, she chuckled. "One thing I know, I've never before been lured out into the country to be seduced."

He reared up. "That's not the way of it, Cassandra, I swear it isn't!"

"I know; I know it isn't, Troy. I was just being facetious. Where's your sense of humor?"

"I don't like to joke about something that I feel so deeply," he said gruffly.

"All right." She touched his cheek with her fingertips. "Leave now. We've got to get some sleep."

Troy left her side and went to his own sleeping bag.

Cassandra was on the verge of sleep when he spoke, "Cassandra?"

She sighed. "Yes, Troy?"

"Where's your hand?"

Without hesitation, her hand found his, and they went to sleep that way, holding hands.

Twenty

Hera was furious. "You deliberately disobeyed me! I specifically told you that I didn't want Randle informed of Cassandra's whereabouts."

"I think he has every right to know," Aphrodite said firmly. "The poor fellow's had the devil's own time of it, and he's trying desperately to find her. They're in love, Hera! That's why I sent him the note. Besides, I think that it would be better if he did find her. He was once a policeman, he can protect her far better than we can."

"She came close to getting killed twice while in his presence."

"But she came through alive, my dear Hera," Aphrodite pointed out.

"Well, be that as it may, I don't want any strangers getting involved in this affair."

"Jake Randle's not a stranger to Cassandra, and she is still in great danger, perhaps more so now than before."

Hera said, "Hermes will protect her."

"Troy is a boy," Aphrodite said scornfully. "A sweet boy, but a boy nonetheless. He can't protect her against the likes of Ares and Zeus."

Hera glared. "You are to refer to him as Hermes. You know the rules!"

Lisa van Horne shrugged. "I'm getting sick of the rules. This is no longer a game, if it ever was. I like Cassandra and don't wish to see her hurt. We got her into this, it's up to us to see that she comes through safely."

"She will, I'm confident of it. Now, you will obey me, Aphrodite," Hera said sternly. "Do not contact Jake Randle! Just because your namesake was the goddess of love, doesn't mean that you have to concern yourself over young lovers."

"What will you do if I don't? Whip me? Lock me away? Kill me? I'm too old and tired to worry about what you may do to me."

Jake had taken a room in the Lindos Bay Hotel, and he had spent the remainder of the day before and this morning methodically combing the village for some clue as to where Cassandra might be. To get around the language barrier, he hired a Greek lad who worked part-time as a tourist guide; the boy had enough command of English to make Jake's questions understood. Finally, in a sports shop that sold camping equipment, Jake received the information that a young man and woman had bought backpacks, two sleeping bags, and hiking clothes the day before. According to the shopkeeper, the woman loosely matched Jake's description of Cassandra.

Jake paid the guide off and had lunch in an outdoor cafe off the plaza while he mulled his options. Was it possible that Cassandra had gone hiking across the countryside with this man? But why would she? It made no sense. Unless, he thought suddenly, she was being taken to her father. It was a slim hope, but it was all he had.

There wasn't much to go on. He had no idea in what direction she might have gone, which would be a severe handicap. Rhodes wasn't a huge island, by any standards, yet it would take many days to cover it all, and he could easily just miss Cassandra everywhere he went. He was struck by the uncomfortable fact that she seemed to be evading him. Everywhere he went he seemed to just miss her.

Deciding that he had no choice but to at least look for her, Jake paid his bill and trudged back to his hotel. He would keep the rented car and drive inland; to try and find her on foot would be an exercise in futility. They had only a day's start on him; surely he could find *someone* who had seen an American answering to Cassandra's description.

In his room he had just completed packing his few belongings when the telephone rang. He stared at the instrument. He had told no one where he was, not even Bruno. But it might be Cassandra, or at least some word of her. He snatched up the receiver. "Hello?"

"Is this Jake Randle?" a woman's deep voice asked.

"Yes. Who is this?"

"Thank the gods! I've been calling and calling, I thought I had missed you."

Jake's hand tightened on the receiver. "Is this about Cassandra? Is she all right?"

"As of last evening she was fine."

"Just who are you, may I ask?"

"My name is Lisa van Horne. I don't know if the name means anything to you—if Cassandra mentioned me."

"Lisa van Horne? Oh, yes, Cass did mention your name. You were a passenger on the *Star*."

"That is correct."

"Cassandra, where is she?"

"Last night she had dinner in a taverna about a day's walk from where you are in Lindos. I should have word from her again this evening."

"You mean she calls you?"

"Oh, no, not at all," Lisa van Horne said with a little laugh. "There is a young man with her . . . Oh, not *with* her in a romantic sense. He is one of us, a companion along to protect her."

"'One of us'? What does that mean?"

There was a brief pause before the woman said, "I'm sorry, I am not permitted to tell you anything more than that. I'm not even supposed to be telling you this much, but Troy, the young man with her . . . Well, I'm not sure just how well he can protect her."

In a flash of intuition Jake said, "Miss van Horne, did you write those lavender notes? The ones to Cassandra, the one I found in my hotel in Rhodes?"

A sigh came over the line. "I'm afraid I am guilty, yes, but please don't ask me anything more at this time."

Jake felt a pulse of anger. "You're asking a lot, you know. This has all changed Cassandra's life. You must know that she has come close to being killed, three times that I know of."

"Yes, Mr. Randle, I am all too well aware of that, and I regret my part in it. Our intentions were all to the good; we never dreamed that she would be placed in such peril."

"If I was filled in on what this is all about, I might be of more help."

"I'm sure you are correct in that, but the decision isn't mine to make. As I said, I'm not even supposed to be telling you this much. But you have my promise on this . . . All will become clear before long, within a matter of days."

Jake made a sound of exasperation. "I suppose I'll have to settle for that. So, what do you want of me?"

"I should think that would be obvious, Mr. Randle. I want you to find Cassandra and keep her safe until such a time as all will be revealed. I'll tell Troy when he calls tonight to inform her that you are on your way to her."

"Are you going to just disappear into the woodwork again after this call?"

"Not at all. I will be available to you night and day from this moment on. I have suite fourteen at the Metropolitan Capsis Hotel in Rhodes Town. Call me as soon as you find her. Perhaps we will have a meeting with Jason arranged by that time."

"Does that mean you know where he is? You've known all along?"

She gave a dry laugh. "No, we haven't known all along. Jason Kanaris is an elusive fellow."

"But he is alive; he does exist?"

There was a brief hesitation before she said, "You'll have to judge that for yourself when the time comes."

"That's a strange answer. Am I to tell Cass she'll finally meet her father or not?"

"To a great extent that's up to Jason. And if that strikes you as an ambiguous answer, it's the best you'll get from me at this time, young man."

She gave him the name and the location of the taverna where contact had been made last night with the young man accompanying Cassandra, then hung up abruptly.

On their second night out, there was no village or taverna. Troy told Cassandra to wait for him while he went to an isolated farmhouse. "They have a telephone." He pointed to a single strand of wire running overhead. "And

I'm sure I can buy some food from them. But I'd rather they didn't know about you, Cassandra."

"You sure you don't want to tie me up out here until you get back?" she said with some asperity. "So I won't run away?"

He looked hurt. "Please don't be like that, Cassandra. I'm not afraid you'll run away, but I'd just rather no more people than necessary know about you."

"Oh, go on, Troy, just go on." She flapped a hand at him. "Of course I won't run away. Where would I run to?"

Still, he hesitated, looking hurt and very young. "I would hope that you'd stay for another reason."

"And what would that be?"

"Because of me, because of what happened last night."

"Troy . . ." She shucked the backpack and sat down on a boulder by the side of the road. "Just go on and do what you have to do."

He went, looking back over his shoulder at her. Cassandra rubbed her shoulders where the straps had chafed. She felt cross and out of sorts. She was hungry, tired, and she longed for a bath; she'd had about all of the outdoors that she could stomach. In the beginning it had appeared as something of a lark, but another night spent sleeping out under the stars had very little appeal.

Last night with Troy had been a pleasant interlude, and it was flattering to be the object of an infatuation—her bruised ego could stand a little bolstering. But despite its sexual intensity, last night's episode had the air of frolicking children, and she suspected that it would soon pall . . .

She saw Troy returning, carrying a sack, and she noticed that he seemed somewhat agitated. "Troy . . . Is something the matter?"

"No, no, everything's fine. I didn't get too much in the way of food. A jar of milk, some cheese, a loaf of bread, and some fruit."

"Did you make your telephone call?"

He nodded. "Yes."

"When do I see my father?" she asked eagerly.

"Soon, very soon."

"You keep saying that!" she snapped. "You're hedging, Troy."

"Perhaps a little." He sat down on the boulder beside her and began taking food out of the sack. "I'll be frank, Cassandra. I've been told that Jason is unavailable at the moment, but they expect to locate him any day now."

"Unavailable, or doesn't want to see me?" She accepted some bread and cheese.

"Oh, I'm sure he will want to see you, as soon as he knows you're here."

"Why doesn't he already know that I'm on Rhodes? Those notes I received said that he was here. If I could be told that much, why wasn't he informed that I was coming?"

"Jason isn't always that easy to find. I think they've been trying to let him know."

Cassandra was silent, nibbling at the cheese and bread, and drinking the milk. The cheese was superior to that served in the taverna. She looked speculatively at Troy, who was also eating. "It strikes me that you're talking a little more freely, although you're still not telling me a great deal. Are you avoiding telling me something? What else did you learn from your phone call?"

"Nothing, Cassandra. Just what I told you." Still, he wouldn't look at her.

"There *is* something; I know there is! Is there someone after us, is that it?"

He got to his feet, returning some of the food to the sack. "We'd better move on. We have at least an hour yet before darkness." He held out a hand to help her up.

She brushed it aside. "Apparently you've decided that you've told me enough for one day. But I'm tired of all the walking. Why can't we just stay here, close to the house? For one thing I'd really like a bath, Troy. Pretty soon, I'm going to start to smell like one of those goats. Surely the people in the farmhouse would let me take a bath."

He shook his head, setting his lips. "No, Cassandra. They don't know who's with me, and I don't want them to know."

"Then someone *is* after me!"

"Yes, Cassandra! Now does that make you happy? That's why I want to move on while it's light."

"It doesn't make me happy; it scares the devil out of me. Who is it?"

"What difference does it make? If we don't want them to catch up to us, we have to move on."

This time he fastened his hand around her wrist and hauled her up. Cassandra offered no more opposition, going along meekly enough. He set a rapid pace, moving fast along the narrow, dirt road. She almost had to run to keep up, but the fact that somebody was back there, on their trail, caused her fear to grow, and she matched his pace until darkness fell.

All at once, she balked, stopping dead still. Troy proceeded on for a few steps before he noticed. He halted, looking back. "Come on, Cassandra."

"No, I've gone as far as I'm going tonight," she said stubbornly.

"Just a little farther," he coaxed.

"No, dammit! I'm tired and one place is as good as another to unroll a sleeping bag. This is as far as I go."

Stepping off the road and under a stunted tree, she unstrapped the backpack.

"All right," Troy said with obvious reluctance. "I suppose this is as good a place as we'll find." He came back to her. "Here, let me help you unroll your bag . . ."

"No!" She slapped his hand away. "I'll do it."

When her sleeping bag was spread out, she said, "Is there an apple in that food sack?"

"Yes. Here."

Sitting tiredly, Cassandra munched on the apple for a few

minutes. Then, removing only her boots, she crawled into the sleeping bag. What was the use of taking off anything else? She was rumpled and dirty. No matter what Troy said, she was going to have a bath tomorrow, somewhere.

Troy had unrolled his bag right next to hers. As she crawled in and tried to arrange herself comfortably, he caught her hand, and then loomed over her, blotting out the stars. She allowed him to kiss her, but as he became insistent, Cassandra turned her face aside.

"No, Troy, please! I'm just too tired to think of anything but sleep." Sensing more than seeing his hurt expression, she gave him a hug. "I'm sorry I've been so cranky, but I feel dirty and disgusting, and worn out. Okay?"

Reluctantly, he answered, "Okay. Tomorrow, we come to a fair-sized village. We should be able to get a room and a bath for the night."

"Fine. I'll be looking forward to it. Good night, Troy." She was asleep almost before she finished speaking.

She came partly awake sometime later at the sound of a vehicle somewhere not far away, but went back to sleep immediately.

The next time she came awake with a start; the moon was up now. Disoriented, she couldn't understand what had awakened her—a strange unease, and a feeling of danger in the air, like the foul scent of sulphur. Then she tensed, puzzled at sounds to her left, like the noise of animals scuffling.

She raised her head cautiously, turning her gaze toward Troy's sleeping bag. The light from the moon showed her a grotesque figure, moving with what seemed to be the motions of sexual intercourse. And then she realized that a man straddled Troy's body, which was thrashing wildly. A hand was clamped over Troy's mouth, and as Cassandra watched, frozen in horror, a hand rose up, moonlight glinting off steel, and plunged down.

A whoosh of air escaped from Troy; his body rose in a

straining arch; then he slowly collapsed and was still. Cassandra could hear the breath of his assailant rasping like a bellows.

She made a small sound, and the man's face snapped around at her. It was a ruined face—nose smashed flat and bandaged, one eye puffed almost shut, and discolored. The one visible eye glared at her, evil and gloating, striking terror into her.

"So we meet at last, Miss Kanaris, face to face," the killer said in a hissing voice. "Now it's your turn, and this time there is no escaping me."

The sound of his voice broke her stasis, and she started to move before realizing that she was trapped in the sleeping bag as effectively as in a straitjacket. As she struggled to free herself the bloodstained knife was ripped out of Troy's lifeless body and was raised high, and then began to descend toward her.

Cassandra found her voice and screamed.

Twenty-One

Jake made fairly good time after he finally left his hotel in Lindos, but it was almost dark when he reached the small village from which the man named Troy had called Lisa van Horne. Jake stopped at the taverna she had mentioned, not to inquire about Cassandra, but to use the telephone.

Sipping at a beer, he dialed Lisa van Horne's hotel in Rhodes Town. She answered on the first ring. "Hello?"

"Miss van Horne? This is Jake Randle . . ."

"Thank the gods! I've been hoping you'd call."

He frowned at the phone. He could hear a series of clicks; maybe the connection was bad. "You have word of Cassandra then?"

"Yes, Troy called me not a half hour ago. She is still all right, and a day's walk farther along the road from you."

Jake breathed a sigh of relief. "Good! Then I should catch up to them by morning at least. I don't know if it's a good idea to try tonight; I might drive right past them in the dark."

She said slowly, "I think it might be advisable to at least try."

Jake tensed. "Why do you say that?"

"Well . . ." She hesitated. "I may have made a mistake. I told Troy that you were going to catch up to them, as I told you I would. I thought it was something that Cassandra would be happy to know. Troy reacted rather strangely when I told him. I'm not sure what to make of it."

"Acted strangely? How, exactly?"

"Well, he didn't seem at all pleased, and he was very vague about where he was calling from."

"Do you trust this Troy? Could he have sold out?"

"Oh, no, I'm sure not," she said instantly. "I'd trust Troy with my life. If you knew him, you'd say the same. It's just that . . ." She laughed uneasily.

"Just what?"

"Well, you may find this hard to believe, but I think Troy is jealous. He knows about you and Cassandra. I really think he wants her all to himself."

"Oh, great," Jake growled. "That's just what I need about now, a jealous rival. If harm comes to Cassandra, I'll wring this guy's neck."

"Oh, I'm sure he'll protect Cassandra with his life."

"That may not be enough. Jealousy tends to distort reality, and it certainly clouds a man's judgment. So I'd better hang up and get on their trail again."

"Mr. Randle! When you find them, have Troy call me at once. Will you do that, please?"

"Yes, of course. Good-bye, Miss van Horne."

Jake hung up, paid the moustachioed proprietor for the beer, and hurried out to the rental car. He didn't think he had much hope of catching up with them before dark, and this proved to be all too true. When darkness fell, he kept going, but very slowly, trying to peer into the dark on both sides of the road. Of course it was impossible to be sure he hadn't passed them somewhere along the way.

Cursing in a monotone, he had about decided to park the car and pack it in for the night when his headlights picked up another car parked by the side of the road, lights off and unoccupied.

Jake pulled the rental in behind it and got out warily, something nagging at him. Then he had it—this was the black Renault that had followed him to Lindos from Rhodes Town! Ian Macomber must have recovered and followed him here . . . not the Rhodes police.

No, that wasn't right. Jake hadn't seen another car behind him all day, and the Renault had arrived first anyway. Then he remembered the clicks he'd heard on the line during his phone conversation with Lisa van Horne. Her telephone was bugged! That was how Macomber knew about Troy and Cassandra; he, or a confederate, had listened in on Lisa van Horne's conversation last night with Troy.

Tension gripped Jake, and he went very still, straining his ears. And then he heard it—a shrill scream some yards down the road. He threw open his car door while groping in the glove compartment for the .38 he'd taken from Macomber and for a flashlight.

Then he proceeded quickly toward the source of the

scream, trying to make as little noise as possible, stopping every few yards to listen intently. On one of those stops he heard scuffling sounds and the beginning of another scream, abruptly choked off as though a hand had clamped over the screamer's mouth. The sounds were quite close now.

With the quickness of a great cat, the killer was astride Cassandra, his cold smile like a knife slash. She recognized him now—the *Star* passenger Ian Macomber, who had tried twice to kill her. A small part of her mind wondered what had happened to his face, but such concerns went out of her mind when he spoke again.

"You've caused me nothing but grief, girl," he said in a chilling voice. "You're going to pay for that now."

Just before he had vaulted astride her, Cassandra had been able to free her hands and arms from the confines of the sleeping bag, but his weight now prevented her from worming farther out of the bag. She cast about frantically for a means of escape.

Then the knife, in a two-handed grip, swung high, the moonlight glittering off it, and began to descend.

Cassandra had only one option, and she used it. Doubling her hands together, she drove them with all the strength she could muster into his crotch. He yowled and fell sideways, just enough to deflect the slashing knife into the ground.

Cassandra squirmed, trying to pull herself out from under his weight and out of the bag. Finally, she was free, and she got quickly to her feet. Macomber was moaning behind her.

She started to run toward the road, and a hand clamped around her ankle. Cassandra screamed and fell, sprawling headlong. In falling she dislodged his hand, and she was up again instantly; but so was Macomber, bent over like a hunchback. His eyes had a mad glitter, and he still had the knife.

He seized her by the arm, and struggle as she might, he pulled her inexorably toward him. His mouth opened, a horrible black hole, and he roared unintelligibly.

All of a sudden, a light blazed, pinning them in a circle of brightness, and a voice shouted, "Cassandra! Drop, drop down!"

The voice was achingly familiar, yet she was too frightened to think about it at the moment. She tried to jerk her arm free of Macomber's grasp and failed. He turned with her, keeping her between himself and the light, the knife now at her throat.

The voice behind the light spoke again. "Macomber, let her go! I have a gun. Your gun, remember?"

It was Jake! How could he be here? It was a miracle, but she was too relieved to question it.

"You see the knife, Randle?" Macomber said in a snarling voice. "You don't dare shoot. I'll cut her throat."

Cassandra stopped struggling and let herself go as limp as a wet rag. She sagged in Macomber's grip. He still retained his hold on her arm, but taken by surprise as he was, she had fallen to her knees before he could stop her.

A gun roared—once, twice, two shots in rapid succession. Cassandra heard Macomber grunt, and then she was free as he was thrown back. She felt a brief prick of pain along her neck, as she was falling free and to the ground. She rolled across the earth three times, and then came up on her elbows, staring back at Macomber, who was on the ground, pinned like a bug in the circle of light.

The flashlight beam moved toward her. "Babe, are you okay?"

"I . . . I think so." She laughed shakily, touching her neck with her fingers. "He scratched my neck with the knife, but it's not serious."

Now Jake stood over the prone figure of Macomber. He

squatted and felt for a pulse. "He's dead, finally. I was beginning to think that he'd keep popping up in my life forever." He stood, swinging the light around until it found Troy. "Is that the guy who was with you?"

"Yes, that's Troy Brooke. He's dead, isn't he?"

Jake bent to examine Troy's body. "I'm afraid so, Cass. He's been stabbed repeatedly in the heart." He stood up. "Macomber, I suppose?"

"Yes. Poor Troy, he was only trying to protect me. But he was much too innocent to stand up to people like Macomber." She remembered, with a feeling of great sadness, that she had refused to let him make love to her last night; now he was dead.

Jake was bending over her, holding out his hand. Cassandra took it, and he pulled her up.

All of a sudden, she was in his arms, clinging to him, the fear and horror of the last few minutes pouring out in the sobs that shook her. Jake held her, his lips in her hair, stroking her neck and shoulders.

"It's all right, babe," he said softly. "It's all over now."

She shook her head, unable to speak. After a moment she got the sobs under control, then stood back, dashing the tears from her eyes.

"That's the thing, Jake, it's not all over. It's far from over."

"What do you mean?"

"I still haven't seen my father, and somebody is trying to stop me from doing so."

"And I suppose that you're more determined than ever to find him? I don't suppose you'd consider turning around and going back home?"

"Of course not!" she said indignantly. "After all I've gone through, and after I left my job?"

"Knowing you, I didn't think you would," he said dryly, "but I thought it was worth a shot."

"Besides, I now know that he's alive," she said. "At least that's what Troy told me. But Jake . . ." She reached out to touch his face. "What happened to you? I was afraid I'd never see you again. And how did you find me?"

"Which question do you want answered first?" he said with a rueful laugh. "It's all a long, involved tale, babe, and we'll get to it in time. But right now we have to get to a telephone and report all this to somebody, the police, or probably first to Lisa van Horne . . ."

"Lisa van Horne?" Cassandra said sharply. "What does she have to do with all this?"

"A great deal, as you'll find out. For one thing, she's the lady who wrote you all the notes. We've become sort of bosom buddies the past couple of days. She's the one who told me your approximate location."

"Is she the person Troy's been calling?"

"I would assume so. Either that or he was calling somebody who passes messages on to her. By the way, did he tell you I was on my way to you?"

"No, he didn't."

"Lisa and I figured he didn't."

"But how did he . . . ? Oh, I understand. He did tell me that somebody was behind us, but he led me to believe that it was one of them." She glanced at the bodies with a faint shudder. "Are we just going to leave them . . . out here?"

"I don't see any other choice, do you? Unless you stay here while I go call the police? Or you go call and I'll stay?"

"Oh, no! I'm not letting you out of my sight again." She came against him, hard, one hand stroking his cheek. "I've missed you terribly, Jake. And whenever I thought that I might never see you again, I thought I would die."

"I've missed you, too, Cass," he said gruffly. "And I was beginning to think that I'd have to chase you halfway around the globe."

They walked hand-in-hand back to Jake's car. He turned it around and headed back the way they'd come. "Where did this Troy call from last night?"

"A farmhouse a few miles back."

"They'll all be asleep this late. I'll drive on back to the small village. It'll be close to morning when we get there, anyway."

As he drove, Jake told her everything that had happened to him since he'd left the *Star* in Genoa.

"My God!" She groped for his hand and squeezed it. "You're lucky to be alive. These people—it seems they'll stop at nothing. I'm sorry, darling, that I got you involved in all this."

"If somebody had told me I would find myself in this kind of situation, I would have said they were crazy. But actually, I haven't had so much fun in ages. It would help a lot, however, if we had a better idea of just what the hell is going on!"

"At least now we know someone who *should* know what's going on—Miss van Horne."

"Did this Troy guy know anything?"

"Some of it. He told me a little, that my father was alive, but I got very little else out of him. One thing I have concluded, on my own, Jake. Everybody connected with this thing is rich, very rich, both sides, if there *are* two sides. Sometimes I'm not sure but what they're all a part of the same bunch."

He glanced sidelong at her. "Rich people? I fail to see what that has to do with anything."

"I don't, either, but it's true. Everybody on board the *Star* had the luxury penthouse suites. Miss van Horne, Eric Johanson, the man I told you about who saved my life. Ian Macomber, he had one of the suites. For some reason Marshall Paris didn't, but he's rolling in money, as well as his guests on the *Olympus*. Even Troy was a rich man."

"You may be right, but I still doubt that it's germane." He looked at her again. "This Marshall Paris, just who is he?"

She shrugged. "All I know is what he told me. His father was a very wealthy man; he's originally from Chicago; he owns a yacht that cost God only knows how much; and he once starred in a movie, *The Olympians*, which, I understand, he also helped to finance."

"He boarded the *Star* in Genoa?"

"Yes."

"It strikes me that you were taking a hell of a chance kiting off on board the yacht of a man you'd just met."

She nodded. "I can't argue with that, Jake. I made a mistake. God, did I ever! But at the time he invited me, he seemed a nice, harmless, playboy sort, and his invitation offered me a base from which to search for my father. Or so I thought. Was I ever wrong!"

"You know what I felt when I first heard about it?" Jake asked diffidently. "I was jealous as hell. I thought, I'm gone a week and she blithely sails off with another man."

"Ah-h, Jake! Darling, you were hardly out of my mind for a minute." She slid across the seat toward him, hand on his leg. "My accepting Marshall's invitation had nothing romantic about it, at least not on my part. He did make a move on me, but I was onto him by that time. You saw him, didn't you?" I'm only lying just a *little*, she thought.

"Yes, when I came charging to his yacht looking for you, with the police as I mentioned, I met Mr. Paris."

"Then you know what I mean. He's too good-looking to be believed, and God does he know it! There was another man on his yacht, a late-arriving guest, by the name of Alexander Chato." She shivered. "Did you see him?"

"A tall man, with a dead face?"

"That's him. He frightens me, Jake. I've never met anyone who gives off such a stench of evil. I think he's capable of anything. And I have the feeling, although it was never confirmed, that Marshall takes orders from him . . ."

Cassandra broke off as the car lights picked out the buildings of the village. Jake pulled up before the taverna. It, and every other building, was dark. Jake peered at his watch in the glow of the dashboard. "It's four o'clock. Soon daylight. I think it's better that we wait, instead of trying to roust anyone out." He put out an arm and pulled her against him. "You're probably worn out, babe. Why don't you try and catch a few winks?"

She snuggled against him with a sigh. "I think I will."

"Maybe you'd be more comfortable in the backseat?".

"No, no." She clutched at him. "Now that you're finally back, I don't intend to let go of you so easily."

It was after sunrise when Jake shook Cassandra awake. "It's late, Cass." He looked sheepish. "I didn't intend to sleep, but I did. It's time to make my calls."

Cassandra got out of the car, combing her hair with her fingers and trying to shake the wrinkles out of her clothing. "Who're you calling first?"

"The cops, I suppose. The longer we put off letting them know about those two dead men, the harder it'll be on us."

She took his arm. "I think you should call Miss van Horne first."

He looked down at her. "Why?"

"I don't know, I just have a feeling. Besides, what will be lost? Five minutes, more or less?"

"I suppose you're right. I did promise to call her."

The taverna was locked, but the owner came to the door, grumbling, after Jake had knocked loudly a few times. Jake managed, with gestures, to make his wishes known, and they were led to a telephone.

Even as early as it was, Lisa van Horne answered at once, "Hello?"

"Miss van Horne, this is Jake Randle. I'm afraid that I have some bad news . . ."

"Cassandra! Something has happened to Cassandra!"

"No, no, Cassandra's fine. In fact, she's standing right here beside me." Jake paused for a moment as he once again heard those puzzling clicks on the line. "It's your man, Troy Brooke, he's dead."

"Oh, no! What happened?"

"They were asleep in their sleeping bags, and this man jumped Brooke with a knife, killed him, and then attempted to kill Cassandra. She fought him, and I was lucky to get there just in the nick. He's dead as well."

"Who's dead? What other man?"

"Do you know a man named Ian Macomber? At least that's the name I knew him by. I suspect it wasn't his real name."

"Oh, yes. Ares."

"Ares?" Jake echoed blankly.

"Never mind," Miss van Horne said briskly. "It's far too complicated to explain over the phone. Tell me everything that happened."

Succinctly, Jake related the events as he knew them, then said, "I'd better call the police now, and I'm not looking forward to that with any great relish. I'm already in dutch with them."

"No, don't you call them, I'll have somebody do it for you."

Jake was dubious. "I'm not sure that's such a good idea. I was once a cop, remember, and we were never too pleased when, in cases like this, someone else other than the person involved called in."

"Don't worry about it, it will be all right," she said decisively. "You will probably have to wait there, you and Cassandra, and go with the authorities to the site of the incident, and you'll probably be interrogated as well, but I'll dispatch someone to be with you at all times, so it'll be relatively easy for both of you."

"I don't know how easy it'll be if we're arrested."

"That will never happen, Mr. Randle, believe me," she said without hesitation. "Now, when you finally get free of them, return to your hotel in Lindos, both you and Cassandra, and I'll be in touch with you shortly."

"All right," Jake said slowly. He looked around at

Cassandra. "Babe, do you want to speak to Miss van Horne?"

Cassandra said, "Yes, I do."

"Not now, I have nothing to say to her now," Lisa van Horne said, and hung up.

Jake shrugged, replacing the receiver. "She didn't want to talk to you, it seems."

"Darn it, Jake! She knows who's behind all this, and I'm certainly entitled to an explanation."

"I agree, and she has promised us one. We're to wait in Lindos, she'll be in touch."

"That's what everybody keeps saying. That's all I get, is promises. Troy promised, now he's dead. What if . . . ?" She stopped, appalled at what she had been about to say.

"Let's hope that doesn't happen, babe. At any rate, one thing at a time. Let's get the police off our backs before anything else."

On leaving Lindos Jake had given up his hotel room, and he was fearful that he wouldn't be able to get another, since it was the height of the tourist season, yet he wasn't too surprised to find when they returned that there was a suite—not a room or rooms, but a suite—reserved for them in his name. He had already learned just how much power was wielded by Lisa van Horne and her cohorts.

When the police had arrived on the scene, they had been accompanied by a Greek lawyer, one Andreas Constantine. He spoke excellent English, and he interposed himself smoothly but firmly between Jake and the police whenever a clash loomed. As a result Jake and Cassandra were allowed to go on their way before too long, in exchange for a promise to keep themselves available in the event they were needed.

The police also insisted that Jake turn Macomber's .38 over to them. He had expected as much, yet he wasn't too happy about going around unarmed after all that had happened. If he hadn't had the gun when he confronted Macomber, Cassandra would probably be dead now, and a similar situation might very well arise again.

He was glad that at least George Pangalos wasn't with them. If he had been, Jake doubted that even Constantine could have prevented them from going to jail.

As Jake and Cassandra had prepared to leave, Constantine had leaned into Jake's window. "I don't believe there will be any legal repercussions, Mr. Randle," he said. "I was told of the Genoa policeman's interest in Ian Macomber, and I had a brief conversation with him prior to my coming out here. I am confident that I shall have no difficulty in convincing the police here that Macomber murdered Troy Brooke, and then tried to do the same to Ms. Kanaris. Since none of those involved, victims or yourselves, are Greek"—he smiled gently—"they will not pursue the case as, shall we say, diligently as they would if their own had been involved. So you may go on your way with untroubled hearts and minds. By the by, Mr. Randle, Marcus Bruno sends his regards, and he is waiting for your call."

It's amazing how money and power can grease the wheels of justice, Jake had thought sardonically as he had driven away. It was no different, no matter what the country. Constantine would do just fine in the States, he concluded; he would be very popular indeed!

At the hotel Jake signed them in, and a bellman took their meager belongings up to the suite.

On the way Cassandra lamented, "I simply have to buy some clothes. I left practically everything on board Marshall's yacht when I jumped ship, and I'm afraid to ask for them back."

"Didn't I tell you? There's nothing of yours on board the *Olympus*, unless the things are well hidden. We searched it from stem to stern and didn't find a thing belonging to you.

My hunch is that Paris tossed everything overboard. But count yourself lucky, babe." He squeezed her hand. "It could have been you."

The suite was spacious, with a marvelous view, but Cassandra started immediately for the bathroom. "I'm taking a bath, a *long* bath. I've never felt so in need of one in my life. If I'm not out in about an hour, maybe you'd better check and see if I haven't washed down the drain."

"Should I order up some food? I don't know about you, but I'm hungry."

"I'm starved, but remember, not for an hour," she called back just before she shut the bathroom door.

Jake stared after her, grinning foolishly. He was so relieved at having her back, and all in one piece, that he felt he could take whatever happened next in stride. And that reminded him . . . He called the desk from the room phone. No, there had been no calls, no messages. He hung up with a frown, wondering why Lisa van Horne hadn't called, as she had promised. But even as he was debating putting through a call to her hotel, the phone rang.

He picked up the receiver. "Hello?"

"Mr. Randle?"

"Yes, Miss van Horne, we just this minute got in . . ." He broke off as he again heard several clicks on the line.

"Did everything go all right?"

"Everything is fine . . . Miss van Horne, I think your telephone line is bugged."

She made a startled sound. "Bugged?"

"Yes, I think it has a tap on it."

"Oh, that can't be!"

"I'm quite certain that it is. Is there another one you can use?"

"Well . . . There are pay phones downstairs in the lobby. Perhaps I could go down and call from one of those."

"Why don't you do that and call me back . . . ." He had an alarming thought. "No, let's do it this way. If there is a tap on your line, they know we're here in this hotel, and this line could easily be bugged as well."

"Mr. Randle, that does sound a little paranoid . . . Well, perhaps not." She laughed nervously. "Then what do you suggest?"

"I'll go down to the lobby here, call you from a pay phone, give you the number, then you find a pay phone there and call me back."

"All right, Mr. Randle, if you think all this is necessary."

"Let's put it this way. What harm can it do?"

Jake hung up and crossed the room to rap on the bathroom door, then opened it a crack. Steam billowed out, as thick as smoke. "My God, babe, aren't you boiling in here?"

"It feels wonderful, darling! Why don't you join me?"

"I have to go out for a few minutes. I'm taking the room key and locking the door. Don't open it for anybody, you hear? Not *anybody*, not until I get back."

She was slow in answering. "Where are you going, Jake?"

"I'll tell you about it when I get back. I won't be gone more than fifteen minutes or so."

He closed the bathroom door and carefully locked the suite door as he left. He wasn't too happy about leaving her alone. If Paris and his people knew they were here, through the wiretap, would they dare force their way into the hotel room in broad daylight? He could only hope they wouldn't be that bold.

In the lobby he called Lisa van Horne in Rhodes Town, and gave her the number of the phone he was using. In less than five minutes she called him back. "Now Mr. Randle, about this foolishness of a 'bug,' or whatever . . . How do you know about this?"

"Two reasons. First, whenever I've talked to you, there are those distinct clicks that often mean a wiretap. And if it isn't tapped, how did Ian Macomber know where Cassandra and Troy Brooke were? He didn't follow me; he was *ahead* of me. So, either he received his information through a wiretap, or through you or one of your associates."

"No, I told no one." She was silent for a moment, then sighed heavily. "You're right, of course. Matters are really getting nasty, aren't they?"

"I would say so, with at least three people dead," Jake said in a dry voice.

"Yes, murder is far more nasty then a wiretap," she said. "Poor Troy. We never expected anything like this to happen."

"No? How about the attempts on Cassandra's life, *and* mine?" he said with some exasperation. "Or perhaps that doesn't strike as close to home as one of your own?"

"Mr. Randle . . . You're angry, aren't you?"

"You're damned right I'm angry!" he said forcibly. "We've been close to death a number of times, and we still haven't the slightest clue as to the reason."

She sighed again. "It all got out of hand."

"*What* got out of hand?"

"Mr. Randle . . . May I call you Jake?"

"Feel free."

"I'm prepared to explain everything to you. Eric and I will be driving down to Lindos later today, to your hotel. We'll arrive sometime after dinner, and everything will be explained to your satisfaction then. At least I hope so."

"Is this your decision, Lisa, or someone else's? I gather that several people are involved."

"Yes, other people are involved, which is one of the reasons for all the secrecy. And yes, it is my decision, but that is of small importance. Jake, I want you to believe one thing." Her voice became intense. "We had no idea it would ever come to this. Harm coming to Cassandra was the furthest thing from our thoughts."

Jake regarded this statement with some suspicion, since he knew that this woman had known of the danger to

Cassandra for some time, but he decided not to make a point of it over the phone.

"All right, we'll expect you then."

"Since you believe it is known where you're staying, Jake, do you think it wise to remain there?"

"Probably about as safe as anywhere else. We'll decide on that when you get here. Will Jason Kanaris be with you?"

"No, it's not time yet. We'll discuss that as well as everything else tonight."

Jake hung up and glanced around the hotel lobby. He felt nakedly exposed. If their presence here was known, he could well be under surveillance at this very moment. No one seemed to be paying him the slightest attention, but then a skilled surveillance team wouldn't give themselves away so easily.

The thought of Cassandra alone and unguarded made him uneasy, and he hurried back to their suite. The door was still locked, which eased his fears somewhat, yet once inside he couldn't see her anywhere. He started across the room, and felt a chill as he saw the bathroom door cracked a little. No steam was coming out.

Wishing again that he had the .38 that the police had appropriated, he placed just the tips of his fingers against the door and pushed it silently open. The bathroom was empty except for Cassandra sprawled full-length in the tub. She was very still, her eyes closed.

He rushed toward her. "Cass! Are you okay?" He dropped to his knees and felt an immense relief when her eyes fluttered open.

She smiled lazily. "Of course I'm all right, Jake. Why shouldn't I be?"

"You were so still and the door was open."

"I opened it to let the steam out, then got back into the tub. I guess I dozed a little. I was really knocked out."

He laughed shakily. "You know how often people fall asleep in the bathtub and drown?"

She looked at him measuringly. "Something's happened, hasn't it, Jake?"

"Not really, it's just . . ." He broke off, not sure how much to tell her.

"Where have you been?"

"I was talking to Lisa van Horne on the telephone."

She sat up in the tub. "You had to go out to do that?"

"I think her telephone's bugged. I think that's how Macomber was able to find you last night before I could."

"And so they know where we are, right? That's why you were worried that they might have come in here?"

He smiled slowly. "You've got it, babe. Did I ever tell you how smart you are?"

"Did she tell you anything important?"

"No, but she and Eric Johanson are driving down from Rhodes. They'll be here sometime after dinner."

"Jake . . ." She reached out, looping her wet arms around his neck. "Did I ever tell you how much I love you?"

"Not recently. Not recently enough."

"Well, I do, a whole world full." She kissed him, and her wet, bare breasts pressed enticingly against his chest.

"Are you trying to turn me on? If you are, you're succeeding."

"Good! You've been gone forever, it seems."

She kissed him again and nipped at his lower lip gently. He said, "I thought you were hungry?"

"I am, but I can wait if I force myself, and I'm willing to force myself. How about you?"

He put one arm around her back, below the shoulders, and the other under her knees, and stood up with her. "Shameless, absolutely shameless." He started into the other room with her, water dripping off her body. Wet and sleek as a seal, pubic hair plastered flat against the lower curve of her belly, she was incredibly erotic.

"I hope they don't object to water on their carpet," she murmured in his ear, and blew into it.

Jake shivered. "After what we've been through, I'm not about to worry about a wet carpet."

He placed her gently on the bed and stood back, beginning to undress quickly.

Cassandra watched him with heavy-lidded eyes, her breath quickening. He sat down beside her on the bed, cupped her face between his hands, and kissed her long and hard. Then his hands moved down to her breasts, mouth never leaving hers. He cupped the heaviness of her breasts, one in each hand, and lifted them as his mouth left hers, kissing lightly as his head traveled down, tongue flicking. He suckled on first one nipple, then the other, until they stood proud and erect, glistening in their wetness.

His hands moved on, exploring, stroking; her flesh leaped in response under each touch of his fingers, like a live entity separate from the rest of her body. She opened her thighs to him, and he caressed the insides of them with increasing urgency. Sensation sparked from his fingertips like tiny jolts of electricity, racing along her nerves until they reached the center of her being, and then her hips rose off the bed as his hand found her mound; his fingers probed and she cried out.

He muttered, "I love you, Cassandra. I've missed you, like an ache inside me that won't go away."

She combed her fingers through his hair. "I love you, too, and I missed you. I never thought I could miss anyone so damned much!"

Her fingers closed around his hair, and she urged him to her. As his face loomed over hers she raised her mouth to his, and her other hand found him, guiding him to her, and then into her.

As he began to move, slowly, inside her, Cassandra was borne high on a tide of pleasure that grew and grew until she didn't think she could endure it for long. She came to orgasm almost at once; she clenched her eyes tightly shut, tightened her arms around Jake's neck, and held his mouth to hers.

As Cassandra's hips convulsed again and again, Jake ceased moving, throbbing mightily inside her, until her spasms ceased. Then, as she fell back, lying still for a few moments, he began to thrust again. For just a moment, thoughts of Troy, poor Troy, passed through her mind, and were as quickly gone.

Now she started to rise and fall again, adjusting her movements to his, until they were in perfect rhythm. She was amazed to discover that same marvelous feeling sweeping over her once more, a breathtaking spiral carrying her to even greater heights.

Jake sped up, driving at her roughly, and Cassandra gloried in a violent feeling of sweet, wild abandon. For the very first time in her life she felt that she was one with another person, that they were two parts of a whole.

He took his mouth away, breath coming in short gasps. He said hoarsely, "Now, babe?"

"Now, Jake! Oh, yes, now!"

He went rigid, crying out, his head thrown back until the tendons stood out in his neck like cords, only his hips moved, and then even they were still; the only movement was that part of him inside her as he shuddered out his orgasm.

As her own pleasure broke, Cassandra stilled, cleaving to him, locking herself to him in a seizure of unbearable ecstasy.

When he finally lay beside her, half-turned, his chest against her breast, she could feel the trip-hammer rhythm of his pounding heart.

She gave a low laugh. "I'll probably have to take another bath after that."

"I'll join you. Cass . . ." He raised up on one elbow. "I

know I wasn't supposed to push, but I am anyway. I'm asking you again to marry me."

"All right."

"Maybe you can't give me an answer right now, but . . ." His eyes widened. "What? What did you say?"

She laughed softly. "I said, 'all right.'"

"But I thought . . . Never mind what I thought!" He gave a whoop of laughter. "You said yes, that's all that matters."

"I'll have to tack on one condition." She touched his lips with her fingers. "I'll marry you when and if this is all over, if I, if we, come out of it all in one piece."

"Oh, we will; I'll see to that." He scooped her up in his arms, raining kisses on her face. "I'll dedicate my life to seeing that everything goes all right from now on. Like they say, all a man needs is the proper incentive."

Twenty-Two

The room service waiter was just removing the dinner dishes, when Lisa van Horne and Eric Johanson arrived at the suite.

Lisa went to Cassandra at once, embracing her. "My dear Cassandra, I am terribly sorry for what happened to you. And Troy, that poor boy! Horrible, horrible!"

Cassandra suffered the embrace, not wishing to appear

rude, but finally she drew back, her eyes searching the old woman's face. "You speak as if Troy had been related to you. Was he?"

Lisa looked startled. "Related? Good heavens, no! But he was one of us, and a very dear friend."

Eric Johanson, as dapper as ever, took Cassandra's hand and bowed over it. "Dear Cassandra, I'm happy to see you unharmed."

Cassandra, about to retort that it was no thanks to him, changed her mind, and smiled in spite of herself. It was very difficult to dislike this pair; they were so warm and charming. "Thank you, Mr. Johanson." Then, as her anger dissipated, she said, "I must confess something. You were right about Marshall Paris. I should have listened to you."

Johanson shrugged. "Ah, well, Apollo!"

Cassandra stared. "Apollo?"

"Oh, dear," Johanson said in distress.

"Never mind, Poseidon." Lisa patted his hand. "It doesn't matter," she smiled faintly, "since we're going to reveal all."

Cassandra looked from one to the other in bewilderment. "Apollo? Poseidon? What have I done, fallen down the rabbit hole?"

"Your puzzlement is perfectly understandable, Cassandra. May we sit down? This is going to take awhile."

"Of course, I'm sorry," Jake said. He arranged two chairs in front of the couch. "Why don't you two take the couch, and Cass and I will take the chairs. I ordered a bottle of brandy for after dinner. Would you like some?"

"Thank you, Jake," Lisa said. "We would be delighted."

The pair sat, and Johanson took out a cigar and looked at Cassandra with raised eyebrows. "Do you mind, my dear?"

"Of course not." Cassandra motioned impatiently, her gaze never leaving Lisa's face, as Jake served the brandy and then seated himself beside her.

Smiling slightly, Lisa took a sip of brandy and looked at

Cassandra. "I would imagine you know very little about your father?"

"Only what my mother told me, and I've never been certain just how much truth there was in that."

"Probably very little, if it came from Jason. Jason is an accomplished liar, as we all are."

Cassandra leaned forward. "I keep hearing about 'we.' Just who is 'we'?"

Lisa ignored the question. "Did your mother ever mention the Olympians?"

"The Olympians?" Cassandra frowned. "You mean the movie?"

The older woman blinked. "The movie?"

Johanson tapped her knee. "She means Apollo's movie, my dear."

"Oh." Lisa laughed. "That atrocity. Cassandra, how much do you know about the old Greek gods? Those are the Olympians I had reference to."

"Not very much, I'm afraid. What I learned in school, of course. But come to think of it, I've heard more about them these past few days than ever before. From Marshall, mostly."

"Marshall is one of our relative newcomers. New people tend to become obsessed with the subject.

"At any rate, to refresh your memory, I'll give you a brief history. In the beginning were Zeus and Hera, although for the sake of accuracy, I should say in the beginning was Chaos, from which emerged Gaea, Earth, who then bore a son, Uranos, Heaven. Heaven then mated with Mother Earth." Lisa's smile was wry. "Incest was prevalent then, but it was a necessity in the beginning. In time Uranos sired seven Titans, who eventually divided the world among themselves. They ruled under the leadership of Kronos, Time, the youngest of the Titans.

"Eventually, Zeus was born to Kronos and had to be hidden away lest Kronos swallow him, as he had the rest of his children. When Zeus reached manhood, he declared himself sovereign of the heavens and of the earth, but the Titans would not acknowledge him as their master. For ten years a terrible war raged, between Zeus, his brothers, and his father and uncles, the Titans." Lisa smiled. "By then, you see, Kronos had been forced to disgorge the children he had swallowed.

"In the end Zeus was victorious, and he settled down to rule the world, fixing the abode of the gods on Mount Olympus. From there he issued godly edicts, made laws for mortals to follow, and controlled the heavenly bodies. Now, Zeus' mother had forbidden him to marry. In defiance he raped her and courted his sister, Hera. He was unsuccessful until he violated her, shaming her into becoming his wife . . ."

Jake interrupted, saying in a dry voice, "They seem like a nice, wholesome bunch, these Greeks gods."

Johanson laughed, blowing cigar smoke. "You have to understand, Mr. Randle, that they were gods, and human rules of morality did not apply to them."

Taking a sip of brandy, Lisa continued, "As I was saying, Zeus and Hera were married and spent their wedding night, a night that lasted three hundred years, on Samos. In spite of having a large number of children, their union was never a happy one. Zeus was unfaithful almost from the beginning, and soon Hera was unable to arouse his passion. She even borrowed Aphrodite's magic girdle, the wearing of which was supposed to make its wearer irresistible. Some said her failure came from the wedding night being too prolonged. In any event, this set the pattern for the relationship between them down to this very day. They have been estranged now for almost a year . . ."

Cassandra broke in, "To this very *day*? Come on, Miss van Horne, I'm beginning to believe that I *am* Alice in Wonderland! You talk as if these old gods existed, and still exist!"

The other woman looked a little sheepish. "To some of us they are very real, my dear. You see, we have become the Olympians."

Jake snorted. "I agree with Cassandra. This mysterious 'we' is becoming annoying."

Cassandra touched his arm. "Wait, I'm beginning to get it!" She leaned forward. "A bit ago Mr. Johanson said something about Apollo. Is Marshall Paris, Apollo?"

Lisa nodded, smiling. "That is correct. And the man you saw on his yacht is Zeus."

"Alex Chato? And you, you're Hera?"

"No, I am Aphrodite, the goddess of love, known as Venus among the old Roman gods." Her smile turned rueful. "Although I might not fit the image nowadays, I once did."

Johanson took her hand and patted it. "My dear, you were the loveliest Aphrodite of them all, and you still are."

Jake said, "And the man I knew as Ian Macomber, which one was he?"

"Ares, the god of war," Johanson said with a grimace. "The god of evil would be more fitting."

Cassandra said, "And Troy, what was he called?"

"Troy was Hermes, the messenger," Lisa said sadly.

Cassandra leaned back, shaking her head. "I think I'm more confused than ever. You've explained, yet you haven't explained. What does all this have to do with us, with *today*?"

"As I said, many believe in the gods, in the ways of the gods, and long years ago, some people went about making them real."

"And just how did they go about doing that?" Jake asked skeptically.

"A group called the Olympians was organized. Actually it happened long before I was born. They established the old gods again and enlisted a number of subjects, which has grown in size over the years. They were lesser gods and demigods, who could aspire to become major gods in time, when one died or needed to be replaced for any reason."

Cassandra, who was beginning to sense the shape of what was coming, said sarcastically, "Die? How could that happen? The gods of Olympus were immortal, weren't they?"

Lisa sat upright, her eyes suddenly flashing. Then she made an obvious effort to relax. "I know you have every reason to be angry, Cassandra, and perhaps we deserve your scorn, but please try to be patient until I have finished."

"Yes, babe." Jake closed his hand around hers. "We wanted to know what's going on, so let's bear with it, okay? It's only fair."

"I don't know what's fair about it, but okay. I'll listen."

Jake glanced at Lisa. "How many of the gods were there, or are there?"

"Twelve," she said promptly. "There were more of the originals, but it was decided that twelve was a good number."

"How are the god selected?"

"By vote of a nominating committee. And before you ask, Zeus, our sovereign, is also selected by the committee."

Jake said, "That all sounds very exclusive, a sort of a club for the privileged."

"Of course it is, Jake. Don't you see?" Cassandra said harshly. "Think about it. They're all wealthy people. Remember my telling you that? They're all bored, with nothing but time on their hands, so they become gods, so they can play their little games. This whole thing with me must be one of their games."

"That is not true, Cassandra," Lisa said with dignity. "Sometimes we play elaborate games, that is true enough, but . . ."

"Yes, you play god. You manipulate people, have them do your bidding, for your private amusement."

"Not in your case. There was a purpose behind bringing you here. You make it all sound so . . . so evil!"

"Well, isn't it?" Cassandra said relentlessly. "Your *Olympians* have tried to kill me several times, and two people have died. Three, if you count Ian Macomber, one of your own 'gods.'"

Lisa nodded mournfully. "I cannot deny that, but it wasn't always so. Oh, perhaps we played games at times, and some of them were mischievous, even wicked, but we never knowingly harmed anyone. Most of the time we have accomplished good things, changing people's lives for the better. That is a god's privilege, isn't it?"

"It is only recently, after Alexander Chato became Zeus, that everything turned sour. His wickedness is what caused the schism among us. Hera, Jennifer Chato, was Alex's wife, and was supposed to rule in tandem with him. But just as with the gods of old, Zeus and Hera, they began to quarrel, mostly because of some of the vicious things Alex did. Hera finally broke with him, determined to fight him, and a number of us joined with her. Myself, Eric here, Troy, and others. Unfortunately, we didn't have the resources, the wealth and power that Alex has at his command, as Zeus.

"You see, gradually over the years, the Olympians have acquired financial holdings all over the world. We became a financial colossus—to our detriment, I truly believe. We own hotels, shipping lines, an airline, valuable real estate. The Nordic Line, Cassandra, even belongs to us. The corporate wealth of the Olympians is staggering."

"My father," Cassandra asked, "is he one of your twelve gods?"

Lisa hesitated. "He was. He was once Zeus. Things were much better then . . ."

"Wait!" Cassandra interrupted. "You said *was*. That must

mean that he's dead then. You said yourself that a new god was selected only when one dies."

Lisa was shaking her head. "That's not precisely what I said, my dear. I said, 'when one died, or needed to be replaced for any reason.' No, Cassandra, Jason Kanaris is very much alive, as you shall soon see for yourself."

Cassandra drew a quick breath of relief. "What happened then? Why was he removed?"

"Alexander Chato happened." The older woman sighed. "He is used to running things, whatever he does, wherever he is. When he became one of the Olympians, he wanted to rise to the top immediately. All that wealth that I mentioned is a tempting target to a man like Chato. Whoever is Zeus has almost unlimited control over all that money.

"He used dirty tactics, politics, bribery, any means to get his way. As in any organization, there are always dissidents. He found them with an unerring instinct and used them to unseat Jason. Jason refused to fight back. He said that if he wasn't wanted, so be it. He abdicated, went into seclusion, and Chato was selected to take his place. That was more than a year ago."

Jake said, "I had a check run on Jason in Cassandra's behalf, and according to my information, Jason has been a near recluse for twenty years."

Lisa smiled. "The Olympians shun publicity. Outside of our members, very, very few people even know of our existence. I think you'd find that Chato is also considered a recluse since he became Zeus . . ."

"And when Chato became our leader," Johanson said, "everything went wrong. Aphrodite and . . . Lisa and I, and a few others, have bent all our efforts toward thwarting him."

Cassandra said, "None of this explains why I was brought into it."

"Since leaving the Olympians, Jason has lost all interest in life," Lisa responded. "We thought that if he was brought face-to-face with you, he might regain his former vigor, and join with us in wresting control back from Chato."

"Then he *does* know about me? Troy either didn't know, or wouldn't tell me."

Lisa nodded. "Oh, yes, Jason knows."

"I'm not sure, now, that I wish to meet him. All these years he has never tried to get in touch with me, and he deserted my mother even before I was born. Was my mother telling the truth? Were they ever actually married?"

"Yes, my dear, they were married. But that was just at the time, shortly after they were married, that Jason was chosen to take his rightful place as Zeus. One of the rules of the Olympians is that gods may marry only gods. If they do not, they must remain single, so your father had to make a choice. To be Zeus, or to stay married to your mother. It was a very difficult choice for him to make . . ."

Cassandra laughed harshly. "There is no doubt which choice he made, and I can't say I admire him for it. And what about me, his daughter? Did I enter into his decision at all?"

An expression of sympathy passed over Lisa's face. "My dear, they were only married two weeks. He had no idea that your mother was enceinte. He did not learn of your existence until after you were born, and by then he had staged his 'death,' and his position as Zeus was a fait accompli. Also, you must take into consideration the fact that becoming Zeus, ruling hundreds of our members and controlling a great deal of wealth, is as close to becoming a real god as a man can become here on earth. Men would kill for the opportunity, and some have, as witness Alex Chato."

"Okay, let's see if I have everything straight," Cassandra said slowly. "This club, or whatever you choose to call it, is divided into two opposing factions, the good guys and the bad guys. I was lured here to meet my father, to help the good guys. Is that substantially correct?"

Lisa nodded regally. "Pretty much."

Cassandra was frowning. "I can't say that I think much of your methods. Why couldn't someone have approached me openly? But then, I suppose that would have been breaking the rules of the game, wouldn't it?"

Lisa winced. "To us, it was never a game. To the others, some of them at any rate, like Ares, Apollo, and Artemis—Artemis is the woman you know as Daphne Moray—to them, it was probably a game. But not to us, and I think not to Chato. It was too threatening to him. Given the wealth of the Olympians there was too much at stake."

"Then tell me this, why did they try to kill me?"

"In the beginning I don't think Chato's intention was to have you killed. He hoped that you might lead him to Jason. He doesn't know where Jason is, you see, but he knows there's a plan afoot to depose him, so he wants Jason dead. I think the first two tries against your life were Ares' own doing. He was a vicious man, a psychopath, who took pleasure from killing."

Johanson said, "You can be sure that Jason would never have anyone like Ares around him."

"But then Chato learned that we had in mind to use you to pressure Jason to enter the fray again," Lisa continued, "so he wanted you dead as well. You can be sure that he will kill you now if he gets the chance. That's the reason Hera instructed Troy to keep you in the backcountry, out of harm's way."

"It didn't work too well, did it?" Cassandra said. "If it wasn't for Jake, I'd be dead by now."

"I had no way of knowing that my telephone line was tapped." Lisa glanced at Jake. "Do you suppose this room is, what do you call it, bugged?"

"I don't think so. I checked just before dinner. Of course,

without the proper equipment, you can never be one hundred percent sure."

Lisa shrugged. "Hopefully, after tomorrow, it won't matter."

"What happens tomorrow?" Cassandra asked.

"Tomorrow, you meet your father. Hera is arranging it now. To make doubly sure that none of Chato's people know of the place or the time of the meeting, Hera is using a 'secure' phone."

Cassandra got up and walked to the window to stare out.

"What's wrong, my dear?" Johanson asked.

She spoke without looking around, her voice tight. "I'm not sure I want to meet him."

Lisa said in dismay, "But why not, Cassandra? You came all this way, and you're not going through with it?"

"It isn't as if I came on my own, I was lured here. I was manipulated into this situation." She whipped about, her anger surfacing anew. "And just because I'm of his blood, doesn't mean that I feel toward him as I should toward a father. It takes more than blood to make a relationship. A father is much more than that. Not only did he desert my mother, but in all these years he has never once tried to make contact. And it can't be said that he didn't know where I was. *You* knew, Lisa, or at least found out. So could he have, if he had cared, or really wanted to."

"Oh, he always knew where you were. I recall a conversation with Jason when you became an assistant cruise director. He was so proud of you."

"*Proud*?" Cassandra said scathingly. "Apparently not proud enough to get in touch."

"By that time he feared that it was not a good idea. Too much time had passed, and he was afraid that you would not forgive him."

"Well, he had that right, anyway. What kind of a father has he ever been to me?"

"There's something that you don't know, I now realize.

Your mother apparently never told you about the money that was sent, every month up until her death."

Cassandra said flatly, "I don't believe you."

"Oh, it's true," Lisa said. "I saw the money orders. There was never any message or return address, but the money went out regularly, and your mother must have guessed where the money came from. How do you think she brought you up, Cassandra? She never held a job in her life."

"She inherited money when her father died."

Lisa was shaking her head. "No, my dear. The money, all of it, came from Jason. He stopped sending it when she died because he figured you could take care of yourself, and he worried you might guess he was still alive if you saw the money orders."

Cassandra was dazed by this news. "Then you think my mother always knew that he was alive?"

"Yes, I do."

Cassandra was silent, thinking back. She had always suspected that her mother had lied, at least covered up part of the truth, yet not to this extent. Now she could see how it was possible. She supposed she should be angry at the deception, but it was much too late for that.

In a sudden decision, she said, "All right, I'll meet him. I suppose it would be foolish of me not to, after I've come all this way, after all I've been through to get this far."

"Excellent!" Lisa clapped her hands together, softly. "I'm sure you'll never regret it."

"I wish I was as sure." She frowned at the other woman. "But one thing I will not promise. I won't promise to try and persuade him to fall in with your scheme. Why should I care about the Olympians? The way I see it, it's because of them that I've been denied a father all these years."

Lisa received the statement with equanimity. "Perhaps you're right, my dear. That's a judgment others will have to make. As for your persuading Jason as to his future course of action, that is a decision *you* will have to make. We will respect whatever it may be. In a way I no longer care. I'm old now, perhaps it's time I became," she smiled sardonically, " a mere mortal again. But I am pleased to be a part of bringing you and Jason together. It's something that should have happened long ago."

Cassandra softened. "I am grateful to you for that at least, Lisa. And I do thank you. I know that you had my happiness in mind, and I'll always be grateful to you for that." She felt the sudden sting of tears in her eyes.

Seeing them, Lisa smiled tenderly and put her arm around Cassandra. Cassandra didn't cry, but she yielded to the reassurance and comfort of the woman's embrace. Perhaps it was a poor substitute for her own mother, but then her own mother had betrayed her . . .

She gave herself a mental shake. No, that wasn't true; her mother hadn't betrayed her. In fact, Cassandra saw with sudden clarity, her mother had handled it the right way; she had protected her. She had been better off all these years, thinking that her father was dead. In that way there had been a memory to romanticize. Was she any better off now that she knew the truth? She didn't know. Maybe she would know the answer to that question when she finally saw Jason Kanaris face-to-face.

She heard Jake clear his throat embarrassedly. "So, when do we learn the time and place to meet Jason Kanaris?"

Cassandra sat back in time to hear Johanson say, "Sometime tomorrow, as Lisa told you. Hera is making the arrangements, and we'll know the details in the morning. Suppose we all meet for brunch? We'll know by then."

"And it won't be 'we,' Jake," Lisa said. "Jason will wish to see Cassandra alone. I doubt if he would even come, should he know you are to be along."

Jake scowled. "I'm not too crazy about that, letting Cass out of my sight, with those weirdos still on the loose."

Cassandra smiled wanly, and leaned across to touch his

hand. "I'll be okay, Jake. Now that I've decided to go through with it, I don't want anything to blow it now."

Cassandra felt a deep contentment the next morning. They had spent hours at ardent, passionate love last night, and then both had slept deeply and well, and Cassandra was happy that she was to see her father at last.

They were to meet Lisa and Eric Johanson for brunch at eleven, so it was late when they finally left their hotel suite. The day was cloudless, the sun hot, the sky a brilliant blue.

In the hotel lobby she hugged Jake's arm to her. "We still have some time before we meet them. Let's walk for a bit."

"Okay by me," he said.

Outside, they mingled with the people on the streets, strolling toward the center of town. Cassandra stretched, her head back, eyes closed against the glare of the sun. "I feel great this morning," she said happily. She opened her eyes and craned up to kiss him on the cheek. "Mostly due to you, dear Jake. Last night was something like a honeymoon night."

He smiled absently, and said in a grumbling voice, "I'd be far happier if I was accompanying you to this rendez-vous."

She patted his cheek. "Nothing will happen, darling. I have this feeling."

He snorted. "Save me from women's intuition!"

"Don't be such a grump." She linked arms with him. "Let's walk."

They soon entered the small plaza at the beginning of the village. Cassandra noticed that Jake continually glanced behind them. "What is it, Jake?"

"I can't help but feel that we're being watched."

She laughed. "Now who has a 'feeling'?"

"When you've been a cop as long as I have, it's much more than a feeling."

They had crossed the plaza and stopped at the railing.

Cassandra looked down the slope, at the beach, and then out into the bay. All of a sudden, she froze.

Jake said in alarm, "What is it, Cass?"

"Look!" She pointed out into the bay.

Floating at anchor, at almost the identical spot where it had been before, was the *Olympus*.

Marshall Paris and Daphne Moray stood at the yacht railing, looking toward Lindos.

Marshall faced about as Alex Chato came striding toward them from the wheelhouse. As Chato stopped before them his dark eyes blazed with an unholy triumph.

"I just received a call from shore. They're here, just as I suspected! The girl and the detective, as well as Aphrodite and Poseidon."

"How about Ares?" Marshall asked. "Is there any word of him?"

Chato's face darkened. "Ares is dead," he said in a grating voice. "The blasted fool took it on himself to try and kill the girl. He did kill Hermes, but in turn Randle killed him."

Marshall clucked. "Ah, that's bad news."

"Not bad news at all. We're better off rid of him. Ares had lost what little sanity he had left, I think. He's no great loss to us."

"Then shall we take them, Zeus?" Marshall asked eagerly. "I would dearly love to get my hands on him."

Daphne Moray laughed. "Your pride still smarting, Apollo? That's probably the first woman you haven't been able to work your charms on. She saw right through you, didn't she?"

Marshall wheeled on her, his face livid. "I've had enough of your infernal insolence, Artemis! One more word out of you and I . . ."

"That's enough!" Chato barked. "We have enough on our plates without you two being at each other's throats constantly."

Marshall asked, "Then when do we take them? They might not stay in Lindos long."

"We don't touch them, not yet. They'll be in Lindos until they meet with Jason, and they're being watched every minute. I'm confident they'll lead us to Jason. He's the one I want. When they meet, I want to be there." His eyes blazed fiercely. "I want to confront him face-to-face. I want the pleasure of killing him myself. When he's taken care of, *then* we will rid ourselves of the girl and the detective!"

Twenty-Three

Jake said explosively, "No! I won't have it!"

Lisa van Horne, across the table from him, glanced around the crowded restaurant. "Please, Jake, keep your voice down. That's why we're talking here, so no one can overhear what we say."

"I'm sorry," Jake said in a softer tone. "But I will not allow Cass to go up there alone. They've tried repeatedly to kill her, and her luck can't last forever."

Johanson said, "Do you think her own father would try to kill her?"

Jake wasn't sure, he wasn't sure of anything, except that Cassandra would be placing herself in grave danger. The rendezvous was arranged to take place at midnight and at the Acropolis on the hill above Lindos. He said, "You know the yacht is out there. They're just waiting for a chance at her. And at midnight, for God's sake!"

Lisa said, "That was Jason's stipulation. For one thing, he can't get here much before then, and he wants to be sure he meets Cassandra alone. As for Chato and his people, if they try to kill anyone now, it will be Jason. He's been their main target all along. Once Cassandra and Jason meet, why should they have any further interest in her?"

"Because they're all crazy, for one reason. For another, both Cassandra and I were witnesses to some of the things they've done, or tried to do." He stared at Lisa intently. "Or are they all above the law?"

"Not completely, perhaps, but to a certain extent they are. To have either Chato or Marshall arrested, there would have to be strong evidence of their crimes, not just your word, Jake."

Jake said, "This Ian Macomber, or Ares as you call him, was out to kill us simply because we had thwarted him. He was out for blood for no other reason."

Lisa shrugged. "Ares was a psychopath, as I have explained. There was no logic to his actions."

"I'm not so sure they're not all psychos," he said.

"Jake . . ." Cassandra spoke for the first time since being told that she was finally to meet her father. She had been staring straight ahead. Now she touched his hand and smiled at him. "If my father says meet him alone, that's the way it will be. I've come too far, gone through too much, to let any threat get in the way of my finally seeing him." As he started to speak, she held up a staying hand. "Don't argue, that's the way it's going to be." She softened her ultimatum, by another smile. "You know how stubborn I can be."

"Yeah, I know very well," he said glumly.

"Jake, access to the Acropolis is limited," Lisa said. "It would be very difficult for anyone else to get up there without being seen. If it'll make you feel any better, you can go with her on the main path two-thirds of the way up, but no farther. You can remain there and keep watch. You won't be so far away that you couldn't hear Cassandra if she called for help."

"Isn't the place guarded at night?"

"Not too well," Johanson said. "It's nothing to worry about. There are ways to get around that."

"Bribery, you mean?"

Johanson shrugged negligently. "Call it that, if you like."

"I sure as hell don't like it, I don't like any of it," Jake said angrily. "But it seems I have little say in the matter."

When they left the hotel shortly after ten that evening, Jake was still disgruntled. "This is a damn fool thing for you to be doing, babe. It's a risk you shouldn't have to take."

She squeezed his hand. "It's what I've been looking forward to for weeks, Jake. Tonight should be the end of it, one way or another."

"That's what I'm afraid of."

"Ah, come on, darling! Lighten up. I promise you, if anything, anything at all, doesn't look right, I'll scream my head off."

"Anything could happen before I could get to you. Hell, I don't even have a gun. I tried to get one, without any luck. I even asked Johanson for one, and he froze up, said he didn't have one and didn't know where to get one. Maybe they're afraid I'd shoot their precious Jason . . . I'm sorry, Cass, I didn't mean it that way."

She patted his arm. "It's all right, I understand."

They walked for a little while in silence. She looked up at the night sky. The moon was still full, but the night was partly cloudy, and clouds often obscured the moon's face. Soon they were out of the village and starting the climb. The path was deserted.

Beside her, Jake stumbled. Righting himself, he cursed. "Goddamnit, why couldn't they have selected a more civilized place for a meeting, like a cocktail bar?"

Laughing, she pinched his arm. "They couldn't do that, you know very well. If what Lisa says is true, my father is risking his life as it is."

They strode on, the climb steeper now. Cassandra kept a careful watch. When she judged they were about a third of the way from the top, she said, "This is as far as you go."

"Just a little farther? Who's to know the difference?"

"*I* will. We promised. I'll go on alone from here. And you promise me right now." She gripped his arm. "Promise me that you won't sneak up after me once I'm out of sight."

He grunted. "Okay. But you have to promise me to sing out if something doesn't smell right."

"I already have. Don't worry, I will."

Then suddenly, she was in his arms, clinging to him.

"What's wrong? Are you frightened?"

"No, you big lug," she said shakily. "It's just that I love you."

"I love you, too, you know that." He gripped her shoulders painfully. "I'm going with you . . ."

"No!" She stepped back out of his arms. "You promised! I'll be fine, Jake. Good-bye for now."

She turned and started up the steep path, but just before she turned the corner that would obscure her from Jake's sight, she glanced back. He was standing where she had left him, moonlight illuminating his features, and for an instant she almost turned back as a wave of love for him swept over her. It would be so easy just to turn and walk back into the protection of his arms. Yet she must go on, she must see this thing through. If she did not, she would be left wondering about her father for the rest of her life and she would feel, she knew, as if she had failed in some way.

Resolutely, she turned her back on Jake and began again to climb.

She didn't pause until she came to the steep flight of steps leading up to the entrance to the Acropolis. Once the steps had been wider, but time, and millions of footsteps, had eroded the left-hand section, until only the right side was usable. Above, she could see the archway to the Acropolis, a dark, open mouth, and a part of ancient wall loomed up on her left.

Breathing deeply from the exertion of the climb, Cassandra stared at the black maw of the entry arch. The moon was again hidden, and she hoped the clouds would pass, but they did not, and she could wait no longer. She tried telling herself that there was nothing to fear. There was no one in the Acropolis except her father, and he surely didn't intend to harm her.

Still, she shivered as she entered the dark, tunneled archway, and almost ran toward the pale arch of light that she saw at the other end.

As she emerged into the Acropolis proper, the erratic clouds again unveiled the moon, illuminating the stark lines of the ruins, and she caught her breath at their beauty. The columns threw long shadows, and as her gaze raked the area, she could see no one.

Where was her father?

Moving slowly into the main portion of the Acropolis, she debated calling out, but somehow she couldn't bring herself to break the serene silence that surrounded her, and then a voice softly spoke her name, "Cassandra?"

Heart pounding, she whirled about to see a tall figure approaching.

The moon was once more covered, and she could only ascertain that the figure was unusually tall, broad-shouldered, and walked toward her with a certain, dignified grace. Her heart was thudding wildly, and she felt that she couldn't breathe, the suspense was too great.

He stood before her, and as the moon slowly emerged from behind a cloud, she saw his face, looking down at her with an expression of melancholy and love.

Her mother's assessment of his looks was at last confirmed: he was indeed a handsome man. His good looks were classic, with a touch of wry humor around his mouth, and the warm glow of his deep-set eyes gave his face a character that Marshall Paris, for all of his incredible good looks, would never possess.

Two strong hands gripped hers as he leaned toward her. "Your pictures don't do you justice, Cassandra. You are far lovelier than I had imagined." His voice was deep and pleasant.

Cassandra's tongue felt cleaved to the roof of her mouth. He seemed to realize her predicament and smiled gently.

"You seem surprised. Yes, I have pictures of you, and have had down through the years. Despite what you may think, I have kept a close watch upon you, and you are, and have always been, very dear to me."

"Yet you never let me know you were alive," Cassandra managed to whisper, unable to keep the bitterness out of her voice.

He winced. "I deserve that, of course, and probably anything else you might say to me, but I want you to know that I have always loved you and protected you as best I could. In my own defense, I can only say that for several years I wasn't even aware that I had a daughter. By the time I found out, it was far too late to change the direction that my life had taken. All I could do was check on you, see that you were well and happy, and that you didn't want for anything."

Cassandra swallowed, seeking to ease the dryness of her throat. "What I wanted and needed was a father. Why did you leave my mother? Why did you choose this game, this club, over my mother, the woman you supposedly loved?" Her words came out as a cry, a plea, and she felt herself burn with embarrassment.

He reached out and pulled her close to him, and she found herself yielding willingly.

"I did care for you, Cassandra. You must believe that, but you must also understand that I was very young, and very impressionable. All of my life I had known of the Olympians, and when I was finally admitted to their ranks, as a lesser member, I was ecstatic. I knew of course of the Olympian rules, that a major god could only marry another god, but at that time I had no real hope of ever becoming one of the twelve. Also, when a young man thinks he is in love, all considerations become negligible.

"By then I had met your mother. She was beautiful and charming, and I wanted her above all else, at that precise moment. Since she was, what at that time was known as a 'good girl,' she wouldn't give herself to me without marriage. And so I married her, not really thinking of the consequences. We had an all too brief time of bliss and happiness, here at Lindos, and then I found out that the Olympians had decreed that I was to be the next Zeus."

Cassandra, her head against his chest, listened almost calmly, as a child might listen to a fairy tale. Her father's story seemed only a continuation of the stories her mother had told her, and somehow, because of this, a feeling of strange peace stole over her.

"Can you possibly understand what that meant to me?" Her father's voice trembled. "It was the greatest honor I could conceive of, something I had only dared daydream about. I would be a living god, with power, prestige, and honor. On the other side of the scale was a young woman, beautiful, true, and desirable, but one whom I actually hardly knew. Still, it was a difficult decision, for I had really begun to care for your mother for more than just her physical attributes.

"Of course, the Olympians advised me, showing me all that I could have, all that I could be, and in the end I succumbed. The lure of the godhead was too great. Since there were no grounds for divorce, it was decided that a fake death was the best means to sever the relationship. The drowning was arranged, and your mother returned to her own country, believing that her husband was dead. I realized that it was a cruel thing to do, even then. Yet it seemed the only solution. I had no idea at the time that she carried the seed of my child in her womb."

Cassandra gently removed herself from his embrace and looked up into his face. She asked softly, "Would it really have made any difference?"

Jason Kanaris stared down at her, his eyes mirroring the conflict within him. "I should like to think so," he said slowly, "but to be honest, I'm not sure. At the time, being Zeus meant a great deal to me."

"And still does?"

He nodded. "Now more than ever, for now our purpose has been perverted by Alex Chato, and it is my responsibility to set it right."

"Your purpose? I'm not sure the Olympians have a purpose besides that of amusing themselves." Cassandra found herself experiencing a mixture of feelings: righteous anger, real curiosity, and the desire to understand her father and the Olympians, to find something good in what they were doing and had done.

Jason was slow in answering. "Yes, there is a purpose, or there was, until Chato's influence was felt. You may believe the Olympians to be simply a hobby of the idle rich, a means of relieving boredom, but that is far from the whole story. I will admit that we manipulated people's lives, but it was for good, not evil. We were truly like the old gods, seeing to it that the lives of the members of our worldwide organization were full and fulfilling. And we helped others, as well. The hungry, the homeless, in all parts of the world. We had power, but I like to believe we used it wisely.

"It is true that the twelve gods are all wealthy, but they have earned it, if not on their own, while working as directors of our various enterprises. They are all shrewd business people, of one sort or another. It is through their efforts that we have become such a financial giant. Most of the twelve could take charge of any corporation and run it brilliantly."

Cassandra, wanting desperately to believe what he was telling her, still had to press on. She had to be sure. "But what about the games? Didn't you play games with people's lives?"

Jason shook his head. "The games are an invention of Chato's. He was bored with doing what he called our 'good samaritan work.' And while we have been content, of late years, with income from our various enterprises, as against further expansion, Chato is not. He wants to use our financial reserves and power to take over more and more corporations.

"In addition, he craves excitement, thrills, and unfortunately he was able to influence others to his way of thinking. He challenged me for the right to be Zeus, as I understand you already know. Chato was always on the attack, and many of the Olympians seemed to side with him. Perhaps I should have fought him harder, but my disgust at his tactics and at what I saw as the weakness of the others caused me to throw up my hands and turn my back. I let him take over, and now I'm very sorry."

Cassandra found herself wanting to comfort this man. Despite all the years of his neglect, she felt the beginning of a bond, a closeness. She said, "And I was brought here to influence you. To get you to challenge Chato again. They want you back, Father. They want you to be Zeus again."

He nodded, smiling. "Can't you tell that I'm already convinced? Chato tried to have you killed. For that alone I would fight him. And he will eventually destroy the Olympians, if he has his way. Yes, I will fight him." A note of confidence had crept into his voice. "And I will win."

Cassandra said hesitantly, "And after that? What will happen after that? Will you disappear from my life again?"

His smile widened. "Never again. I shall always be near you, dear girl. The role of Zeus demands a certain seclusion, but we will see one another, I promise. And if you ever need me, I will be there for you."

She caught herself smiling back at the tall man who was her father. His words, warmly and sincerely spoken, seemed to heal an old wound. She knew that she would not see him often, but she would see him, and she truly felt that his love would always be there.

As she stared into her father's eyes, his gaze shifted, looking over her head, and his expression became cold and hard.

Feeling a chill ripple down her spine, Cassandra slowly turned and saw, limned in the moonlight, the figure of Alex Chato.

For the first time she saw a smile on Chato's thin lips. "So, Jason. I've finally run you to earth. You've come out of hiding."

Jason, gently pushing Cassandra aside, said calmly, "I was never hiding from you, Chato."

"I am Zeus," Chato said arrogantly, "and you will so address me!"

"You are an imposter, a pretender," Jason said with a gesture of contempt. "You are not worthy of the throne."

"We shall see here, tonight, who is worthy. Only one of us will walk away from this meeting alive, and that will be me."

In the moonlight Jason's smile was taunting. "What will you do, Chato? Hurl your thunderbolts at me?" In an undertone he said, "Leave, Cassandra. Leave here now, while there is still time."

Cassandra didn't move. She watched, fascinated, as Jason began to walk toward Chato. There was a commanding presence about her father. He walked tall, supremely confident. Her glance darted to Chato, and she saw a sudden look of uncertainty on that customarily dead face. He took a few steps backward, toward the cliff's edge.

Jason continued his advance. "Don't run, Chato. As you said, now is the time to finish this."

Chato stiffened, squaring his shoulders. "I am not running! I am not afraid of you. I broke you once and I will do so again!"

Jason kept on. "Perhaps you should be afraid of me," he said with an undertone of amusement. "I'm going to see to it that you and your cohorts pay the penalty for the crimes you've all committed in the name of the Olympians."

They were only a few feet apart now, as Jason continued his steady, inexorable advance. Until this moment Cassandra had never realized quite how tall both men were. They were both formidable men, although Chato was the younger by at least fifteen years. A phrase flashed through Cassandra's mind, the battle of the Titans.

In the moment before Jason reached him, Cassandra saw Chato's hand snake in and out of his coat; it emerged holding a pistol.

"A gun, Chato?" Jason said, unafraid, voice mocking. "Is that your thunderbolt?"

Abruptly, a bank of clouds moved across the moon, plunging the Acropolis into darkness. Cassandra squinted, but she could see nothing.

And then the darkness was split by a sudden flash of light, followed by a sound like a clap of thunder. She cried out involuntarily and took several steps toward where she'd last seen Jason and Chato. Again, the flash, and again the blast of sound.

As she took another uncertain step, the clouds parted, and she began to run toward the cliff edge before she realized there was no one there. Both men were gone!

She cried out, "Father?"

She skidded to a stop perilously close to the precipice, peering down. All she could see was the glint of water far below.

"Oh, no!" she cried. "Dear God, no!"

Had both men gone over the cliff? Had she come all this distance just to watch her father killed?

"Cassandra? I'm all right, Alex Chato is dead. He has paid for what he tried to do to you."

Cassandra whirled around. Although the moonlight was bright, she could see no one and could not tell where the voice was coming from.

"Father? Where are you? Come out and let me see you."

"It is better that we part this way. You must go home now, live your own life. Marry your young man and be happy. But remember, I will always be there for you if you need me. I love you, my child. Remember me."

The voice faded, leaving Cassandra alone in the silent Acropolis. He had gone, but she felt as if he had left her something, something valuable—the sense of being cherished and loved.

Suddenly, she stiffened, as she heard the hard pound of running footsteps on stone. Then she relaxed as Jake burst into view. He plowed to a stop, looking around.

"Cassandra!" he bellowed. "Where are you?"

Still basking in the residue of her father's love, she happily turned to this new source. "I'm here, Jake. I'm here."

He hurried to her and took her rather roughly into his arms. "When I heard those shots I cursed myself for promising to stay on the path. Are you all right?"

"I'm fine," she said shakily, burrowing her face into his shoulder, welcoming the comforting scent of him, the feel of his hard muscles.

"What happened? What was the shooting all about?"

"Shooting?" she said vaguely. Of course, it must have been the sound of gunshots she had heard. After all, Alex Chato had had a gun, yet they hadn't sounded like gunshots at all. She looked up to find Jake staring down at her with a puzzled frown.

"Babe? Are you sure you're all right?"

She hugged him tightly. "I'm fine. Honestly. It's just that what happened here was so strange."

He pushed her away and looked into her eyes. "Strange in what way? Just what did happen?"

She hesitated; it was all so bizarre. How much should she tell him? Jake had been with her, all the way. He deserved to know the truth. The trouble was, she thought, what *was* the truth?

"I met my father," she said slowly. "He was all that my mother had said, and he explained to me why he did what he did. I'll fill you in on all the details later. While we were talking, Alex Chato appeared, and he drew a gun. That must have been the shots you heard. But by that time, clouds had covered the moon, and I couldn't see a thing. But afterward, I heard my father speak to me. He told me that he loved me and that I would see him again.

"You see, after the moon came out, they were both gone, Father and Alex Chato. I can only suppose that Chato went over the cliff, and that my father slipped away under cover of darkness, so that our parting would be easier."

"I didn't see anyone on the path," Jake said dubiously. "If anyone had passed me, I would have seen him."

"There is another way down."

"But it is very difficult, babe."

"Still, that is the only thing that could have happened."

Jake hesitated before speaking. "Well, if that is the only thing that could have happened, that must be what happened."

She shivered slightly in his embrace, and Jake pulled her close. "We'd best get back down the hill. It's growing cool, and you've had quite an experience."

They began to walk toward the tunneled archway. "Tell me something, Cassandra," Jake said softly, "was it worth it? Was it worth everything that you went through to find him?"

"Oh, yes, it was worth it!" she said fervently. "I found out that my father does love me, and that he was never as far away from me as I thought. Also, he gave me some very good advice tonight, advice that I intend to follow."

He looked at her quizzically. "And what advice is that?"

"He told me to go home and marry my young man, and live happily ever after."

"Oh, that's good advice, that's very good advice."

And then Jake began to laugh, and hand-in-hand they started down the steep path toward the lights of the city below.

ABOUT THE AUTHORS

A few years ago PATRICIA MATTHEWS was office manager for The Associated Students, California State University at Los Angeles, and a part-time writer who dreamed of making her career writing.

The mother of two sons, Patricia had to struggle to find time to turn out her poems, short stories, and novels which were published under her prior name, Patty Brisco. But the success of her first historical romance, published in 1977, changed all that, and Patricia Matthews' own true life story has proven to have a Cinderella ending. Today she is America's leading lady of historical romance with thirteen consecutive bestselling novels to her credit and millions of fans all over the world.

For CLAYTON MATTHEWS, author of more than one hundred books, fifty short stories, and innumerable magazine articles, writing is not only his profession but his hobby. Born in Waurika, Oklahoma in 1918, Matt (as he is known to his friends) worked as a surveyor, overland truck driver, gandy dancer, and taxi driver. In 1960 he became a full-time author with the publication of *Rage of Desire*. More recent books by Clayton Matthews include his highly successful book *The Power Seekers* (winner of the West Coast Review of Books Bronze Medal for Best Novel in 1978), *The Harvesters*, *The Birthright*, and *The Disinherited*.

FROM THE BESTSELLING AUTHOR OF
THE PROUD BREED

W I L D
S W A N

by Celeste De Blasis

Sweeping from England's West Country in the years of the
Napoleonic Wars when smuggling flourished and life was led
dangerously, to the beauty of Maryland horse country—a
golden land already shadowed by slavery and soon to be
ravaged by war—here is a novel richly spun of authentically
detailed history and sumptuous romance, the story of a
woman's life and the generations of two families interwoven by
fortune and fate, told as it could only be by the bestselling
author of THE PROUD BREED.

Don't miss WILD SWAN, available in paperback July 1,
1985, from Bantam Books.

The #1 national bestseller—now in paperback!

LEON URIS
AUTHOR OF EXODUS AND TRINITY

THE

H
A
J

Leon Uris returns to the land of EXODUS in a mighty epic of Arab and Jew, hate and love, vengeance and forgiveness to bring to life a spellbinding epic that probes to the heart of a centuries-old conflict . . . a powerful and moving testament that tells one of the greatest stories of our time.

Don't miss THE HAJ, now on sale wherever Bantam Books are sold. Or use the handy coupon below for ordering:

PATRICIA MATTHEWS

Now You Can Read All These Books By One Of America's Queens Of Historical Romance

SPECIAL
MONEY SAVING
OFFER

Now you can have an up-to-date listing of Bantam's hundreds of titles plus take advantage of our unique and exciting bonus book offer. A special offer which gives you the opportunity to purchase a Bantam book for only 50¢. Here's how!

By ordering any five books at the regular price per order, you can also choose any other single book listed (up to a $4.95 value) for just 50¢. Some restrictions do apply, but for further details why not send for Bantam's listing of titles today!

Just send us your name and address plus 50¢ to defray the postage and handling costs.

THE LATEST BOOKS IN THE BANTAM BESTSELLING TRADITION